CANADIAN WOOD-FRAME HOUSE CONSTRUCTION

CMHC offers a wide range of housing information. Turn to the inside back cover for a listing of related publications.

Cette publication est aussi disponible en français sous le titre :
Construction de maison à ossature de bois—Canada 61199

The information contained in this publication represents current research results available to CMHC, and has been reviewed by a wide spectrum of the housing industry. The Corporation, however, assumes no liability for any damage, injury, or expense that may be incurred or suffered as a result of the use of this publication.

Canadian Cataloguing in Publication Data

Kesik, Ted J. (Theodore Jonathan), 1954-
　　Canadian wood-frame house construction

Rev. ed.
Issued also in French under title: Construction de
　　maison à ossature de bois - Canada.
Includes bibliographical references and index.
ISBN 0-660-17294-1
N° de cat. NH17-3/1997E

　　I. Wooden-frame houses—Canada—Design and construction. 2. Wooden-frame buildings—Canada—Design and construction 3. House construction—Canada. I.Canada Mortgage and Housing Corporation. II. Title.

TH4818.W6K48 1998　　694　　C98-900058-3

First Combined Imperial/Metric Edition
Revised 1998
Reprinted 1998, 2001, 2003

Printed in Canada
Produced by CMHC

ACKNOWLEDGEMENTS

Canada Mortgage and Housing Corporation wishes to acknowledge the many individuals and their organizations for contributing to this latest edition of *Canadian Wood-Frame House Construction*.

The following people served as reviewers and performed the important role of ensuring the accuracy and usefulness of the publication for builders and educators, and its relevance to Healthy Housing initiatives at CMHC.

Rick Glanville, Camosun College, Victoria, BC
Louis Kane, Advanced Education and Labour, NBCC, Saint John, NB
Michael Nauth, Algonquin College, Nepean, ON
Eric Jones, Canadian Wood Council, Ottawa, ON
Ross Monsour, Canadian Home Builders' Association, Ottawa, ON
Everett Dunham, CMHC
Darrel Smith, CMHC
Terry Marshall, CMHC

CMHC also wishes to express its appreciation to the authors who updated this edition to conform to the 1995 National Building Code of Canada and enhanced it significantly by adding new, special features.

Ted Kesik, Ryerson Polytechnic University, Toronto, ON
Michael Lio, Michael Lio and Associates, Toronto, ON

CMHC gratefully acknowledges the National Research Council and the Canadian Wood Council for the use of their information included in the tables of this publication.

TABLE OF CONTENTS

vii

PREFACE

Since the first edition of Canada Mortgage and Housing Corporation's *Canadian Wood-Frame House Construction* appeared in 1967, this publication has been the primary means by which builders, carpenters and students of housing technology have learned about wood-frame house construction in Canada. This publication continues to be the most widely-used reference in the field, in community colleges and in many university architecture programs.

This edition retains the convenient format of previous editions, reflecting the feedback from a broad cross-section of users across Canada. It is hoped that readers of this publication will continue to contribute their much-welcomed suggestions for future improvements.

The inclusion of *Healthy Housing* principles throughout this book represents a significant shift in awareness regarding the individual, social, environmental and economic impacts of the housing industry in Canada and around the world. Canadians continue to have good cause to be proud of their wood-frame house construction technology.

This latest edition is one among many continuing efforts toward the goal of providing choice in accessible, affordable and sustainable housing in Canada.

HOW TO USE THIS BOOK

This book presents a concise description of Canadian wood-frame house construction. As well, references to a number of available publications, which can provide a greater depth of information, have been noted. This book should not be considered to be a complete reference on wood-frame house construction. Instead, readers should consider it as the basic framework for learning about and appropriately applying wood-frame house construction technology and healthy housing principles.

Canadian Wood-Frame House Construction is based on the requirements of the 1995 edition of the National Building Code. This book is not a substitute for the National Building Code. We strongly recommend that readers refer to the codes and standards pertaining to housing in their jurisdictions for a complete set of requirements.

The organization of *Canadian Wood-Frame House Construction* corresponds to the construction sequence for a typical Canadian house. The chapters are based on major aspects of wood-frame house construction and reflect typical practices. Actual practices may be expected to vary across Canada. Users of this publication are urged to consult with local building departments, trades and suppliers when designing and building a house.

Ideally, users of this book should gain an overview of its contents before exploring any of the topics in depth. Start at the beginning of the book and work forward through the stages of construction when planning and designing the house. However, if only specific information is required, each chapter has been developed as a stand-alone reference. Experienced builders and tradespeople will, we hope, continue to find this edition a convenient job-site guide — now enhanced with helpful new features.

The feedback and insights of readers is highly valued at Canada Mortgage and Housing Corporation (CMHC). Your views and suggestions on new or improved content are welcome. While every effort has been made to present accurate information, please point out any incorrect or incomplete information. Kindly take the time to help improve this publication. Forward your correspondence to:

Canadian Housing Information
  Centre
Canada Mortgage and Housing
  Corporation
700 Montreal Road
Ottawa, ON K1A 0P7

NEW FEATURES

This edition of *Canadian Wood-Frame House Construction* incorporates several new features intended to provide a better understanding of the practical, environmental and technical aspects of wood-frame house construction.

Since the first edition of this publication, a steady move toward improved energy efficiency and a growing awareness for the need to develop and construct more-sustainable housing has occurred. It has been recognized that these ideal concepts must be practically applied in order to realize any real benefits. The main thrust of the new features focus on linking ideal concepts to practical matters which may be implemented in construction practices. Where applicable, references for more detailed information are provided.

Healthy Housing Insights

CMHC is committed to provide the Canadian housing industry with reliable information on appropriate housing technology that responds to people and the environment. Practical considerations derived from CMHC's Healthy Housing initiatives have been included in this edition.

Healthy Housing Insights, conveniently identified throughout this publication, are presented in the format depicted below.

HEALTHY HOUSING INSIGHT

Healthy Housing Insights are presented throughout this book to enable users to consider and practically apply the following elements of healthy housing to wood-frame house construction:

→ Occupant Health

→ Energy Efficiency

→ Resource Efficiency

→ Environmental Responsibility

→ Affordability

Healthy Housing Insights are intended to help users make appropriate choices that will sustain the health of the house occupants, and the environment. They deal with issues that have not yet found their way into building code requirements, but which are recognized as practical options for building more-sustainable housing.

Planning Ahead and Checking Back Notes

The *Planning Ahead* and *Checking Back* notes have valuable pointers for builders. The *Planning Ahead* notes tell you about factors that affect later stages of construction. The *Checking Back* notes remind you about problems that need to be solved before continuing with building.

The format for these notes is depicted below. Further information on how they may be used to plan and properly construct a dwelling is provided.

PLANNING AHEAD

Planning Ahead notes are intended to identify important factors which may affect later stages of construction. Options for dealing with these related aspects of construction are also presented.

It is recommended that you review all of the **Planning Ahead** notes during the design stage of the house. Resolving conflicts on paper is much easier than on site, and generally less expensive.

➜ Points like this identify key factors to consider when using **Planning Ahead** notes.

Planning Ahead notes are cross-referenced with **Checking Back** notes to ensure that critical aspects are appropriately resolved at every stage of construction.

CHECKING BACK

Checking Back notes are intended to flag aspects of earlier stages of construction which may affect a present stage of construction. They are conveniently referenced to **Planning Ahead** notes.

In case a **Planning Ahead** note has been overlooked, **Checking Back** notes are helpful reminders of the need to resolve potential problems during the early stages of planning and design, prior to construction.

➜ Points like this identify items to review when **Checking Back** notes are encountered.

Checking Back notes may also be used as a concise checklist when reviewing plans to avoid construction problems.

Examples for Using the Sizing Tables

Examples have been provided for sizing typical structural components of the house.

Imperial and Metric Dimensions

This edition of *Canadian Wood-Frame House Construction* contains imperial as well as metric units. The National Building Code of Canada uses metric units, and these govern when strict interpretations of Code requirements are required. However, imperial units of measure (feet and inches) dominate most of wood-frame house construc-tion technology. For this reason, the imperial units are provided first in this publication, followed by the actual Code requirements in metric units.

Every reasonable effort has been made to provide accurate conversions of metric dimensions to imperial equivalents; however, it remains the responsibility of designers and builders to comply with building code requirements in their jurisdictions.

Note: Consult your local building department on the units of measure-ment required for house plans.

SIZING TABLE

Examples using the sizing tables found in the Appendix have been developed to assist users in their proper application. They may be found in the sections dealing with the actual framing of the house.

By reviewing these examples, readers may correctly apply the tables when sizing structural components of the house. Readers should consult their local building departments to ensure that the sizing of basic structural components has been done properly.

When encountering situations not covered by any of the tables, it is advisable to consult a structural designer.

5

HEALTHY HOUSING

A growing awareness of the relationship between the health of people, the environment and the economy has fostered the Healthy Housing concept in Canada. Wood-frame house construction continues to predominate in the Canadian market, and offers many opportunities to explore and incorporate Healthy Housing principles. In fact, wood-frame house construction continues to represent an environmentally responsible choice. Wood is a renewable resource which, if properly managed and utilized, can enhance our quality of life, sustain our natural environment, and contribute to the economy.

Healthy Housing principles are presented throughout this publication in order to make readers aware of the many options available to them at the various stages of house construction — from siting the building all the way through to interior finishes and landscaping. Before any of these specific topics are discussed, an overview of Healthy Housing principles has been provided.

Healthy Housing represents a collaborative effort supported by CMHC which enables researchers, the building industry and interested groups to engage in an ongoing exploration of environmentally and economically sound design and development techniques. Healthy Housing is founded on the following five fundamental principles.

ELEMENTS OF HEALTHY HOUSING

The principles of Healthy Housing each consist of a number of related elements. Each should be considered at the design stage before beginning house construction. Decisions are easiest to reconsider and revise appropriately at this stage. Incorporating these elements during construction is

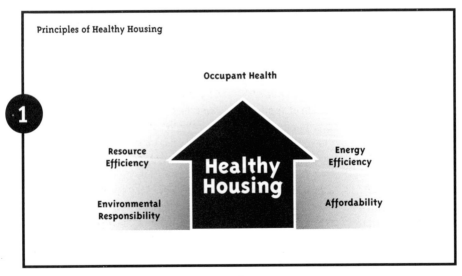

Principles of Healthy Housing

Occupant Health

Resource Efficiency

Healthy Housing

Energy Efficiency

Environmental Responsibility

Affordability

·1

equally important, and makes the difference between a healthful idea and a healthy house.

Occupant Health

Indoor Air Quality: the reduction of the level of contaminants built into the building (material selection), and the removal of any contaminants at the source, coupled with the dilution of house air with fresh outside air (ventilation).

Water Quality: the selection of a safe supply of potable water, and where this is not possible, appropriate home treatment to remove bacteria, chemical contaminants, and unpleasant tastes or odours.

Light, Sound and Radiation: the provision of adequate natural light throughout the house, the isolation of internal and external noise sources, and the avoidance of exposure to electromagnetic fields.

Energy Efficiency

Building Thermal Performance: the reduction of building envelope area (compact design), the improvement of the building envelope through better insulated and more airtight assemblies, and the installation of high performance windows.

Energy for Heating, Cooling and Ventilation: the selection of appropriate house energy sources, and the provision of high efficiency equipment having the proper capacity.

Renewable Energy Technologies: the orientation of the building and the placement of windows to capture solar gains during cold months, and to enhance natural ventilation and cooling of the house during hot months.

Electrical Consumption and Peak Demand: the use of controls to avoid or minimize electrical power consumption during peak periods, typically mornings and early evenings, and the selection of efficient domestic appliances and lights.

Resource Efficiency

Embodied Energy: the selection of renewable, recycled or reused materials where possible, and consideration of the environmental impacts associated with manufactured materials.

Management of Construction Waste: the intelligent use of materials to reduce waste, to enable their reuse, and finally to recycle waste materials into useful products.

Water: the installation of water-efficient plumbing fixtures and appliances indoors, and the careful planning of landscaping and natural drainage to minimize water consumption outdoors.

Durability and Longevity: the construction of a durable building structure, thermal envelope and finishes.

Environmental Responsibility

Emissions and Combustion By-products: the selection of appropriate materials made from environmentally responsible manufacturing processes, and the installation of high efficiency, low emission equipment and appliances.

Wastewater and Sewage: the reduction of wastewater and sewage through water conservation, and the provision of an appropriate treatment technique for private septic systems.

Community Planning and Site Planning Issues: the design of viable communities which are properly sited to minimize ecological damage and to take better advantage of the sun and the wind.

Hazardous Materials — Landfill and Disposal: the avoidance of hazardous materials during construction and in the home, combined with a facility for composting and recycling.

Affordability

Affordability: the availability of suitable housing choice having both an affordable purchase price and long-term operating costs.

Viability for the Construction Industry: the reliance on simple but effective technologies which are adaptable across the range of Canadian climates and markets, and exportable abroad.

Adaptability: the flexibility of design and construction to enable cost-effective renovation and reuse long into the future.

Marketability: catering to the real needs of people and accounting for shifts in demographics and consumer perceptions about housing.

HEALTHY WOOD-FRAME HOUSE CONSTRUCTION

There are many Healthy Housing practices to be considered when designing and building a home. The preceding outline forms the basis for a number of suggestions, presented within the chapters, to follow as *Healthy Housing Insights.* Refer to the previous chapter entitled **How To Use This Book** for a guide on how to consider and incorporate Healthy Housing alternatives into your house construction.

RELATED PUBLICATIONS

Building Materials for the Environmentally Hypersensitive
Canada Mortgage and Housing Corporation

PLANNING AHEAD

4 Rs of Wood-Frame Construction

Many of the chapters contain *Healthy Housing Insights* on the appropriate use of wood to minimize waste and to make the most efficient use of this valuable resource. These are presented according to an approach which the building industry has adopted as the 4 Rs:

→ *Review* conventional procedures and practices;

→ *Reduce* the wastes being generated;

→ *Re-use* materials; and

→ *Recycle* what traditionally has been conventionally seen as waste.

Refer to the *Healthy Housing Insight* on applying the 4 Rs of Wood-Frame Construction in the **Framing the House** chapter.

TYPICAL HOUSE CONSTRUCTION PROCESS

Due to the wide variety of homes in terms of style and size, and the differences between professional builders and the do-it-yourselfer, it is difficult to say exactly what is a typical house construction process. Many factors apply, such as whether a single house or a whole subdivision is being built, as well as other factors such as weather, site conditions and the availability of labour and materials.

The description of the typical house construction process which follows is based on the wood-frame house construction techniques presented in this book. It assumes that a typical two- or three-bedroom house is being built by an average builder employing sub-trades. Special features, such as a sunroom, swimming pool or detached garage or workshop, are not included in this description. Before proceeding, it is interesting to review some Canadian housing statistics to appreciate how innovations in wood-frame house construction technology have decreased the time and effort required to construct a house.

The steady decline in construction time indicated in Figure 2 is due largely to the introduction of sheet and panel goods, such as drywall and plywood, factory-built components such as roof trusses, windows and cabinets, and plastic piping for sanitary plumbing. Specialized power tools and equipment also helped reduce manual labour. The shift from building one house at a time to building dozens, or hundreds at a time, is not specifically reflected in

Canadian wood-frame house construction statistics.*

Year	1943	1956	1965	1975	1985	1995
Housing Starts	59,900	115,420	155,128	180,952	180,000	110,993
Average Size	800 ft^2	1,080 ft^2	1,200 ft^2	1,080 ft^2	1,230 ft^2	1225 ft^{2}**
Average Selling Price	$5,500	$13,000	$17,400	$35,500	$80,500	$103,000
Hourly Wage Carpenter	$1.05	$2.30	$3.46	$8.30	$18.37	$26.20
Minimum Construction Time	30 weeks	20 weeks	10 weeks	9 weeks	8 weeks	8 weeks

2

* These statistics have been gathered from a number of sources. They are indicative of era statistics and should not be treated as definitive.
** Based on 1990 data

these statistics, but should not be underestimated.

These statistics cannot be applied directly to the typical, individual house construction process being described here. Instead, use them as a guide for estimating a reasonable range of time needed to construct a dwelling. Normally, about 16 weeks is required from start to finish. If it is a very large or highly detailed building, 20 or more weeks may be needed. On the other hand, completing a small, simple dwelling may only require eight to ten weeks. This does not account for delays due to inclement weather, inspections, material shortages, custom-ordered items, or busy sub-trades during construction. Prior to construction, additional delays may be incurred while financing and a building permit are being obtained. The traditional need to set aside late spring, all summer and part of the fall for construction has not changed significantly for the single-house builder. At the same time, advances in Canadian home building have made construction an efficient, year-round activity in many parts of Canada.

STAGES OF CONSTRUCTION

There are a number of stages in constructing a house which must be properly planned, co-ordinated and executed by the builder. A short description of these has been provided following the typical construction sequence. It should be noted that the chapters which follow are presented according to this sequence.

Plans, Financing and Permits

This stage is also referred to as the pre-construction stage. The amount of time needed to develop a complete set

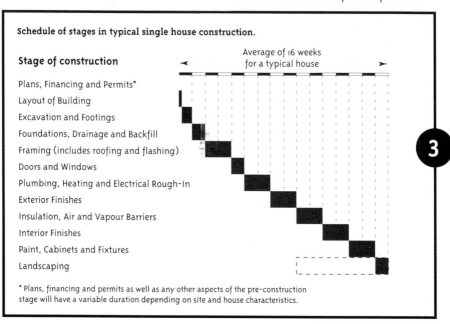

Schedule of stages in typical single house construction.

Stage of construction	Average of 16 weeks for a typical house
Plans, Financing and Permits*	
Layout of Building	
Excavation and Footings	
Foundations, Drainage and Backfill	
Framing (includes roofing and flashing)	
Doors and Windows	
Plumbing, Heating and Electrical Rough-In	
Exterior Finishes	
Insulation, Air and Vapour Barriers	
Interior Finishes	
Paint, Cabinets and Fixtures	
Landscaping	

* Plans, financing and permits as well as any other aspects of the pre-construction stage will have a variable duration depending on site and house characteristics.

3

of plans, estimate the cost of the dwelling, arrange for financing and obtain a building permit and all other required approvals, will vary considerably across the country. Providing access to the building site and arranging for temporary power may also take place during this stage. Because the time required for these factors is unpredictable, it has not been shown in Figure 3, but it should be taken into account.

Layout of Building

The first stage of construction involves layout of the building on the property. To properly observe the by-laws for setbacks to property lines, the services of a land surveyor may be required. Accurately laying out the excavation for the depth and placement of foundations is critical. Layout can usually be performed in a single day provided property boundaries do not need to be established. Site planning, on the other hand, to take advantage of the sun and wind, to manage drainage (runoff) and snow accumulation, and to afford a pleasing view, may require considerably more effort.

Excavation and Footings

Once the building layout is complete, excavation for the foundations may proceed. A single day is often all that is needed, provided appropriate equipment is employed and there is access to the excavation area. Another few days are needed to trench for and rough-in services, form and pour footings, remove footing formwork, layout the foundation walls and columns, and prepare to construct the foundations.

Foundations, Drainage and Backfill

Foundations can be installed in several days by a skilled sub-trade, including curing concrete and removing formwork. Dampproofing, foundation drainage systems and backfill will usually require another day or two. In some cases, unusual site conditions in unserviced areas may require additional measures for foundation drainage, such as sumps, ditching or dry wells. Properly storing topsoil and excavated material suitable for backfilling can eliminate the need to import fill and topsoil. Placement of the granular layer and basement floor slab usually takes place later when the basement plumbing rough-in is completed.

Framing

Generally, about two weeks is needed to complete the framing and install roofing to provide weather protection during subsequent stages of construction. This assumes that temporary power is available for tools and equipment. Chimney installation and the building of stairs or the installation of pre-manufactured stairs is generally considered part of the framing stage. Typical arrangements with carpentry sub-trades vary across Canada. Where window and exterior door installation is included, about another week is needed to complete this stage. Framing decks is usually performed later.

Doors and Windows

Installing doors and windows, usually after framing is completed, requires a few days to a week to complete. Complete installation generally includes flashing and installing locks and related hardware. Jamb extensions and trim are typically part of the finishing carpentry work. The interior air sealing of gaps around window and door openings is commonly performed by the insulation and air/vapour barrier contractor.

Plumbing, Heating and Electrical Rough-in

This stage usually does not start until all framing is completed. Plumbing is brought from the service connections and roughed-in to the fixtures. Bathtubs and any large shower enclosures are generally installed at this time. The furnace and ductwork or piping is installed, along with ductwork for exhaust fans and mechanical ventilation equipment such as heat recovery ventilators (HRVs). Electrical wiring, smoke alarms, telephone and computer lines, and cable TV is roughed-in throughout the dwelling. The work requires about two weeks to complete, but does not include items such as woodstoves and fireplaces.

Exterior Finishes

Depending on the type of exterior finish being applied to the dwelling, between one and two weeks is needed to complete this stage. If an exterior air barrier, such as a house wrap, is being used, it is usually applied at this time, but it may also have been installed during the framing stage. Brick, siding and stucco along with soffit, fascia, eavestroughing, downspouts, and window and door caulking are all part of the exterior finishes stage. Exterior trim and millwork, staining and painting may also be carried out at this stage.

Insulation, Air and Vapour Barriers

This stage may be performed at the same time as exterior finishes, provided the insulation is protected against moisture damage caused by wind-driven rain. Installing insulation, air and vapour barriers requires a few days to complete when all of the detailing around penetrations, fixtures and outlets is included.

Interior Finishes

This stage typically begins with installing ceiling, wall and floor finishes. Finishing carpentry for interior doors, frames and trim along with stair balusters and handrails is generally carried out immediately after the floor, wall and ceiling finishes are prepared for painting and varnishing. The interior finishes stage normally requires about two weeks to complete, but significantly more time may be required depending on the type of finishes selected.

Paint, Cabinets and Fixtures

Painting and varnishing are usually performed at the beginning of this stage. Cabinets and items such as ceramic tile backsplashes are then installed. While this is proceeding, plumbers complete the installation of the plumbing fixtures, and electricians finish connecting circuits, receptacles, switches, light fixtures and smoke alarms. Connections to equipment such as furnaces, water heaters, mechanical ventilation systems, stoves and clothes dryers are also performed at this time. The heating contractor will install all grilles and registers for forced-air systems, and radiators for hydronic or electric baseboard systems. In some cases, appliances such as refrigerators, dish washers, stoves and dryers will also be installed at this time. All of the trades should ensure that their installations have been inspected and function properly, and then hand over any operating instructions and warranties to the builder or owner. A final clean-up of the dwelling concludes all work. About two weeks is normally required to complete this stage of construction.

Landscaping

This final stage includes finish grading, driveways, steps, walkways, groundcover, shrubs and trees. Carpentry work associated with decks and fences, and plumbing work for items such as underground sprinkler systems are also carried out at this time. Approximately one week is needed to carry out this final stage; however, the time will vary depending on the nature of the landscaping, and any special features such as decks and pools.

A summary of the stages of house construction, showing their sequence and duration, is depicted in Figure 3. Again, this should be viewed as a guide. It is important for do-it-yourself and less experienced builders to obtain advice on local conditions and practices. It is also important to add in several weeks time to allow for unavoidable delays.

APPROVALS, PERMITS AND INSPECTIONS

The system of approvals, permits and inspections for house construction can be quite complex for inexperienced and do-it-yourself builders. Practices differ among localities. However, the most important consideration before proceeding with house plans and specifications is to ensure that the property is zoned for residential use. For example, properties located in areas under the jurisdiction of a conservation authority may have many restrictions and requirements which apply to dwellings. Some properties may have development regulations, covenants or restrictions, governing the size, location and finishes of the house. Without knowing the zoning and environmental guidelines for construction, it is not prudent to proceed with the house design.

Requirements for plans, permits and inspections vary across Canada; however, most municipalities will conform to the basic requirements described in the National Building Code of Canada for plans. Plans should be drawn to scale and provide sufficient detail to enable a plans examiner to confirm that the house conforms to Code requirements. Most building departments will indicate the preferred format for house plans and the minimum information needed to obtain a building permit. Good plans also enable suppliers and sub-trades to properly supply and install materials and equipment. A complete set of plans and specifications should be prepared by a competent designer, the cost of which is often more than recovered through avoided extras and unforeseen problems.

Figure 4 shows the process of approvals, permits and inspections which may apply to a new house. It is recommended that readers consult their local building departments to obtain a complete list of forms and procedures. In some areas, it may be necessary to observe additional registration and inspection requirements by warranty programs for new houses. The scheduling of inspections to avoid lengthy delays is very important. It is advisable to determine exactly what work must be completed prior to calling for a particular inspection, as well as the amount of notice required. This

Approvals, permits and inspections process for new houses.

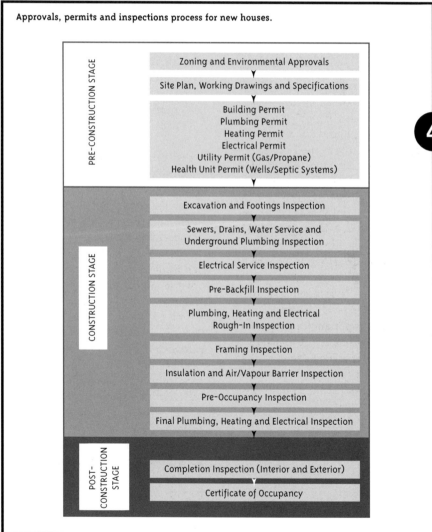

is most critical in remote communities where inspectors must travel long distances to perform inspections.

The many systems of approvals, permits and inspections in Canada are intended to maintain minimum levels of health and safety in new houses. It's important to understand the local requirements and plan ahead, so that the legal and adminis- trative aspects of house building do not interfere with the actual construc- tion of the house. Builders and their sub-trades can focus solely on the quality of their work when the paper- work associated with approvals, permits and inspections is handled properly. The following chapters present aspects of these stages of house construction in greater detail.

LOCATION AND EXCAVATION

MARKING THE EXCAVATION AREA

Before the exact location of the house on the site is decided, it is important to check with the municipality or township for minimum setback and side yard requirements, because these can be determining factors in placing the house.

Always check with local utility companies prior to digging to ensure that the excavation will not interfere with buried services. Inadvertently

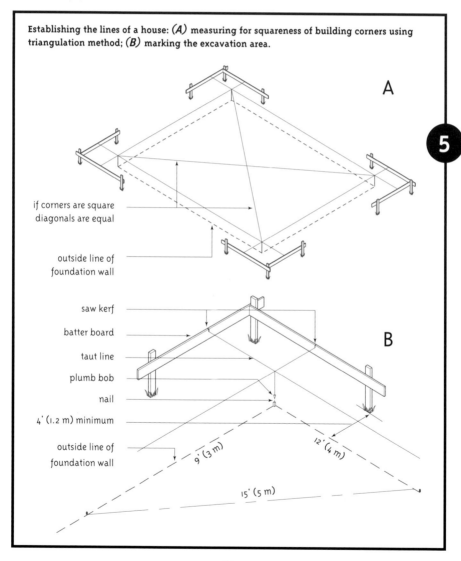

Establishing the lines of a house: **(A)** measuring for squareness of building corners using triangulation method; **(B)** marking the excavation area.

A

if corners are square
diagonals are equal

outside line of
foundation wall

saw kerf

batter board

taut line

plumb bob

nail

4' (1.2 m) minimum

outside line of
foundation wall

B

9' (3 m)

12' (4 m)

15' (5 m)

cutting telephone, gas or power lines can prove costly and can result in personal injury.

After the site is cleared, the perimeter of the house is marked using the exact location of the corners of the lot as a reference. These are usually determined by a certified survey. The corners of the house are marked by small wooden stakes, accurately located at each corner, with nails driven into their tops indicating the outside line of the foundation walls.

Because these stakes will be eventually lost during excavation, additional markings are needed. Offset markings may be located by extending the lines of the foundation walls from the established corners, and fixing these offset markings either with stakes on the ground or marks on surrounding, but permanent, objects. These markings are used after the excavation to set up an arrangement of batter boards (Fig. 5B). However, if the foundation shape is simple, the site area unconstrained and the excavation carefully done, the batter boards can be erected at this point.

The area to be excavated is staked out usually 24 to 28 in. (600 to 700 mm) wider than the corners of the house. This extra width is needed for easy handling and erection of the formwork, placement of the drain tile, application of dampproofing, and placement of the exterior insulation, if applicable. Allow for a slope on the sides of the excavation where the depth exceeds 4 ft. (1.2 m). This creates stability of the slope and the safety of the workers.

An alternative approach to marking the perimeter of the excavation, especially when the foundation shape is not a simple rectangle, is to spray fluorescent paint directly on the ground.

EXCAVATION SIZE AND DEPTH

In most case, the quickest and least expensive way to excavate is to use a bulldozer or power shovel. Before this is done, however, all topsoil should be stripped and stored for reuse. The subsoil from the excavation is usually carried away for disposal unless grading requirements allow its use on the site. The depth of the excavation and, consequently, the elevation of the foundation usually depend on the elevation of the street, sewer and water services, the profile of the lot, and the level of finished grade around the perimeter of the house. The elevation of adjoining houses and surface drainage patterns must also be considered.

The basement headroom and the elevation of the floor above grade also affect the depth of the excavation. Basement headroom should be at least 6 ft. 5 in. (1.95 m) to the underside of beams or joists, but a headroom of 6 ft. 7 in. (2 m) is preferable. If the basement is to be used as a living space, however, the minimum headroom should be 7 ft. 7 in. (2.3 m), the same height as the other finished floor areas. The elevation of the first floor should allow for a minimum distance from finished grade to the beginning of exterior finishing (normally starting at the foundation top) of 6 in. (150 mm) for masonry and metal siding, and 8 in. (200 mm) for wood siding, plywood, hardboard and stucco (Fig. 6). This is intended to minimize damage to siding caused by melting snow and rainwater bouncing off the ground.

At times, the depth of the excavation will also be affected by the type of soil encountered. The excavation may be deepened until suitable soil is encountered. Similarly, the depth of the water table or encountering bedrock can affect the depth of the excavation.

The rough grade around the house should be kept at least 4 in. (100 mm) below the line established for the finished grade to allow for subsequent placing of topsoil or paving material.

If a granular base is to be used under the basement floor slab, the excavation should be made deep enough to accommodate this base. Normally, this depth is also sufficient to accommodate the thickness of the footings. If the site is well-drained and only a dampproofing membrane is used without the granular base underneath, the excavation is stopped at the elevation established for the top surface of the footings. When this is done, the footings are formed by trenching. Adequate space must be provided for the drainage pipe beside the footing.

The steepness of the excavation's back slope is determined by the type of subsoil encountered. With clay or other stable soils and depending on the depth of the excavation, the back slope can be nearly vertical. When sand is encountered, the banks must be cut back.

Be sure that the excavation does

Finish grade sloped for drainage.

8" (200 mm) minimum for wood-based siding and stucco

6" (150 mm) minimum for masonry or metal siding

slope for drainage (10% slope recommended)

finish grade

foundation

HEALTHY HOUSING INSIGHT

Siting for Sun, Wind and Water

In addition to local requirements for location of the dwelling on the lot, such as setbacks from property lines, consideration should be given to solar access, wind effects and water runoff. Careful consideration of these factors can minimize environmental impacts, save energy and promote healthy housing. Here are some important points that should be considered when siting and orienting the dwelling.

Solar Access

➜ In order to take advantage of passive solar heating, the preferred orientation for windows is within 15° west of south and 20° east of south. Plan the layout of the house plan and its solar orientation to take advantage of the sun's free energy.

➜ Today's high performance windows allow for good natural light and generous views while saving energy and promoting occupant well-being. Passive solar heating opportunities are attainable.

Principal Wind Direction

➜ The wind can be harnessed to provide natural ventilation through operable windows on the windward and leeward side of the house if they are aligned with principal wind directions.

➜ Proper landscaping and site grading can minimize uncomfortable winds in outdoor living areas, and reduce snow removal. The local weather office can provide information on principal wind directions over the seasons.

Water Runoff and Site Drainage

➜ Attempt to maintain natural runoff patterns when draining the site of rainwater and snowmelt. Do not site the building in low spots or where it obstructs the natural path of water runoff.

➜ Convey water from roofs and drives to areas where it may infiltrate the soil and replenish groundwater. Avoid connecting downspouts from eavestroughs to weeping tiles or sumps.

➜ Collect and store rainwater in rain barrels or cisterns to use for watering gardens or washing vehicles.

not affect the foundations of adjacent buildings. Care must always be taken when excavating below the level of footings of adjacent houses. Local building departments should be contacted in these situations.

Remember to always protect the excavation in winter. Building on frozen soils can cause a number of problems that are costly and very difficult to remedy.

PLACEMENT OF THE HOUSE

After the excavation is completed, the next step is to establish the lines and elevation for the footings and foun-

dation walls. Figure 7 shows a convenient arrangement of batter boards for this purpose.

Using the previously established location of the foundation walls, three stakes of suitable length are placed at each corner at least 4 ft. (1.2 m) beyond the lines of the excavation. Boards are then nailed horizontally, as shown in Figure 7, so the tops of all the boards are level and at the same elevation. Wire or stout string (called carpenter's dryline) is stretched across the tops of opposite boards at two corners and adjusted exactly to follow the line of the outside edge of the foundation wall. By cutting saw kerfs 1/4 to 3/8 in. (6 to 8 mm) deep or driving nails where the lines touch

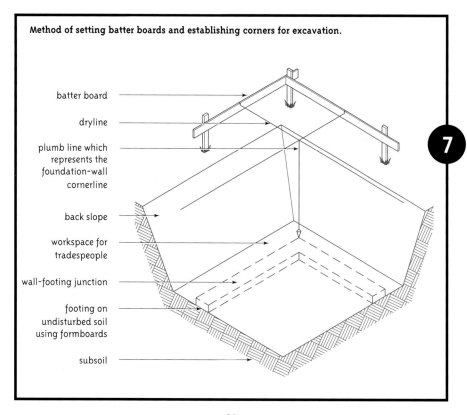

Method of setting batter boards and establishing corners for excavation.

batter board

dryline

plumb line which represents the foundation-wall cornerline

back slope

workspace for tradespeople

wall-footing junction

footing on undisturbed soil using formboards

subsoil

7

the boards, the lines may be replaced if broken or disturbed. After similar cuts are made in all of the batter boards, the perimeter of the house foundation will be established.

Two methods determine whether the building corners are square. The first is to measure the diagonals. If the diagonals are equal, the building corners are square (Fig. 5A). Another method, called triangulation, measures along one side of the corner a distance in multiples of 12 in. (300 mm) and along the adjacent side the same number in multiples of 16 in. (400 mm). The diagonal, or hypotenuse, will have an equal number of multiples of 20 in. (500 mm) when the corner is square (Fig. 5B).

RELATED PUBLICATIONS

Glossary of Housing Terms
Canada Mortgage and Housing Corporation
1995 National Building Code of Canada
National Research Council of Canada

CONCRETE WORK

Concrete, both plain and reinforced, is used for a variety of purposes in houses, such as concrete foundations, and basement and garage slabs-on-ground.

READY-MIX CONCRETE

Ready-mix concrete is available in most locations. When ordering ready-mix concrete for footings, interior slabs, and foundation walls, it is important to specify a minimum strength of 2200 psi (15 MPa). For garage and carport floors, exterior steps and driveways, a minimum of 3600 psi (25 MPa) air-entrained concrete must be specified. Air entrainment for these applications must be between 5 to 8 percent. Air-entrainment will produce a concrete that contains a system of minute air bubbles that make the concrete more workable and more easily placed than plain concrete. Most important, when cured, air-entrained concrete is many times more resistant to damage from frost action. It is a must for all exterior concrete work and is recommended for other applications to improve workability and durability. In areas where soils are sulphate reactive, admixtures are recommended to protect the concrete.

ON-SITE MIXING

Avoid adding water to concrete at the construction site to facilitate its placement. Additional water will lower strength, increase permeability and decrease freeze-thaw resistance. If more workability is required, the concrete supplier should be asked to adjust the mix, because the concrete may need a plasticizer to improve workability and placement.

When mixing must be done on site, water and aggregate should be clean and free of organic material or other substances which might damage the concrete. The aggregates should also be well-graded.

The air-entraining admixture should be added strictly according to the manufacturer's recommendations, because too much admixture will decrease the strength of the concrete. Contact the manufacturer's representative, if possible, for advice about the proper proportion for a specific use. Air-entraining admixtures should be used only if the concrete is mixed in a motorized mixer.

For concrete in footings and foundation walls, not more than 4.4 imp. gal. (20 L) of water should be used for each 88 lb. (40 kg) of cement. For other concrete work, not more than 4 imp. gal. (18 L) of water should be added to each 88 lb. (40 kg) sack of cement. These amounts are based on average moisture content in the aggregate.

The proportions of fine and coarse aggregates, cement and water should be properly adjusted to produce a mixture that will work readily into angles and corners without allowing the material to segregate or free water to collect on the surface. The concrete mixes shown in Table 2 are generally considered acceptable. Aggregate used in these mixes must not be larger than one-fifth the distance between vertical forms or one-third the thickness of the flat-work. The slump for mixes from Table 2 must not exceed 6 in. (150 mm) for footings and foundation walls, and 4 in. (100 mm) for slabs-on-ground.

PLACING CONCRETE

Whenever possible, concrete should be placed into the forms continuously in horizontal lifts not exceeding 12 to 18 in. (300 to 450 mm) in depth. Concrete should not be allowed to fall into the forms from a height of more than 5 ft. (1.5 m) as this causes the concrete to segregate. For higher drops, the concrete should be deposited through a suitable vertical pipe. Buggies, wheelbarrows or chutes may be used to move the concrete if all points in the forms are not accessible to ready-mix trucks. The chutes should be metal or metal-lined with round bottoms and sloped with a rise-to-run inclination between 1:2 and 1:3.

The concrete should not be deposited in a pile but should be spread out and leveled by raking or shoveling. Vibrators may be used to consolidate the concrete, but should not be used to assist placement. Concrete can also be placed by pumping, if proper equipment is available.

If it is necessary to interrupt the placing operations, the surface of the concrete placed in the forms should be leveled off and the concrete allowed to partially set. The surface should then be roughened to provide a good bonding surface for the next lift. When work resumes, the surface should be cleaned and slightly dampened prior to placing the concrete. Bonding agents or grout of 1 part of cement to 2 parts sand should be spread about 1/2 in. (12 mm) thick over the rough-ened surface to provide a good joint between the two lifts. The new lift should be placed immediately after the placement of the grout.

When being placed, the concrete should be uniformly compacted by means of tamping hand tools (puddling sticks) or, preferably, by a vibrator.

When the air temperature is at or below 41°F (5°C) or when there is a possibility of it falling to that level within 24 hours, concrete operations should, if possible, be suspended. When placing concrete, ensure that its temperature is maintained between 50°F (10°C) and 77°F (25°C) while being mixed and placed. It must be main-tained at a temperature of not less than 50°F (10°C) for a minimum of 72 hours while curing. To do this, the water to be mixed into the concrete may have to be heated. The concrete should not be placed against frozen soil, and any ice and snow should be removed from the formwork.

CURING CONCRETE

Curing involves keeping freshly-set concrete moist or preventing it from drying out and shrinking for several days after placing. The cracking of concrete walls and floors can often result from improper attention to curing. Proper procedures for curing must be followed to ensure concrete is able to achieve its potential strength, water tightness and durability. To aid in the curing process, wall forms should be left in place as long as practical, at least for three days.

The curing of walls should be carried out after the forms are removed for at least another day if the temperature of concrete is kept above 70°F (21°C), and for another three days if the temperature of concrete is kept between 50°F (10°C) and 70°F (21°C).

A good method of curing is to place a soil-soaker hose around the top of the wall allowing water to run down the wall. When water curing cannot be carried out (for example, in cold weather), spray-on curing compounds that inhibit evaporation may be used. If a dampproofing compound is applied to the wall, no further curing of that face is required.

In hot weather, concrete should be protected from rapid drying. During hot dry weather, wood forms should be sprinkled with water while they are in place in order to prevent excessive drying out.

In freezing weather, freshly placed concrete may be protected with a thick layer of straw or other insulating material. In addition, it may be necessary for the concrete to be protected by an enclosure and the space heated with fuel-burning heaters to ensure appropriate temperatures during the curing period.

Concrete slabs-on-ground can be cured by use of water sprays, by covering with burlap kept continuously moist, or by covering with polyethylene sheeting or other means to prevent moisture loss. Unless curing is carried on for about a week after placing the concrete, the exposed surface of the slab may show unsightly, cracking or be otherwise weakened.

Allowing concrete to cure properly is an important step in the construction process. Attention to this step helps to avoid costly problems.

RELATED PUBLICATIONS

Concrete Construction for Housing and Small Buildings
Canadian Standards Association
Avoiding Concrete Foundation Problems (Video)
Canada Mortgage and Housing Corporation

FOOTINGS, FOUNDATIONS AND SLABS

FOOTINGS

Footings receive the house loads through posts or foundation walls and then transmit these loads to the soil. The type and size of footings should be suitable for the soil conditions, and located far enough below ground level to be protected from frost action. Frost action can also be avoided by providing good drainage around the foundation to direct water away from the building. In some cases, insulation can be used to provide frost protection for shallow foundations. Competent design is normally called for when using this approach.

The distance between the footings base and the finished grade should usually be at least the depth of frost penetration. Table 3 shows the minimum depths for several soil conditions. Where fill has been used, the foundation should extend below the fill to undisturbed earth or be designed to suit the condition of the fill.

Wall Footings

The size of the wall footings should comply with building code requirements. Table 4 presents the size of concrete footings on average stable soil. However, if the distance of the water table from the bearing surface is the same as the width of the footings, the footings sizes listed in Table 4 should be doubled. Unless soil conditions and design allow for sharply cut trenches, side forms should be used for footings.

Footings should project beyond each side of the wall at least 4 in. (100 mm), and without reinforcement their

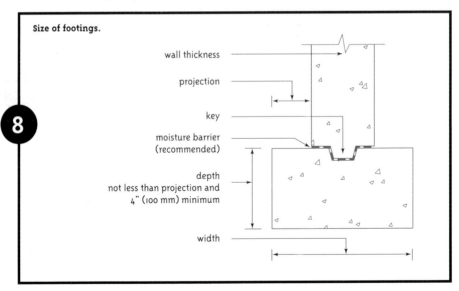

Size of footings.

wall thickness

projection

key

moisture barrier (recommended)

depth
not less than projection and
4" (100 mm) minimum

width

8

thickness should be no less than the projection beyond the wall. Footings must never be less than 4 in. (100 mm) thick (Fig. 8). If the soil is of low loadbearing capacity, wider reinforced footings may be required. Local building officials are often in a position to provide useful advice on local conditions.

A key carved into the top of the footings is a good practice that helps the foundation wall resist the lateral pressures from the earth pushing against it.

If the footings excavation is uneven and in places too deep, a compacted granular mat can be used to level the excavation. Excavated material should not be used as a base.

Pipe trenches directly under wall footings should be backfilled with concrete.

Wood Footings

For preserved wood foundations, continuous wood footings are usually more practical and economical than concrete footings. Wood footings and the granular drainage layer act together to distribute loads from the structure to the undisturbed soil. Sizes of interior and exterior footings and construction practices are given in the Canadian Wood Council publication *Permanent Wood Foundations*.

Column Footings

Footings for posts or columns (Figs. 9 and 10) should be placed so that the members they are supporting will be centered. Footings vary in size depending on the allowable soil pressure and the load they support. On average stable soil, common sizes are 4.3 sq. ft. (0.4 m2) (about 25 x 25 in. (640 x 640 mm)) for one-storey houses and 8 sq. ft. (0.75 m2) (34 x 34 in. (870 x 870 mm)) for two-storey houses. The minimum thickness of column footings without reinforcement must be at least 4 in. (100 mm). The thickness must also never be less

---

Steel column supported on steel bearing plate resting on footings. Base of column embedded in concrete floor. Table 4 provides minimum footing sizes for normal conditions.

layer of sheathing membrane or polyethylene around steel column to break bond of concrete to slab

steel column

concrete floor

dampproofing

granular fill

steel bearing plate

thickness

projection

concrete footing

The thickness of the footing must not be less than the projection and never less than 4" (100 mm).

Wood column supported on concrete footings. Polyethylene layer separates wood from concrete. Base of column may be soaked in wood preservative for additional moisture protection.

10

- wood column
- concrete floor
- dampproofing
- granular fill
- layer of polyethylene around wood column
- thickness
- projection
- concrete footing

than the column footings pad projection measured from the edge of the column base plate to the edge of the footings pad. Footings for fireplaces and chimneys are usually placed at the same time as other footings.

Stepped Footings

On steeply sloping sites, or where an unstable soil is encountered in part of the excavation, stepped footings may be required. They may also be required in split-level houses. The vertical part of the step should be placed at the same time as the footing. The bottom

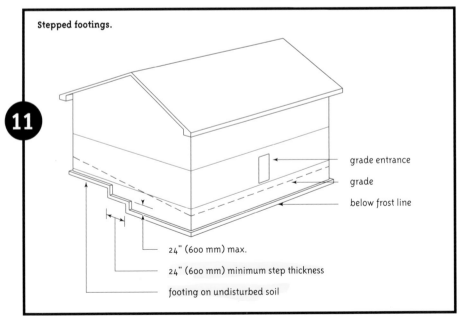

Stepped footings.

11

- grade entrance
- grade
- below frost line
- 24" (600 mm) max.
- 24" (600 mm) minimum step thickness
- footing on undisturbed soil

of the footing is always placed on undisturbed soil or compacted granular fill with each run level.

The vertical connection between footings at the step should be of concrete at least 6 in. (150 mm) thick and the same width as the footings (Fig. 11). On steep slopes, more than one step may be required. Except in rock, the vertical distance between steps should not exceed 24 in. (600 mm), and the horizontal distance between steps should not be less than 24 in. (600 mm). For sand or gravel, a vertical distance between steps of no more than 16 in. (400 mm) is recommended. For very steep slopes, where these limitations cannot be maintained, special footings may be required.

FOUNDATIONS

The foundation wall carries the floor, wall, roof and other building loads (including snow and occupant loads) down to the footings. The three materials commonly used are cast-in-place concrete, concrete blocks and preserved wood. Precast concrete or steel foundations may also be used.

Wall thickness of concrete and concrete block walls may vary from 6 to 12 in. (150 to 300 mm) depending upon their depth below grade and the lateral support provided by the floor-framing system. Table 1 shows minimum foundation wall thickness for solid concrete and concrete masonry units in stable soils.

Where unstable soils are encountered, construction of foundation walls should follow proven local practices or be specifically designed by an engineer.

Formwork for Foundations

Crushed stone or a coarse granular mat is used around the perimeter and under the basement slab for drainage, and for radon mitigation should it be discovered to be a problem. It is advantageous to spread the layer of stone around the footings in advance to provide a clean, dry surface on which to work.

Formwork for concrete walls must be tight, well-braced and tied to withstand the pressure of the concrete. Reusable forms are made of plywood or steel, and use steel form ties to hold the two sides of the formwork together (Fig. 12). The ties are usually broken off to remove the forms when the concrete has set. If these forms are not available, the formwork may be made with lumber (tongue-and-groove or shiplap) or plywood, together with the necessary framing members. They can be built in sections and then erected.

Combination steel form ties and separators are generally used to hold the forms together and to maintain the necessary width. Where wire ties are used, wood spacer blocks, whose length equals the finished thickness of the wall, are placed between the faces of the form. Where wood spacer blocks are used, they must be removed and not left in the concrete. Wire ties hold the forms rigidly against the spacer blocks. Chalklines, pour strips or nails may be used on wood forms to show the elevation at which the concrete will be placed.

New insulated form products are emerging across Canada. These provide both the formwork and the insulation for the concrete wall. They

Concrete formwork and combination form ties.

wall thickness

break point

12

reusable forms —
plywood or other
facing

waler

horizontal
bracing

diagonal brace
if required

form tie

stake

block

anchor bolt

cast-in-place
concrete wall

strip footing

eliminate the need for form stripping and in some situations provide real advantages.

Frames for basement windows, doors and other openings, along with the boxes that will form notches for the ends of floor beams, are set into place when the formwork is built. Framing and bracing are used to keep the forms vertical and in place until the concrete has set (Fig. 13). It is important to check the diagonals of the frames to ensure that the frames are square.

If wood beams at or below grade are not treated with preservative to prevent decay, the wall notch or pocket for such beams must allow at least 1/2 in. (12 mm) of clearance at the sides and ends of the beam for air

Concrete frames and braces: **(A)** window installed in cast-in-place concrete wall; **(B)** framing/bracing around door frame.

A

wood plate

window frame set to inside face of wall

temporary bracing (sash panel removed)

B

slope to exterior

8" (200 mm) minimum

finished grade line

preservative-treated wood buck (frame)

temporary horizontal bracing

caulking

13

Notches or beam pockets in foundation walls.

$^1/_2$" (12 mm) clearance if beam untreated where beam bottom is below grade

foundation wall

notch or pocket for beam

3 $^1/_2$" (90 mm) minimum bearing

steel bearing plate

14

Note: Separate wood beams installed less than 6" (150 mm) above grade from concrete with dampproofing material such as 2 mil (0.05 mm) polyethylene.

circulation (Fig. 14). These air circulation requirements do not apply to steel beams.

Where a masonry chimney is to be incorporated in the outside walls, provision should be made for it at this stage.

Forms should not be removed until the concrete has acquired sufficient strength to support loads imposed during early construction. At least two days are required, but a week is preferable, particularly in cold weather.

After the forms have been removed, all holes and recesses from the form ties must be sealed with cement mortar or dampproofing material.

Cast-in-place Foundation Walls

Concrete should be placed continuously without interruption. During the placing operation, it should be tamped or vibrated to remove air pockets and to work the material under window frames and other blocking.

Anchor bolts for sill plates should be placed while the concrete is in an unhardened condition. Anchorage is commonly accomplished by 1/2 in. (12.7 mm) thick anchor bolts spaced not more than 8 ft. (2.4 m) apart (Fig. 15). Anchor bolts should be embedded at least 4 in. (100 mm) into the foundation wall. The end of the anchor bolt embedded in the concrete should be deformed or bent to provide good secure anchoring. Also ensure that the bolts are free from oil and that the concrete has cured to minimize withdrawal of the bolt.

Control Joints

Uncontrolled cracking can occur in concrete slabs and walls. If this is to be

Method of anchoring floor system to concrete walls, showing anchor bolt for wood sill.

15

header joist

foundation

joist

1 1/2" (38 mm) minimum joist bearing

nut and large washer

anchor bolt

sill plate

mortar bed or foam gasket

Different combinations of slab/footing and slab/wall isolation joints may be used together, as desired.

wall or column

perimeter joint between floor slab and wall column. For details of various types, see sketches below.

16

floor slab

footing

sheathing membrane

polyethylene sheet

premoulded joint filler

1" (25 mm) sand cushion

double layer of sheathing membrane

dampproof course

reglet in slab, sealed waterproofing membrane

Control joint in basement wall.

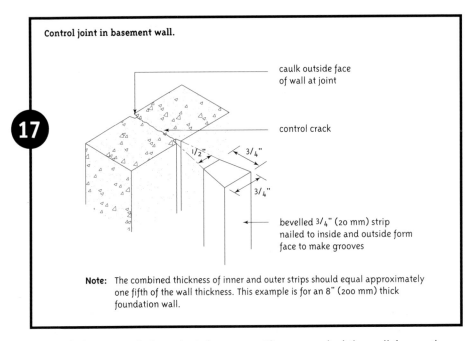

caulk outside face
of wall at joint

control crack

1/2"

3/4"

3/4"

bevelled 3/4" (20 mm) strip
nailed to inside and outside form
face to make grooves

Note: The combined thickness of inner and outer strips should equal approximately
one fifth of the wall thickness. This example is for an 8" (200 mm) thick
foundation wall.

avoided, or controlled, steel reinforcing rods or properly located and
formed vertical control joints should
be used (Figs. 16 and 17). Wall crack
control joints are formed by nailing
strips of wood about 3/4 in. (20 mm)
thick, beveled from 3/4 to 1/2 in. (20 to
12 mm) in width, to the inside of both
interior and exterior wall forms. The
purpose of these is to make grooves in
the wall that will predetermine the
location of shrinkage cracks. Control
joints are necessary in walls longer
than 82 ft. (25 m). Shorter walls are
also susceptible to cracking. Control
joints in these walls are also recommended.

Control joints should be located
first at the natural planes of weakness,
such as windows and doors, and then
within 10 ft. (3 m) from the corners,
and 20 ft. (6 m) apart. The sides of
windows or door openings, if present,
should be chosen as joint locations.

After removal of the wall forms, the
groove in the exterior face of the wall
should be carefully caulked with a
good-quality joint sealer (Fig. 17). The
dampproofing material, applied after
the caulking operation, should be
compatible with the caulking material used. A supplier should be
contacted for advice regarding the
compatibility of caulking materials.

Concrete-block Foundation Walls

Concrete blocks are available in various sizes and shapes, but the most
widely used come in modular sizes 8
in. (200 mm) high, 16 in. (400 mm)
long, and 6, 8, 10 or 12 in. (150, 200,
250 or 300 mm) wide. The actual size
is 3/8 in. (10 mm) less than the modular size to allow for the mortar joint.

Block courses (rows) start at the
footings and are laid up with 3/8 to 1/2
in. (10 to 12 mm) mortar joints. No joint

should exceed 3/4 in. (20 mm). All joints should be tooled smooth to resist water seepage. Full bed and head joints should be used in the bottom course. Succeeding courses may be laid with mortar applied to the contact surfaces of the block. Pilasters are column-like projections that normally protrude into the basement space. They are sometimes required by building codes to strengthen a wall or support a beam. Ensure that they are placed at a height where they can properly support beams if necessary. In these situations, they will often need to be at a height lower than the top of the foundation.

Special concrete blocks, such as universal, pier or sash blocks, should be used to frame the sides of openings for basement doors and windows. For example, sash blocks (Fig. 18) have a keyed face or recess into which the frames are connected, thus providing rigidity and preventing air infiltration. Proper sill and lintel details should also be used to achieve the same effect.

Block walls should be capped either with 2 in. (50 mm) of solid masonry or concrete, or with a mortar filling in the top course of blocks. Alternatively, where termites are not a problem, a wood plank 2 in. (38 mm) thick and the same width as the wall may be used. At grade, another separation should be introduced to prevent convection currents in the cores of hollow masonry walls. This separation can be achieved with a strip of polyethylene between the top two courses, by filling the top course with mortar, or by using a solid masonry unit.

In all cases, the siding should

Concrete blocks for foundation construction.

Stretcher — 8" (190 mm), 16" (390 mm), 8" (190 mm)

Corner — 8", 16", 8"

Beam or lintel — 8", 16", 8"

Sash — 16" (390 mm), 8" (190 mm), 4" (100 mm), 4", 2" (50 mm)

Solid top — 8", 16", 8"

Beam or lintel — 8", 8", 8"

Note: All dimensions are nominal dimensions

18

overlap the foundation wall by at least 1/2 in. (12 mm) so that the rainwater cannot reach the top of the foundation. Pilasters supporting beams should be capped with 8 in. (200 mm) of solid masonry.

Freshly-laid block walls should be protected from below-freezing temperatures. Freezing of the mortar before it is set will result in low adhesion, low strength and joint failures. Mortar mix proportions should conform to those shown in Table 5.

Concrete-block walls should be parged on the outside with at least 1/4 in. (6 mm) of Portland cement plaster. A cove should be formed on the outside perimeter joint between the footings and the wall (Fig. 19). The wall should then be dampproofed by applying at least one heavy coat of bituminous material over the parging

up to the proposed ground level. For added protection where quantities of water accumulate in the soil, two layers of bitumen-saturated membrane may be mopped on and coated overall with a heavy coating of bituminous material. This covering will prevent leaks if minor cracks develop in the blocks or joints between the blocks.

Preserved Wood Foundations

Preserved wood foundations are constructed by the same methods employed in house framing with some additional bracing requirements. The foundations usually consist of a pressure-treated wood footings plate resting on a granular drainage layer, with pressure-treated bottom and top plates, studs and blocking and pressure-treated plywood as outside

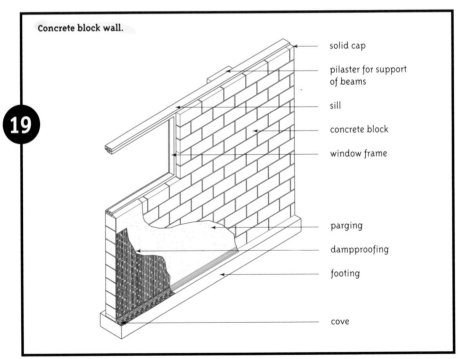

Concrete block wall.

- solid cap
- pilaster for support of beams
- sill
- concrete block
- window frame
- parging
- dampproofing
- footing
- cove

19

PLANNING AHEAD

Minimum Foundation Wall Thickness for Exterior Insulated Masonry Veneer Walls

When determining the minimum thickness of foundation walls required in Table 1, it is important to consider:

→ how the exterior walls will be framed;

→ the thickness of exterior insulation materials;

→ the width of the air space; and

→ the thickness of masonry veneer, such as brick or stone.

brick veneer

air space

exterior insulation

offset stud wall

minimum thickness required in Table 1

minimum thickness required to accommodate insulation and support brick veneer above

Review the *Wall Framing* chapter for framing options and details. Check the *Wall Sheathings and Exterior Finishes* and *Thermal Insulation* chapters when calculating the required thickness for foundation walls supporting masonry veneer.

PLANNING AHEAD

Sill Anchors in Concrete and Masonry Foundations

Before pouring a concrete foundation, or completing the final courses of a masonry foundation, it is necessary to determine how the floor joists will be anchored and supported. The two most common options are illustrated below. If a sill plate is going to be employed, then its location on top of the wall must be known in order to establish the centre-line for sill anchor bolt placement. Refer to the **Floor Framing** chapter for sill anchor bolt placement and use.

Options for anchoring and supporting floor joists

floor joists nailed to sill plate anchored to concrete or masonry foundation wall

floor joists embedded in top of concrete or masonry foundation wall

anchor bolt

→ When building in areas where high winds due to hurricanes or tornadoes are known to occur, additional measures for anchoring the floor framing to the foundation may be considered.

→ Consult a competent structural designer for specific details in such cases.

cladding, covered with a polyethylene sheet for dampproofing. The space between the studs may be filled with insulation and the interior finished to provide a well-insulated living space partly or entirely below ground level.

In preserved wood foundations, all wood used in the foundation system must be pressure treated with chemical preservatives in accordance with Canadian Standards Association (CSA) Standard O80.15. The chemicals permanently impregnate the wood cells to levels of penetration and concentration that make the wood highly resistant to attack by decay organisms and insects such as termites. The dried wood is odorless, and is only slightly coloured. Properly treated lumber and plywood can be identified by a certification mark showing that the material has been treated by a plant certified according to CSA Standard O322 (Fig. 20).

Wood foundations are suitable for low-rise or multiple dwellings. They can be built with a conventional concrete slab floor, a wood floor on sleepers resting on a granular drainage layer, or a suspended wood floor (Fig. 21). They must be designed to carry not only the vertical load of the house and its floor and roof loads but also the horizontal loads of the

---

Facsimile of certification mark.

> Company name and logo
>
> (SA) **CERTIFIED 0322**
> **CERTIFIÉ**
>
> **PWF — FBT**
> **L/B·P/C CCA 2577**

20

The certification mark contains the following information:

 – identifies the certifying agency

O322 – identifies the standard, CSA O322, under which the material is certified

PWF and FBT – identifies the intended use of the material

L/B and/or P/C – the plant is licensed for lumber and/or plywood inspection

CCA (or ACA) – identifies the preservative used

2577 – the first two digits identify the treating plant, the last two the year of treatment

Preservative-treated wood foundations: *(A)* with concrete floor slab and wood footings; *(B)* with wood sleeper floor; *(C)* with suspended wood floor; *(D)* on concrete strip foundation (see next page).

A

typical wood-frame wall

finished grade
(minimum slope
of 1 in 12)

framing strap

treated wall stud

treated plywood cover

2" x 4" (38 x 89 mm)
treated blocking between
studs (backing at panel joint)

backfill

treated
exterior plywood

treated wall plate

treated footing plate

polyethylene
(stops at grade)

treated screed board

concrete slab

gravel bed
5" (125 mm)
minimum

polyethylene

12" (300 mm)
minimum

B

treated subfloor

treated floor joist

polyethylene

treated wood sleeper

treated blocking between
studs (backing for panel joint
and nailer for interior finish)

2" x 6" (38 x 140 mm) ledger

C

subfloor

floor joist

treated top wall plate

treated stud

treated wall plate

polyethylene

Note: Shaded areas indicate those members that are preservative treated.

Preservative-treated wood foundations (cont'd): **(D)** on concrete strip foundation.

D

treated wall plate

treated screed board

concrete strip footing resting on undisturbed soil

water passages 2 1/2" (60 mm) minimum diameter at 4' (1.2 m) o.c.

21

concrete slab on polyethylene

compacted granular drainage layer

Note: Shaded areas indicate those members that are preservative treated.

Concrete footings resting on granular drainage layer.

sheathing

exterior wall studs

screed board

concrete slab floor

polyethylene sheet, sand or other bond breaker

granular drainage layer

5" (125 mm) minimum

undisturbed soil

22

Note: Shaded areas indicate those members that are preservative treated.

backfill material. The required size, species and grade of studs and thickness of plywood depend on stud spacing and backfill height and the number of storeys supported.

SLABS

Concrete slabs are used for basement floors and for houses or portions of houses constructed at grade. In small buildings, they are generally supported by the ground below and not by the structure at the perimeter.

Basement Floor Slabs

Basement floors are usually installed after the roof construction is completed, the building enclosed, sewer and water lines installed, and the basement floor drain in place. While curing, concrete gives off moisture which can seriously affect finish flooring, drywall or millwork. The basement should be ventilated to allow moisture to escape before finish flooring or millwork is installed.

Basement floor slabs should be at least 3 in. (75 mm) thick and sloped toward the floor drain. There should be at least one drain (or sump pit), located near the laundry area if provided.

The following summary provides a reminder of the requirements, the good practice and the sequence of events in the construction of concrete basement floor slabs.

1. Complete the installation of sewer lines and other subsurface work before the slab is placed. Compact backfill in trenches.

2. Put at least 4 in. (100 mm) of crushed rock or coarse gravel under the floor slab to restrict the passage of moisture by capillary action from the ground to the slab and to facilitate soil gas remediation if necessary.

3. Apply a layer of 6 mil (0.15 mm) polyethylene sheet or Type S roll roofing below the slab to dampproof the floor. Dampproofing is especially desirable when a finish floor will be attached later to the slab by an adhesive. Where the water table is high, waterproofing the slab, as detailed below, will be necessary to avoid problems. To prevent the entry of soil gas, polyethylene that is lapped at least 4 in. (100 mm) at the joints can be used (Fig. 22).

4. In order to allow for slight movement due to shrinkage of the slab during drying and settling of the subbase, a premoulded joint filler or double layer of sheathing paper (Fig. 16) between floor slab and wall or column should be provided.

5. After the concrete has been placed and consolidated, it should be struck off with a straightedge to the proper elevation. This can be determined by measuring down from the bottom of properly leveled floor joists. In order to eliminate local high or low areas and to embed large aggregate particles, the surface is then immediately smoothed using a large float of either the darby or bull type or by using other appropriate means. Tools used for air-entrained concrete should have a magnesium surface. Care must be taken not to overwork the concrete, because this will result in a less durable surface.

6. After the water sheen has disappeared and the concrete has stiffened slightly, edging, jointing and floating operations can begin. Any of these operations performed while bleed water is present will cause serious dusting or scaling.

7. If minor random cracking in the slab is to be avoided, proper control jointing or grooving may be necessary. Control joints should be placed on line with interior columns and at changes in width of floor slab (Fig. 23). The maximum spacing of control joints should be between 15 to 20 ft. (4.5 and 6.0 m) in either direction. Joints may be formed in the freshly placed concrete by cutting grooves by hand with a jointing tool as soon as the concrete is firm enough. The depth of joints should be about one-quarter of the thickness of the floor slab.

Location of control joints.

1. control joints within 10' (3 m) of corners.
2. spacing of joints 20' (6 m) maximum
3. joints incorporate side of opening.
4. perimeter joint between floor and wall
5. control joint in floor slab
6. floor slab joint spacing of 20' (6 m) maximum
7. control joint around column footings
   (see note)

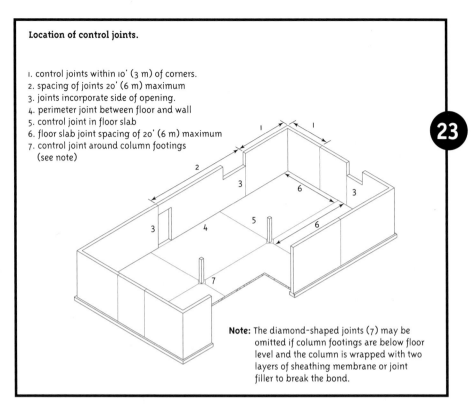

23

Note: The diamond-shaped joints (7) may be omitted if column footings are below floor level and the column is wrapped with two layers of sheathing membrane or joint filler to break the bond.

8. As soon as the floor surface has been finished, curing should begin. Curing should continue for at least five days at air temperature of 70°F (21°C) or higher, or for seven days at temperatures of 50°F (10°C) to 70°F (21°C). Curing may be carried out by ponding water on top of the slab (by temporarily plugging all floor drains), or by covering with burlap, which is kept continuously wet. If this is not practical, liquid membrane-forming curing compound spread on the concrete surface may be used. If the finish is to be tile, caution should be used, because curing compounds may not be compatible with adhesives.

Slabs-on-ground

Because the requirements for slabs-on-ground are similar to basement slabs (Fig. 24), the steps and precautions described above apply here as well. An important difference is the need to establish the finish floor level at a sufficient height above the natural grade so that the finished grade will provide good drainage away from the house. The top of the slab should be at least 8 in. (200 mm) above finished grade.

It also important to remember that all debris, stumps and organic matter from the unexcavated areas under the building should be removed to provide a smooth surface free of soft pockets. As well, the soil should be tamped where loose.

Independent concrete floor slab and foundation wall. Slab is supported on 5 in. (125 mm) of coarse fill and on a ledge formed in the foundation wall.

stud

air/vapour barrier

insulation

drywall

finish flooring

concrete slab reinforced

metal or vinyl siding

sheathing membrane

sheathing

base flashing

6" (150 mm) minimum

$1/2$" (12 mm) cement parging on wire lath

well-compacted fill under slab

rigid insulation

sand cushion

foundation wall

vapour barrier

sill gasket

A water-repellent type of rigid insulation should be installed around the perimeter of the slab. Rigid insulation should be protected from physical or ultraviolet damage by using parging or a board finish. The slab should also be reinforced with approximately 0.15 in. (3.6 mm) thick reinforcing steel bars spaced 2 ft. (600 mm) on centre in both directions. (The steel bars have a metric product designation of 10M.) Alternatively, a welded wire mesh can be used that forms a grid of 6 in. (152 mm) squares in which the thickness of the steel is 0.15 in. (3.4 mm). (The metric product designation of this grid is 152 x 152

MW9.1 x MW9.1.)

A topping is generally not needed since the finished surface resulting from mechanical troweling is very smooth. When a topping is used, it should consist of 1 part cement to 2 1/2 parts well-graded sand. A layer 3/4 in. (20 mm) thick is placed after the concrete slab has set. The layer should be troweled to a smooth level finish.

Footings and foundations for houses with slabs-on-ground have similar requirements as those for crawl spaces and are constructed in the same manner.

FOUNDATION DAMPPROOFING AND WATER-PROOFING

Foundation dampproofing on the exterior face of the foundation is intended to control the movement of soil moisture into the foundation. On the interior face of the foundation, it is also used to prevent the movement of moisture from concrete or unit masonry foundation walls into interior wood framing that supports insulation or interior finishes. Dampproofing takes many forms. Most commonly, a heavy coat of bituminous material, polyethylene or other sheet material is used.

Waterproofing, on the other hand, is intended to deal with severe water problems normally associated with high water tables. Whereas dampproofing is necessary for all foundations, waterproofing is required only for foundations that are subject to hydrostatic pressures. Special attention of a qualified professional is normally recommended for these buildings. Often special steps need to be taken to deal with the water and the forces that are superimposed onto the foundation.

Concrete and unit masonry walls below grade should be dampproofed with a heavy coat of bituminous material applied on the exterior surface from the footings to the finished grade line. Such a coating is usually sufficient to make the wall watertight against ordinary seepage that may occur after a rainstorm or from soil dampness.

Added protection from moisture can be provided by special dense glass-fibre insulation or by other commercially available drainage layers, which will be discussed later.

In poorly drained soils, waterproofing walls may be necessary, and should consist of an impermeable membrane such as two layers of bitumen-saturated felt. The two layers of felt should be attached to the wall and each other, and covered with liquid bitumen.

Where hydrostatic pressures exist, waterproofing the foundation involves more than the two layers of impermeable wall membrane as noted. It also requires that the floor slab is waterproofed with a membrane sandwiched between two layers of concrete each not less than 3 in. (75 mm) thick. The floor membrane must extend to the wall membrane forming a complete seal. In many cases, foundations subjected to hydrostatic pressure are also equipped with a means of relieving the water pressure, preventing structural damage.

It should be clear that foundations that are waterproofed do not need to be dampproofed. Waterproofing can provide all of the protection that dampproofing normally provides.

Care must be taken when backfilling walls to prevent damage to the dampproofing, waterproofing, insulation or drainage layer.

Dampproofing is also required on the interior of concrete or unit masonry walls that come into contact with interior wood framing that supports insulation or interior finishes. The dampproofing, installed between the foundation wall and interior framing, prevents moisture in the foundation wall from coming into contact with the wood framing. The dampproofing must extend from the basement floor and terminate at the exterior finish grade level.

FOUNDATION DRAINAGE

In most locations, it is necessary to drain away any subsurface water to prevent damp basements and wet floors. Drainage is required in most areas unless it can be shown that natural, free-draining soil makes it unnecessary. Foundation drainage normally consists of a drain tile installed around the perimeter of the basement and at times a wall drainage layer. A layer of granular material can often substitute for the perimeter drain tile as noted below.

Drain tile should be laid on solid undisturbed soil around the footings, making sure that the top of the tile is below the level of the basement floor

or crawl space, with a slight slope to the outlet. The tile is then covered with a minimum of 6 in. (150 mm) of coarse, clean gravel or crushed rock (Fig. 25).

The drain tile should be connected with a tight joint pipe to a storm sewer or other satisfactory outlet. Adequate drainage to prevent the infiltration of water into the basement is essential. A sump may be necessary in some cases.

On wet sites, special drainage features, such as lateral drain tiles under the floor slab, may be needed to avoid hydrostatic pressures on basement walls and slab. Note that foundation drainage is not intended to deal with high water tables. Buildings sited on high water tables normally will require involving a professional engineer or architect in the design.

If a preserved wood foundation is used, a granular layer must be employed in combination with a sump. The bottom of the excavation is sloped so that it drains to the sump, which is subsequently drained by

Drain tile at foundation wall.

25

dampproofing

6" (150 mm) coarse gravel or crushed stone

footing

perforated plastic drain tile

gravity or mechanical means. The granular layer should extend at least 12 in. (300 mm) beyond the footings plate and, if thicker than 8 in. (200 mm), should be compacted.

This granular layer technique is applicable to any type of foundation. With concrete footings placed on undisturbed soil, water passages of 2.5 in. (60 mm) in diameter and at regular 4 ft. (1.2 m) intervals should be put in the footings to permit draining water to the sump (Fig. 26).

Wall drainage layers are required by building codes in some regions of the country. Consult the local building department in your area. Drainage layer materials are normally applied to the outside of the basement wall. They are intended to direct infiltrating rain water, that comes into contact with the foundation wall, down to the drain tile, and prevent the water from entering the basement through cracks or poorly sealed tie rod holes that might exist.

Wall drainage layers normally consist of 3/4 in. (19 mm) or thicker mineral-fibre insulation with a density of at least 3.6 lb./cu. ft. (57 kg/m3) or other commercially available wall drainage materials. Alternatively, free-draining granular material may be used as backfill. It is important that the drainage layer directs water to the drain tile avoiding any possible ponding of water at the base of the foundation wall. The granular fill that surrounds the drain tile should also cover the base of the wall drainage layer.

As with foundation walls, surface drainage should be directed away from basement windows. Basement windows that extend below ground level require window wells (Fig. 27). Galvanized sheet steel, corrugated for added strength, is commonly used for this purpose. This type of window

Concrete footing resting on undisturbed soil

undisturbed soil

sheathing

exterior wall studs

treated wall plate

treated screed board

concrete strip footing resting on undisturbed soil

concrete slab floor

26

polyethylene sheet, sand, or other bond breaker

compacted granular drainage layer

water passages 2 1/2" (60 mm) minimum diameter at 4' (1.2 m) o.c. around perimeter

Note: Shaded areas indicate those members that are preservative treated

Window well at basement wall.

27

building foundation

slope directing surface drainage away from building

basement window

corrugated metal window well

backfill

drilled hole leading to weeping tile

well is available in a variety of sizes to suit various window openings. For concrete window wells, forms are installed and the concrete placed after the backfill has been compacted.

When the backfill is not a granular material, the bottom of the window well should be drained by a tube or hole 6 in. (150 mm) in diameter drilled down through the backfill material to the drain tile and filled with crushed stone.

BACKFILLING

Backfilling foundation walls should not be carried out until the floor joists and subfloor are in place. This applies to concrete, masonry and preserved wood foundation walls. Table 1 presents the maximum height of the finished grade for both laterally

supported and laterally unsupported foundation walls.

Backfill material should be free of all large rocks, clay clumps and construction wastes. These materials can cause undue pressure on the foundation wall, and, among other problems, can cause settlement and uneven drainage. Ensure backfill material is suitable, preferably with good drainage characteristics.

Sudden pressures against foundation walls brought about by loads of backfill material may cause the walls to move, resulting in damage such as cracking in the wall. It is important, therefore, that backfill material be deposited gradually and uniformly around the perimeter in small lifts, with each lift being compacted to the appropriate density before the next lift is placed. Care

PLANNING AHEAD

Weeping Tiles, Sumps and Sewage Ejectors

The means by which the foundation and basement plumbing will be drained requires careful planning, particularly in areas without sewers.

Foundation drainage may consist of weeping tile or a granular drainage layer, or both. When the house is located on a site where gravity drainage of the foundation is possible, a sump pump is not required. However, in flat or low-lying areas without storm sewers, a sump pump will be required to pump the water to a ditch or dry well. In areas with storm sewers, it may also be required when the foundation drainage lies below the storm sewer.

When plumbing fixtures are installed in the basement of a house located below the sanitary sewer, or without municipal sewer services, a sewage ejector is required to pump sewage up to the sewer or septic system. Some key factors to consider in such cases include:

→ Always check with the building department for local requirements regarding foundation drainage and basement plumbing.

→ Avoid leading water from roofs and driveways into the foundation drainage system. Drain this water away from the house.

→ Use gravity drainage of foundations and basement plumbing in areas without municipal sewer services whenever possible. Plan the location of the building and septic system accordingly.

→ Plan site drainage to divert water away from wells and septic systems.

→ Only use sump pumps and sewage ejectors with tight seals to avoid odours and soil gases from entering the dwelling.

→ Never combine the use of a sewage ejector as a sump pump when it is connected to a septic system. The water will dilute the effluent in the septic tank and impair its proper digestion.

→ Consider the location of any other services entering at or beneath the foundation to avoid conflicting interference.

Refer to the *Eavestroughs and Downspouts* chapter for more information on dealing with roof drainage. The *Surface Drainage, Driveways and Walkways* chapter discusses options for draining runoff.

must also be taken to ensure that externally mounted insulation, drainage material, dampproofing or waterproofing membrane are not damaged.

FOUNDATION INSULATION

Foundation insulation provides a means of reducing the heat loss of the building. Depending on the approach taken, foundation insulation can also provide other benefits, such as acting as an exterior wall drainage layer. The requirements for basement insulation vary from province to province. Check with the local municipality for the local requirements.

Foundations can be insulated on the interior or the exterior of the building. Interior insulated basements may be partially insulated with insulation extending 2 ft. (600 mm) below grade or full depth. Interior basement insulation often requires installing framing to support the insulation and the interior finish. This approach creates a finished basement space that often adds to the habitable areas of the house.

Insulating the basement from the outside provides its own advantages. The insulation often can also provide wall drainage offering additional protection while reducing heat loss. Exterior basement insulation also reduces the temperature swing that the foundation wall experiences, which often reduces thermal stresses and the cracking that sometimes results. The disadvantage of this system is that the insulation often requires protection because it extends above grade.

FOOTINGS AND FOUNDATIONS FOR CRAWL SPACES

Houses with a crawl space are supported on a foundation wall that is carried at least 6 in. (150 mm) above the exterior finished grade.

Trenches are dug for the foundation walls and the footings placed at a depth below grade determined by soil conditions and frost penetration (see Table 3). The sizes of the footings are generally the same as those used to support basement walls. The foundation walls may be built of concrete, concrete masonry units or preserved wood, but since the inside grade is never much lower than the outside grade, the thickness of the foundation walls is usually less than those enclosing a basement. Table 1 shows minimum foundation wall thickness for stable soils.

Footings for columns supporting the floor beams should be placed on solid undisturbed ground, and this may require some excavation. Concrete, masonry or preserved wood columns are generally used to support the beams. The excavated area is backfilled around the base of the columns and footings when the crawl space floor is leveled. Crawl space insulation, which can be installed either at the perimeter of the foundation or in the floor frame under the living space, is discussed and illustrated in the chapter on *Thermal Insulation*.

Crawl Space Ventilation and Ground Cover

Where the crawl space floor is below the level of the outside finished grade, the foundation walls should be damp-proofed. Drain tile is then installed around the footings and connected to a drain. The floor of the crawl space and access trenches is graded toward the drain, and a ground cover of 6 mil (0.15 mm) polyethylene or Type S roll roofing is installed over the surface with the joints lapped at least 4 in. (100 mm). The ground cover prevents ground moisture from entering the crawl space area. The crawl space should also be ventilated. See the chapter on Ventilation.

GARAGE FOUNDATIONS

Foundations for garages are usually concrete or masonry, although concrete slab-on-grade or preserved wood foundations are also used. The minimum depth below grade for a garage foundation attached to a house should not be less than that shown in Table 3.

If fill is required below the floor, a granular material is preferable and should be well compacted to avoid settlement after the floor is laid. With a base of 6 in. (150 mm) of crushed stone or gravel, the concrete floor should be at least 3 in. (75 mm) thick. Unless a floor drain is installed, the floor should be sloped toward the entrance.

Detailing, placing and curing of concrete garage floors should be carried out as described for basement floor slabs. Control joints should be used to produce panels as nearly square as possible. For a single car garage, one control joint should be sufficient.

The foundation walls should not be less than 6 in. (150 mm) thick and should extend at least 6 in. (150 mm) above grade.

Sill plates should be anchored to the foundation wall or slab with anchor bolts spaced about 8 ft. (2.4 m) apart and with at least two bolts in each sill piece. Extra anchors may be required at the side of the main door.

RELATED PUBLICATIONS

Construction of Preserved Wood Foundations
Canadian Standards Association

The Living House: Part 1 - Foundations (Video)
Canada Mortgage and Housing Corporation

The 10.1 Solution: Foundations for Manufactured Homes (Video)
Canada Mortgage and Housing Corporation

Moisture in Atlantic Housing
Canada Mortgage and Housing Corporation

PROTECTION AND CARE OF MATERIALS ON THE BUILDING SITE

The protection of building materials on the site and their storage before use are very important. If materials are stored without protection in inclement weather, damage may be caused that could be reflected in wastage of material and troublesome construction defects.

As much as possible, material should be delivered to the site just before it is to be used. This is especially true of exterior window and door frames and exterior trim materials. Interior finishing materials may be stored in the house once the roof is on.

In the normal staging of construction, the framing lumber and sheathing materials are delivered to the job after the foundation is complete. Structural and framing materials in place before the house is enclosed will be subject to wetting during rainstorms, but the moisture is mostly on the exposed surfaces and can dry out quickly in subsequent dry weather without causing damage.

Lumber stored in close piles, however, may soak up and retain water, causing very slow drying out. This condition should be avoided because it may lead to staining and decay. Piles of lumber should be placed on skids raised off the ground and covered with sheets of waterproof material to shed water. Sheets of polyethylene may also be placed on the ground, under the skids to prevent ground moisture from wetting the lumber.

After the framing is started, the roof shingles may be delivered. Asphalt shingles should be stored so that the bundles can lie flat without bending. Using curved or buckled shingles will result in an unattractive roof.

Windows and doors are usually the next items to be installed after the roofing. If the frames are delivered before they can be installed, they should be sheltered until they are used. Good frames are costly items, and exposure to the weather may nullify their good construction. This is especially true where the frames are delivered with the window sash installed.

Insulation, interior wall and ceiling finish, wood siding and similar items can be stored in the house. Heavy materials such as gypsum wallboard should be distributed over the floor area in order not to overload the floor joists. Heavy loads, concentrated on one spot for any appreciable time, may cause permanent deflection in the floor joists.

Hardwood flooring, interior trim and millwork should not be stored in the house until the basement floor has been completed and allowed to dry. The curing of the slab gives off moisture which may cause the kiln-dried material to swell, resulting in shrinkage after the materials are installed.

LUMBER AND OTHER WOOD PRODUCTS

The primary component of wood-frame construction is dimension lumber. It forms the structural shell which encloses and divides spaces and to which finishes are applied. In addition to lumber, other wood products are frequently used in the construction of the shell and in the interior and exterior finishes. All of these products are intended for specific uses and are manufactured to meet certain standards.

The lumber that is commonly used for framing is 1 1/2 to 3 1/2 in. (38 to 89 mm) thick and is called dimension lumber. Timber is the name given to lumber thicker than 4 1/2 in. (114 mm); there are also decking, boards and finish lumber groupings. Table 6 presents the grades, common grade mixes, principal uses, and grade categories for the various sizes of dimension lumber.

GRADE MARKS

Lumber used in construction is grade stamped in Canada with identifying markings to show that it conforms to the National Lumber Grades Authority (NLGA) grading rules for Canadian lumber. The grading and grade marking of lumber must also conform to CSA Standard 0141, "Softwood Lumber." Grade stamps usually show the name or symbol (or both) of the grading agency, the species or species combination designation, the grade, the moisture content at the time of manufacture, and the mill number.

"S-GRN" in the grade mark signifies that the lumber was surfaced at a moisture content higher than 19 percent to a size which would allow for natural shrinkage during seasoning. "S-DRY" in the mark indicates the lumber was surfaced at a moisture content not exceeding 19 percent. "MC 15" indicates a moisture content not exceeding 15 percent.

Facsimiles of Canadian grade marks are shown in Tables 7 and 8.

LUMBER GRADES

Each piece of lumber is examined and assigned a grade depending on its physical characteristics. In addition to visually graded lumber, machine-stress-rated (MSR) lumber is available in Canada. MSR lumber is identified in grade stamps by its structural properties and, for most wood-frame construction purposes, is independent of species.

Many softwood lumber species in Canada are harvested, milled and marketed together. Those having similar properties that enables them to be used together easily are combined into a single-species combination and marketed under a group designation. The Canadian commercial species combinations and their characteristics are shown in Table 9.

The top grade is Select Structural, which is used only where high strength, stiffness and good appearance are required. Lumber marked No. 1 grade often contains some percentage of Select Structural material, but permitted knots are slightly larger.

Tests have shown that No. 1 and No. 2 grades of lumber have the same strength. These grades are popular for most general construction uses. No. 3 grade lumber is used in general construction where appearance is not a factor.

2 x 4 in. (38 x 89 mm) and 2 x 6 in. (38 x 140 mm) lumber are available as Stud grades. Stud grade is stiff, straight lumber suitable for vertical wall members. 2 x 4 in. (38 x 89 mm) is also available as Construction, Standard, Utility and Economy grades. Construction and Standard grade lumber are used for structural purposes. Construction grade lumber has similar strength properties as No. 3 grade, and Standard grade is lower. Utility and Economy grades are not used for structural purposes. Economy is the lowest grade.

Minimum grades for various uses of lumber in wood-frame construction, such as stud wall framing, plank-frame construction, posts and beams, sheathing and subflooring are set forth in the National Building Code of Canada. Tables giving maximum allowable spans for visually graded lumber and for MSR lumber when used as joists and rafters are available from the Canadian Wood Council. In this publication, a number of tables have been provided which present the maximum allowable spans for structural components using various grades of lumber.

Metric sizes of softwood lumber are the same as those in use in Canada under the imperial system of measurement, but their sizes are expressed in millimetres of actual thickness and width after surfacing. The concept of "nominal size" is not used. Table 10 relates the current metric dimensions to the imperial equivalents actual and nominal.

ENGINEERED WOOD PRODUCTS

In addition to dimension lumber, a wide variety of engineered wood products (EWPs) are manufactured for use in wood-frame house construction. These products can provide equivalent or superior performance to dimension lumber, and are typically manufactured using less wood from small, fast-growing trees. EWPs make better use of forest resources. A description of the various types which are available follows. EWPs include products such as glue-laminated timber, wood I-joists and structural composite lumber.

Dimension lumber and other wood products are often combined in the manufacture of EWPs using glue or mechanical fasteners or both. The most common example is the engineered pitched-roof truss. Less common, but of increasing application, is the parallel-chord truss with metal or wood webs. Wood I-joists consisting of lumber flanges and plywood, waferboard or oriented strandboard webs are also being used more frequently (Fig. 28).

All these products provide greater flexibility in design by virtue of their larger spans and their capability to house services. In addition, when used for the roof structure, they can accommodate higher insulation levels.

Parallel chord trusses and wood I-joist.

metal web

wood web

wood I-joist

28

Structural Composite Lumber

Structural composite lumber is a sub-set of EWPs which includes products such as laminated veneer lumber (LVL) and parallel strand lumber (PSL).

Laminated veneer lumber consists of thin veneer panels laid parallel to each other, coated with a waterproof adhesive, and bonded by heat and pressure. Available in a wide variety of sizes and strengths, LVL may be cut into desired lengths for use as beams, columns, headers (lintels), joists, and as flanges in wood I-beams.

Parallel strand lumber is manu-factured using thin veneer panels cut into narrow strips and then bonded together using a process similar to LVL. Members are available in a vari-ety of widths, depths and lengths, and are primarily used as beams, columns and headers.

Finger-jointed studs are an alter-native to milled lumber.

SHEET OR PANEL PRODUCTS

In addition to dimension lumber, other wood products in the form of sheets and panels are used in wood-frame construction. Plywood, oriented strand board and waferboard, for example, are used to add stiffness to the structural components of the roof, wall and floor, apart from forming a uniform surface for the application of other materials. Fibreboard, parti-cleboard and hardboard are also used in many aspects of interior and exte-rior finishing.

Plywood, one of the most commonly and extensively used wood products, is used in constructing the shell (subfloor, roof sheathing, and so on), exterior finishing, some interior finishing and cabinetry.

Plywood is made of thin layers or plies of wood glued together with the grain of each ply running in a counter direction. Common thicknesses range from 1/4 to 3/4 in. (6.0 to 18.5 mm). Like dimension lumber, plywood is graded for particular uses. Douglas fir plywood (DFP) and Canadian softwood plywood (CSP) are the two most common softwood plywoods produced. All sheathing grade plywood, waferboard and oriented strand board is made with an exterior grade glue. Pre-oiled or overlaid plywood is used for concrete formwork.

Waferboard has the same use as plywood: subflooring, roof sheathing and wall sheathing. Waferboard is made of wide wood shavings and glued together.

Oriented strand board (OSB) is similar in appearance to waferboard, but uses strands instead of wafers. The strands are mechanically oriented in layers, with the outer layers running parallel to the long dimension of the sheet, and the inner layers having a random or cross alignment. OSB is primarily used for roof or wall sheathing, sub-flooring, siding and the webs of wood I-joists.

Fibreboard is made of wood fibres bonded together under pressure. It is available both in a plain and an asphalt-impregnated form. The impregnated version is used primarily for wall sheathing.

Particleboard is generally used in underlay or interior finishing such as shelving and other cabinetry. Often covered with a plastic laminate or other protective and decorative material, it is used to manufacture cabinet doors. The same material is often used as the base for plain or preformed kitchen countertops.

Hardboard is made of wood fibre, like fibreboard, but is denser and harder. It is present in many furniture and cabinetry products. Hardboard siding with a prefinished colour is an alternative to wood, vinyl or aluminum siding. Large panels with prefinished and textured surfaces are often used to create special effects inside or outside the building.

RELATED PUBLICATIONS

Wood Reference Handbook
Canadian Wood Council, 1996

FRAMING THE HOUSE

The structural shell of a one- or two-storey house must be erected before any other work can begin. The shell consists of the foundation, floors, walls and roof (Fig. 29). In some cases, interior walls may be loadbearing, so they must be erected at the same time as the exterior walls. The shell must be framed and sheathed during construction to obtain its rigidity. Generally, temporary bracings and cross bracings are introduced to allow construction to proceed without accidents or damage.

Before starting the framing of the house, it is important to consider the levels of insulation to be used in the different elements of the structural shell, because framing dimensions may have to be increased to accommodate higher levels of insulation. Refer to the chapter on *Thermal Insulation* for more information.

The platform and balloon methods of framing are two ways of constructing a wood-frame house. Balloon framing was the most common method of wood-frame construction in the latter part of the 19th century, and early part of the 20th century. Platform framing has dominated since the late 1940s, and today represents conventional practice in Canada.

PLATFORM CONSTRUCTION

The most commonly used method for framing a house is platform construction. The chief advantage of this

Cutaway of a wood-frame house.

29

57

approach is that the floor system, assembled independently from the walls, provides a platform or working surface upon which walls and partitions may be assembled and erected. Since the studs are one storey high, walls can easily be prefabricated off the site or assembled on the subfloor in sections and erected one storey at a time without using heavy lifting equipment. The bottom and top plates, which are an integral part of the wall framing, provide fire stops at the floor and ceiling and also nailing support for wall sheathing and interior finish.

BALLOON CONSTRUCTION

Balloon framing differs from platform framing in that the studs used for exterior and some interior walls are continuous, passing through the floors and ending at the top plates which support the roof framing. Since the connections between the floor joists and studs in balloon framing do not lend themselves to prefabrication or easy assembly on the site, this method of framing houses is rarely used. However, some of the techniques involved in balloon framing may be used with the platform framing method. For example, ceiling joists or dropped ceiling may be supported on a 1 x 4 in. (19 x 89 mm) ribbon let into the studs. Floor joists may also be supported in this manner where the level of the floors is offset at an adjoining wall in split-level houses. In some two-storey houses, the centre load-bearing wall in an otherwise platform-framed house is balloon framed to provide convenient passage for heating ducts and pipes.

HEALTHY HOUSING INSIGHT

Applying the 4 Rs of Wood-Frame Construction

Wood-frame construction has the potential to remain one of the most environmentally appropriate building choices, provided we make the most of our wood resources. Currently, about 20 percent of a typical new house is made up of wood, yet some 40 percent of construction waste is made up of dimensional lumber and manufactured wood products. Clearly, there is a significant opportunity to waste less of this valuable resource. Canada's building industry has responded to this challenge and taken the 4 Rs approach to wood-frame construction: Review, Reduce, Reuse, and Recycle. Here are some important 4 Rs considerations.

Review

Wood-frame house construction follows traditional practices which evolved when wood was abundant and waste management was not an issue. It now makes economic and environmental sense to review how the house will be designed and built.

Continued on page 59

Continued from page 58

→ Review current trade practices and procedures to see if these pose a barrier to the efficient use of wood, as well as any other building materials.

→ Check plans to ensure that standard sizes and maximum spans are used wherever possible — get more house for less cost and waste.

→ Identify alternatives to dimensional lumber, such as engineered wood products (EWPs), and more efficient framing practices.

Reduce

Lumber represents the greatest component of the waste stream for new housing. Better use of our natural resources is possible by reducing inefficient and wasteful practices.

→ Cut all wood in one area on the site. Most waste is generated by poor cutting practices. Organize off cuts so that short lengths are easily visible and readily accessible — use up warped or twisted full length pieces first when a shorter piece is needed.

→ Order materials in packages corresponding to the stage of construction. Avoid having all materials shipped at once. Only order what is needed — make adjustments with each order.

→ Store materials properly to avoid damage. Damaged wood is the second highest cause of wood waste, after poor cutting practices.

→ Use simplified framing techniques, such as constructing walls at 24 in. (600 mm) on centre, wherever possible.

→ Use engineered wood products, such as wood I-joists, laminated veneer lumber and trusses, which provide equal or better performance using smaller trees.

→ Reduce the inefficient use of space in the house. Reduced permit fees and property taxes prove that bigger is not necessarily better.

Reuse

In some cases, materials may be reused, while in other cases, used materials may be purchased or obtained free of charge.

→ Plan ahead to reuse lumber wisely. For example, reuse footing formwork lumber as bracing or strapping.

→ Check with demolition contractors for used building materials. In many cases, these materials will provide acceptable service at a fraction of the cost.

→ Buy recycled rather than new materials.

Continued on page 60

Continued from page 59

Recycle

When it is not possible to eliminate waste entirely, consider recycling.

→ Sort and securely store materials for recycling - avoid using a single waste bin without dividers.

→ Offer waste products to schools or community groups that may have a use for these in shops and crafts.

→ Use the dimensional lumber as kindling wood. In addition to providing warmth and light, burning wood responsibly is the natural way to recycle. *(Note: Do not burn preservative-treated wood.)*

→ The *Healthy Housing* principle of resource efficiency applies not only to wood, but to all building materials. Additional and more specific insights on the 4 Rs of wood-frame construction are provided in a number of the sections which follow.

FLOOR FRAMING

In a wood-frame house, the floor framing consists of sills, headers, beams and joists. In the interior, load-bearing stud walls are sometimes used instead of posts and beams to support the floor joists and the centre-bearing partition. All framing lumber should be well-seasoned and have a moisture content not exceeding 19 percent at the time of installation, as required by the National Building Code of Canada.

SILL PLATES AND ANCHORS

The sill plate should be leveled carefully. If the top of the foundation is level, the sill plate may be laid directly on the foundation and the junction caulked. Alternatively, the sill plate may be placed on a closed-cell foam gasket or other air-impermeable material of the same width as the sill plate. If the top of the foundation is uneven or not level, the sill plate may be laid in a full bed of mortar. All sill plates must be anchored to the foundation wall with 1/2 in. (12.7 mm) minimum diameter bolts or other approved anchors.

COLUMNS AND BEAMS

Wood or steel columns are generally used in the basement to support the

---

CHECKING BACK

Requirements for Sill Anchors

Before selecting a floor-framing system, it is important to check back to determine how the floor system will be connected to the foundation wall.

When the sill-plate method of foundation wall and joist connection is employed, the sill plate must be securely anchored to the foundation wall. This is normally done using sill anchors embedded in the top of poured concrete walls, or in the top course of concrete blocks having their holes filled with concrete. The method of connecting the floor system to the foundation wall should be determined at the time the foundation wall is being construction because considerable time and expense is involved in providing sill anchors after the concrete has set.

The following requirements for sill anchor bolt size and placement apply:

→ Anchors must have a diameter no less than 1/2 in. (12.7 mm).

→ Anchors must be fastened to the sill plate with nuts and washers, and embedded no less than 4 in. (100 mm).

→ Anchors must be provided at a minimum spacing of 8 ft. (2.4 m), with no less than 2 anchors per sill plate.

beams, which in turn support the inner ends of the first-floor joists as well as loads from upper floors transferred through walls and posts.

Round, adjustable, structural-steel columns fitted with plates at both ends are commonly used. The top plate should be as wide as the beam it supports and either be bolted to the flange where a steel beam is used or nailed to the wood beam. Columns may be adjusted to length after installation to compensate for movement in the soil or settling caused by shrinkage in the framing members.

Wood columns at least 6 x 6 in. (140 x 140 mm) may be solid or built-up of 2 in. (38 mm) lumber. Generally, 3 in. (76 mm) nails spaced at 12 in. (300 mm) on centre are used to fasten the built-up members together. Wood columns should be the same width as the beam they support and cut to ensure even bearing at top and

bottom. Each column is nailed to the beam at the top and separated from the concrete base at the bottom by dampproofing material such as 6 mil (0.15 mm) polyethylene or Type S roll roofing.

Columns are usually spaced 8 to 10 ft. (2.4 to 3.0 m) on centre, depending on the loading and strength of the beam they support.

Either wood or steel beams may be used in house construction. One advantage of steel is the absence of shrinkage. For steel beams, the I-beam is the commonly used shape. Wood beams can be solid or built-up. The built-up wood beam (Fig. 30) is usually made of three or more pieces of 2 in. (38 mm) thick lumber set on edge and spiked together from each side with 3 1/2 in. (89 mm) nails. The nails are driven not more than 18 in. (450 mm) apart in each row, with the end nails located 4 to 6 in.

Built-up wood beam.

joints should be within 6" (150 mm) of quarter point of clear span

foundation wall

built-up wood beam

sill plate

1/2" (12 mm) air space all around or beam end preservative treated at or below grade

3 1/2" (89 mm) minimum bearing

clear span

metal or wood column

30

PLANNING AHEAD

Accommodating Ductwork and Piping

An important consideration when designing beam and joist layout is accommodating ductwork and piping. Ductwork for heating and mechanical ventilation systems, unlike electrical wiring, is not very flexible. To minimize sharp bends and long runs, consider how ducts will be concealed when designing beam and floor joist layout. Piping is somewhat more flexible than ductwork, however, plumbing components such as soil stacks are usually required to run vertically with few, if any, horizontal offsets. Bathroom plumbing may also be made more difficult if bathrooms are not grouped around a common soil stack. The following items should be considered when beam and joist layouts are being designed:

→ Review the house design with a knowledgeable plumbing and heating contractor at the preliminary stage for an idea of what is required and how it may be accommodated. Consider a higher basement to conceal services above a finished ceiling.

→ Avoid the use of flush beams where floor joists are tied into the sides of beams. Resting joists on top of beams provides a continuous chase over the beam for ductwork and piping.

→ Keep joist spans running in the same direction over the entire floor plan, whenever possible. This minimizes situations where ducts or piping must pass beneath the joists.

→ Use blocking, rather than additional floor joists, under non-loadbearing partition walls running parallel to floor joists. This permits ductwork and piping to enter the partition wall from underneath.

→ Always provide a 2 x 6 in. (38 x 140 mm) wall when it contains a plumbing stack. Alternatively, plan on strapping the wall out to conceal the stack and accommodate any potable water piping.

→ Where possible, align wall studs in partitions with floor joists so that the full width of a stud space may be accessed from beneath.

→ If, in following all of the above points, it appears that it will still be difficult to accommodate ductwork and piping, consider using floor trusses which will permit passage of services between the webs.

→ Be prepared to revise your framing plan to accommodate ductwork and piping.

(100 150 mm) from the end of each piece. Butt joints in each member are located over a supporting post or within about 6 in. (150 mm) of the quarter points in the span. (See Tables 11, 12 and 13).

Alternatives to steel or built-up wood beams and columns include glue-laminated (glulam) and laminated veneer lumber beams, and parallel strand lumber beams and columns (See Table 14).

Ends of beams should bear at least 3 1/2 in. (89 mm) on concrete or masonry walls or columns. There is a decay hazard, however, where beams are tightly set into wall notches, such that moisture cannot escape readily. Therefore, the ends of wood beams, located at or below grade and framed into masonry or concrete walls, should be treated to prevent decay or have a 1/2 in. (12 mm) air space at the ends and sides. Untreated wood beams should also be separated from the concrete with an impermeable membrane where they are at a level of 6 in. (150 mm) above grade or less.

BEAM AND JOIST INSTALLATION

The simplest method of beam and joist framing is to have the joists rest on top of the beam (Fig. 31), in which case the top of the beam is level with the top of the sill plate (Fig. 30). This method is used where the basement has adequate headroom below the beam.

Where more clearance under a wood beam is desired, joists may be supported by joist hangers or other structural connectors attached to the beam. In lieu of joist hangers, the National Building Code allows joists to be supported on ledger strips attached to the wood beams (Fig. 32). The 2 x 3 in. (38 x 64 mm) ledger strip is nailed to the beam with two 3 1/4 in. (82 mm) nails per joist. The ends of the joists may be spliced or notched as shown in Figures 32 and 33.

Joists framed into the side of a steel beam may be supported on the bottom flange or on a 2 x 2 in. (38 x 38

Joists supported on top of wood beam and fastened to the beam by toenailing. Two 3 1/4 in. (82 mm) nails used for each joist.

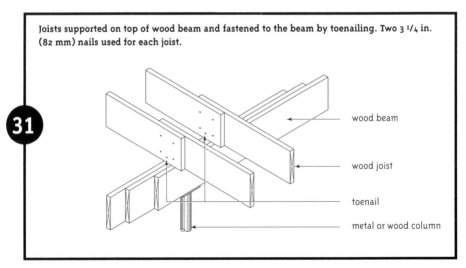

31

wood beam

wood joist

toenail

metal or wood column

mm) ledger strip bolted to the web with 1/4 in. (6.3 mm) bolts spaced 24 in. (600 mm) on centre. The joists should be spliced (Fig. 33) and a 1/2 in. (12 mm) space provided on top of the beam to allow for joist shrinkage.

Joists supported on ledger strip nailed to beam with two 3 1/4 in. (82 mm) nails per joist. Splice nailed to joists with two 3 1/4 in. (82 mm) nails at each end.

- built-up wood beam
- 2" x 3" (38 x 64 mm) ledger strip
- 2" x 2" x 2' (38 x 38 x 600 mm) splice
- wood floor joist

32

Joists supported on ledger strip nailed to beam with two 3 1/4 in. (82 mm) nails per joist. Joists lapped and nailed together with two 3 1/4 in. (82 mm) nails. When a steel beam is used, joists rest on the bottom flange, or a wood plate which is bolted to the beam, and are joined at the top with a 2 x 2 in. (38 x 38 mm) splice.

- wood beam
- 2" x 2" (38 x 38 mm) splice
- joist
- ledger strip
- steel beam
- 2" x 2" (38 x 38 mm) splice
- joist

Alternatively, the joists may be supported on a minimum 2" x 2" (38 x 38 mm) wood ledger bolted through the web of the beam

33

FOUNDATION WALL AND JOIST CONNECTION

The two general types of floor joist construction used over the foundation wall conform either to platform or balloon-frame construction. Platform framing is by far the most common type used. In platform framing, two methods of wall and joist connection are used and are generally referred to as the sill-plate method and the joist-embedded method.

Sill-Plate Method

This method can be used with either concrete or concrete block foundation walls. It consists of a wood sill plate anchored to the foundation wall (Fig.

34) for the support and fastening of the joists and header at the ends of the joists. The sill plate is usually supported on the top of the foundation wall. In this case, the bottom of the sill plate should be at least 6 in. (150 mm) above the finished grade.

Where it is desirable to lower the elevation of the main floor, the top of concrete foundation walls may be reduced to 3 1/2 in. (90 mm) in thickness. If siding or stucco is used as an exterior finish, the wall framing is supported on a sill plate anchored to the top of the wall, and the floor joists rest on a separate sill plate located on a ledge formed in the wall (Fig. 35). Where a masonry finish is used, such as brick veneer, the masonry is supported on the top of the founda-

Sill-plate method used in platform construction.

bottom wall plate

subfloor

floor joist

header

anchored sill plate

foam gasket or mortar

8" (200 mm) minimum for stucco and wood exteriors
6" (150 mm) minimum for other

finished grade

34

tion wall, and the wall framing is supported on the floor framing (Fig. 36). If the thickness of the wall is reduced, as noted above, the height of the reduced section should not exceed 14 in. (350 mm).

Joist-embedded Method

This method can be used only with cast-in-place concrete foundation walls. Beams, joists and headers are positioned before the concrete is placed. Floor framing is temporarily supported on the inside concrete form

and wedges used to level the framing. Filler pieces placed between the floor joists and along the end walls retain the fluid concrete between the joists. These filler pieces are set flush with the inner face of the foundation wall (Fig. 37). Joist headers and end joists serve as outside forms for the concrete. Beam ends are treated to prevent decay when they are located at or below grade. The concrete is then placed so that at least two-thirds of the depth of each joist is embedded in the concrete, thus providing suitable

Floor joists supported on a ledge formed in the foundation wall. Joists are toenailed to header and sill plate. Sill plate is anchored to top of foundation wall with anchor bolts. Wall plate supporting the wall framing is fastened to the sill plate with 3 in. (76 mm) nails spaced 16 in. (400 mm) on centre.

wall finish
vapour barrier
insulation
wall stud
wall sheathing
sheathing membrane
wood siding
wall plate

8" (200 mm) minimum

bottom sill plate anchored to foundation

baseboard
finish flooring
subfloor and underlay

floor joist toe-nailed to sill plate

continuous header

sill plate anchored to foundation

$^1/_2$" (12 mm) air space if untreated

Floor joists are supported on ledge formed in foundation wall. Joists are toenailed to header and sill plate. Masonry veneer supported on top of foundation wall. Wall framing supported on top of the subfloor.

36

wall finish
vapour barrier
insulation
wall stud
wall sheathing
sheathing membrane
brick veneer
base flashing

6" (150 mm) minimum
1/2" (12 mm) air space if untreated

baseboard
finish flooring
subfloor and underlay

floor joist toe-nailed to sill plate

damproof course under sill when less than 6" (150 mm) above finished grade

continuous header

sill plate anchored to foundation

anchor bolt

Floor joists embedded in the top of the foundation wall.

37

end joist
header
floor joist
concrete foundation

Masonry support using joist-embedded method of floor framing.

brick veneer

header

sheathing membrane lapped over flashing

metal flashing

floor joist

concrete foundation

38

HEALTHY HOUSING INSIGHT

Alternative Floor Systems

The Healthy Housing principle of resource efficiency may be applied to floor systems by considering alternatives such as engineered wood products (EWPs). EWPs may take the form of engineered structural members which replace conventional dimensional lumber, or specially manufactured sheathings which replace plywood.

Commonly available alternatives to floor joists are wood I-joists and floor trusses. In addition to being capable of providing stiffer and quieter floors, these systems also make installing ductwork and piping much easier.

On average, wood I-joists and floor trusses use 20 percent less material than a conventional floor constructed with dimensional lumber, and may permit a wider spacing between members leading to even further reductions in material requirements.

Manufactured in lengths which well exceed those available in conventional lumber, these engineered floor systems may often clear span the building, avoiding the need for interior bearing walls. This enhances the future adaptability of the house plan while further reducing the amount of material and labour required.

Alternatives to plywood floor sheathings include waferboard and oriented

Continued on page 70

Continued from page 69 strand board. Waferboard is manufactured using waste wood wafers which are pressed together and bonded to one another with adhesives. Oriented strand board is similar to waferboard, however, alternating layers of wood strands are uniformly oriented to improve strength.

Whenever using engineered wood products, it is important to strictly adhere to manufacturers' installation instructions.

anchorage for the floor-framing members. The filler pieces are removed, together with the wall forms, when the concrete has set. The same method can be used when the finish of the exterior wall is masonry (Fig. 38).

FLOOR JOISTS

Joists are selected to meet strength and stiffness requirements. Strength requirements depend on the loads to be carried. Stiffness requirements, on the other hand, are intended to limit cracking of ceiling finishes under live loads and, even more important, to limit vibrations from moving loads, often a cause of annoyance to occupants.

Wood floor joists are generally 2 in. (38 mm) thick and either 6, 8, 10 or 12 in. (140, 184, 235 or 286 mm) deep. The size depends upon the loading, length of span, spacing between joists, the species and grade of lumber used, and the deflection which may be allowed. Tables 15 and 16 show the spans which are allowable for the various grades and species of lumber and for different loading conditions. The allowable spans shown in these tables are measured between inside edges of the joist supports and have been calculated on the basis of lumber dressed to standard Canadian sizes.

Alternatives to dimension lumber floor joists include laminated veneer lumber joists, parallel chord trusses and wood I-joists. Allowable spans for these engineered wood products are provided by their manufacturers.

Where a sill plate is used, the joists are installed after the sill plates have been leveled on the mortar bed and anchored to the foundation wall. As already described, where joists are embedded in the top of the foundation wall, they are installed before the foundation wall is placed. The joists are located and spaced according to the design.

Joist spacing of 16 in. (400 mm) on centre is most commonly used, although for heavy loads or when space is limited, 12 in. (300 mm) spacing of shallower joists may be substituted. Conversely, if floor thickness is

Floor framing: (1) subfloor nailed with 2 in. (51 mm) nails to joists; (2) 1 x 3 in. (19 x 64 mm) continuous wood strapping nailed at bottom with two 2 1/4 in. (57 mm) nails; and/or (3) 2 x 2 in. (38 x 38 mm) cross-bridging nailed with two 2 1/4 in. (57 mm) nails; (4) header joist end-nailed to joists with three 3 1/4 in. (82 mm) nails; (5) header toenailed to sill plate with 3 1/4 in. (82 mm) nails 24 in. (600 mm) o.c.; (6) floor joists toenailed to sill plate with two 3 1/4 in. (82 mm) nails, one on each side.

joint over joist

joist under partitions parallel to joists

joists lapped over beam

blocking

6

39

anchored sill plate

joist parallel to foundation

1
2
3
4
5

not a limitation, deeper joists at 24 in. (600 mm) spacing may prove more economical. (*Note: Metric joist spacings are nominal, and should not be used since panel products are manufactured in imperial sizes.*)

Any joists having a slight bow edgewise should be placed with the crown on top. A crowned joist will tend to straighten out when the subfloor and floor loads are applied.

A header joist is end-nailed (Fig. 39) or toenailed (Fig. 35) to each joist. In platform construction, each joist including the end joist parallel to the exterior walls is toenailed to the sill (Fig. 39). The inner ends of the joists are supported on top of the beam (Fig. 31) or framed into the side of the beam (Fig. 32).

When a loadbearing wall runs parallel to the joists, it should be supported by a beam or loadbearing wall in the basement.

Floor plans often require a loadbearing wall to be located at right angles to the floor joists, but offset from the joist support. Loadbearing interior walls at right angles to floor joists should be located not more than 36 in. (900 mm) from the joist support when the wall does not support a floor, and not more than 24 in. (600 mm) from the joist support when the

Framing for floor openings where double headers and double trimmers are used: (*3*) second header nailed to first header with 3 in. (76 mm) nails spaced 12 in. (300 mm) apart longitudinally; (*2*) first header nailed to tail joists with three 4 in. (101 mm) or five 3 1/4 in. (82 mm) nails; (*5*) second trimmer nailed to first trimmer with 3 in. (76 mm) nails spaced 12 in. (300 mm) apart longitudinally; (*4*) first trimmer nailed to second header with three 4 in. (101 mm) or five 3 1/4 in. (82 mm) nails; (*1*) first trimmer nailed to first header with three 4 in. (101 mm) or five 3 1/4 in. (82 mm) nails.

40

first header
second header
first trimmer joist
second trimmer joist

length of opening

3
2
5
4
1

joist hangers may be used as an alternative to end nailing tail joists

tail joist

wall supports one or more floors, unless the joist size is designed to support such concentrated loads.

Non-loadbearing partitions parallel to the joists should bear on joists or on blocking between the joists. This blocking should be 2 x 4 in. (38 x 89 mm) lumber and spaced 4 ft. (1.2 m) or less.

When framing for large openings, such as stairwells or fireplaces, trimmer joists are doubled if they support header joists more than 32 in. (800 mm) long. Header joists longer than the 4 ft. (1.2 m) should also be doubled. Where unusually large openings occur, trimmer joists that support header joists more than 6 ft. 6 in. (2 m) long and header joists that are more than 10 ft. 6 in. (3.2 m) long should be designed according to accepted engineering practice.

Nailing and assembly methods generally used in the framing of floor openings are shown in Figure 40.

Joist hangers are often used to support long joist headers and tail joists.

Joists may be kept from twisting by cross bridging, blocking, strapping or a ceiling finish fastened to the underside of the joists. Where a board-type finish is not used, necessary restraint should be provided at intermediate locations between the supports and at distances not greater than 6 ft. 10 in. (2.1 m).

Intermediate support may be provided by the following methods: 1 x 3 in. (19 x 64) mm or 2 x 2 in. (38 x 38 mm) cross bridging or 2 in. (38 mm) full-depth blocking fastened between joists together with continuous wood strapping of 1 x 3 in.

(19 x 64 mm) nailed to the bottoms of the joists. Continuous wood strapping, however, is not required where ceiling finish is provided.

Floor Performance

The floor joist span tables incorporate vibration criteria. The tables recognize that different floor constructions are more "bouncy" or "springy" than others. Therefore, by adding blocking, or increasing subfloor thickness, floor joist spans may be increased. Alternatively, engineered wood products such as laminated veneer lumber joists, parallel chord trusses and wood I-joists may be considered.

SUBFLOOR

Subflooring should consist of plywood, oriented strand board, waferboard or square-edge, shiplap, or tongue-and-grooved lumber no wider than 8 in. (184 mm). The minimum thicknesses of plywood, oriented strand board, waferboard and lumber for subflooring are shown in Table 17.

Plywood is often used as subflooring under wood-strip flooring or as a combination subfloor and underlay for resilient flooring or ceramic tile. When used as a combination subfloor and underlay, the side joints should be supported on 2 x 2 in. (38 x 38 mm) blocking fitted between the joists unless the edges of the panels are tongue-and-grooved.

Plywood panels should be installed with the surface grain at right angles to the floor joists and with the end joints staggered and nailed along the edges at 6 in. (150 mm) on centre and 12 in. (300 mm) at intermediate supports. Ringed underlay nails, which are designed to resist withdrawal and "nail popping," or approved staples should be used where the panels provide a combination subfloor and underlay. (See Table 18 for details of fastening sheathing and subflooring.)

Floor stiffness can be substantially increased, and floor squeaks minimized, by applying elastomeric glue between the floor joists and the plywood subfloor. By using this method, the plywood, adhesive and joists act together as a strengthened floor frame, thus reducing deflection between adjacent joists.

Waferboard panels, including oriented strand board, may also be used as subflooring, and should be covered with an underlay where a vinyl floor covering is used. The panels should be staggered and nailed in the same way as the plywood.

All plywood, oriented strand board and waferboard panels used for subflooring and underlayment should be the exterior type, manufactured with waterproof adhesives.

An underlay is not required where the edges of the subflooring are supported.

For lumber subfloor, 1 in. (19 mm) thick boards are generally used, although this thickness may be reduced to 11/16 in. (17 mm) where joists are spaced at 16 in. (400 mm) on centre. The boards should be applied so that the end joints occur over the joists. End joints are usually staggered throughout the floor. Boards may be applied at right angles to the joists or diagonally at an angle of 45°. When the subflooring is laid at right angles to the joists, strip finish flooring should be placed at right angles to the subflooring unless an underlay is used. Diagonal subflooring permits finish strip flooring to be laid either parallel to or across the joists. The boards should be nailed with two 2 in. (51 mm) nails at each support. Lumber subflooring must be covered with a panel-type underlay where the floor is finished with resilient flooring.

FLOOR FRAMING AT PROJECTIONS

Floor joists sometimes project beyond the foundation wall to provide support for a bay window or additional floor space in the upper rooms. The cantilevered portion of the floor framing should not exceed 16 in. (400 mm) for 2 x 8 in. (38 x 184 mm) joists and 24 in. (600 mm) for larger joists. In either case, this projection should not carry loads from additional floors. If the cantilevered floor joists are to carry additional loads, they must be specifically designed for the appropriate loads according to accepted engineering practice. The subflooring is carried to and sawn flush with the outer framing members. Figure 41 shows a typical second-storey projection.

Insulation should be fitted carefully, and placed on top of the soffit finish under the cantilevered floor and up the inside face of the joist header and end joists. The vapour barrier should be placed on the warm side of the insulation and neatly fitted and fastened in place.

If the joist depth is great enough, the space between the insulation and subfloor is usually left open to let the warm air in the ceiling area circulate between the joist spaces. In this way, the floor in the projected area is heated both from below and above, resulting in an even and comfortable floor temperature throughout the room.

To prevent external air infiltration into the cantilevered area, the soffit under the overhang and other parts of the trim should be carefully fitted and caulked where necessary or wrapped with an air barrier.

RELATED PUBLICATIONS

The Span Book, 1995 Edition
Canadian Wood Council

Floor framing at projections.

- end joist
- subfloor
- bead of caulking
- floor joist
- rigid insulation with caulking
- vapour barrier
- gypsum board
- overhang

- full depth insulation
- header
- soffit covering

41

SIZING BUILT-UP WOOD BEAMS

Problem

Select two built-up beams that can satisfy the conditions noted below.

supported joist length
=12' (3.6 m)

beam end

foundation wall

interior support

built-up beam

beam span = 13' (4 m)

supported joist length

$a_{/2} + b_{/2}$

a

b

beam span

supporting column

Conditions

One-storey, brick veneer house.
Beam supporting main floor only.
Supported joist length is 12' (3.6 m).
Beam span is 13' (4 m).
Commercial designation and grade specified is SPF No. 2 or better.

Selection

Use table 11

Acceptable beams for this application include:
5 - 2" x 10" (5 - 38 x 235 mm) or
4 - 2" x 12" (4 - 38 x 286 mm).

SIZING FLOOR JOISTS

Problem
Select a floor joist that is acceptable for the conditions as described below

joist span = 12'-3" (3.75 m)

Conditions
Joists supporting living room floor.
Joist span is 12'-3" (3.75 m).
Bridging will be installed.
Basement ceiling will be not finished.
Commercial designation and grade specified is SPF No. 2 or better.
Subfloor is 5/8" (15.9 mm) plywood nailed in place.

Also note that drywall or gypsum board ceiling finish can be considered a strapping.
For this example floor joists can be considered braced with bridging and strapping.

Selection
Use Table 15

Acceptable floor joist sizes for this application include:
2" x 8" at 12" o.c.(38 x 184mm at 300 mm o.c.) or
2" x 10" at 24" o.c.(38 x 235 mm at 600 mm o.c.).
Note that any spacing less than 24" (600 mm) for the 2" x 10" (38 x 235 mm) is
acceptable.

WALL FRAMING

The term "wall framing" includes the vertical and horizontal members of exterior walls and interior partitions. These members, referred to as studs, wall plates and lintels, serve as a nailing base for all covering material and support the upper floors, ceiling and roof. All framing lumber should be graded, well-seasoned and have a moisture content not exceeding 19 percent. (See Table 19 for nailing practice.)

Exterior wall studs are the vertical members to which the wall sheathing and cladding are attached. They are supported on a bottom plate or foundation sill and in turn support the top plate. Studs usually consist of 2 x 4 in. (38 x 89 mm) or 2 x 6 in. (38 x 140 mm) lumber and are commonly spaced at 16 in. (400 mm) on centre. This spacing may be changed to 12 in. (300 mm) or 24 in. (600 mm) on centre depending on the load and the limitations imposed by the type and thickness of the wall covering used. (See Table 20.) Wider studs 2 x 6 in. (38 x 140 mm) may be used to provide space for more insulation. Insulation beyond that which can be accommodated within a 3 1/2 in. (89 mm) stud space can also be provided by other means, such as rigid or semi-rigid insulation or batts between 2 x 2 in. (38 x 38 mm) horizontal furring strips, or by attaching rigid or semi-rigid insulation sheathing to the outside of the studs.

The studs are attached to horizontal top and bottom wall plates of 2 in. (38 mm) lumber that are the same width as the studs.

Lintels are the horizontal members placed over window, door and other openings to carry vertical loads to the adjoining studs. Lintels are usually constructed of two pieces of 2 in. (38 mm) lumber separated with spacers to the width of the studs and nailed together to form a single unit. The preferable spacer material is rigid insulation. The depth of a lintel is determined by the width of the opening and vertical loads supported. (See Tables 21 to 23.)

PLATFORM FRAMING

There are two methods of framing a house. Balloon framing was common until the late 1940s, but since that time, platform framing has become the predominant form of house construction.

This method of framing wall sections horizontally on the subfloor prior to erection is widely used. The top and bottom plates are end-nailed to each stud with two nails at least 3 1/4 in. (82 mm) in length. Studs are doubled at openings, the jack stud being cut to receive the lintels which are placed and end-nailed through the outer studs.

Wall sheathing is usually applied to the framing prior to erection, thus eliminating the need to scaffold for this operation. Some types of sheathing, such as asphalt-impregnated fibreboard, plywood, oriented strandboard and waferboard, will provide

PLANNING AHEAD

Providing the Required Effective Thermal Resistance

Code requirements for minimum levels of effective thermal resistance in wall and other building assemblies depend on climatic conditions and the type of energy source used for space heating.

It is important to understand the difference between the nominal and effective thermal resistance of insulated building assemblies. The nominal thermal resistance refers to the thermal resistance rating of the insulation which is installed. For example, a 2 x 6 in. (38 x 140 mm) wall cavity containing a glass or mineral fibre insulation batt has a nominal thermal resistance of about R-20 (RSI-3.52). The effective thermal resistance takes into account interior and exterior sheathings and finishes, and most importantly, the effect of the wood studs which conduct heat at a higher rate than insulation. This effect, known as thermal bridging, reduces the nominal thermal resistance of the building assembly and is reflected in the effective thermal resistance rating. For a wall constructed with wood studs at 16 in. (400 mm) on centres, the effective thermal resistance is R-17.4 (RSI-3.06). In general, the effective thermal resistance is lower than the nominal rating. It is important to select an assembly which will comply with the minimum Code requirement applicable to the house being constructed. The following points should be considered when providing adequate effective thermal resistance values:

→ Effective thermal resistance values of common building assemblies are provided in the Model National Energy Code for Houses. It is available from the National Research Council.

→ Wider spacing of framing members reduces thermal bridging and provides higher effective thermal resistance.

→ Select insulation materials with higher nominal thermal resistance values.

→ Use insulating sheathings in place of structural sheathings to increase the effective thermal resistance of wall assemblies.

→ Take into account the effect of thicker building assemblies when designing details at the foundation wall/main floor and wall intersection, and at the wall and roof intersection.

Additional consideration should also be given to factors affecting the amount of labour associated with various insulated wall assemblies, particularly in relation to the placement of air and vapour barriers.

adequate bracing to resist lateral loads and keep the wall square. Others, such as rigid glass-fibre, polystyrene or polyurethane board, will not. In this latter case, the wall should be reinforced with a diagonal wood or metal bracing let into the studs.

The complete wall sections are then raised and put in place, temporary braces added and the bottom plates nailed through the subfloor to the floor framing members (Fig. 42). The braces should have their larger dimension on the vertical and should permit adjustment of the vertical position of the wall.

Once the assembled sections are plumbed, they are nailed together at the corners and intersections. A second top plate, with joints offset at least one stud space away from the joints in the plate beneath, is then

Wall framing used with platform construction: (*1*) top plate end-nailed to each stud with two 3 ¹/₄ in. (82 mm) nails; (*2*) top plates nailed together with 3 in. (76 mm) nails 24 in. (600 mm) on centre; (*3*) stud toenailed with four 2 ¹/₂ in. (63 mm) nails or end-nailed to bottom plate with two 3 ¹/₄ in. (82 mm) nails; (*4*) top plates at corners and loadbearing partitions are lapped and nailed together with two 3 ¹/₄ in. (82 mm) nails or the plates are butted together and tied with a metal plate fastened to the top plates with three 2 ¹/₂ in. (63 mm) nails on each side of the joint; (*5*) doubled studs at openings and multiple studs at corners and intersections nailed with 3 in. (76 mm) nails 30 in. (750 mm) on centre; (*6*) bottom plate nailed to joist or header joist with 3 ¹/₄ in. (82 mm) nails 16 in. (400 mm) on centre.

42

butt joint with metal tie or lap top plate

1
2
3
4

temporary brace
stud and jack stud
cripple/trimmer stud
window opening
lintel

5
6
bottom plate
subfloor
let-in bracing or metal strapping when no or non-structural sheathing is used

PLANNING AHEAD

Installing Special Items Prior to Wall Framing

After the main floor system is completed, and prior to the framing of exterior walls, careful consideration should be given to any special items which need to be installed. One-piece bath or shower units and other large fixtures or equipment that cannot pass through door or window openings must be placed within the building before walls are erected. Similarly, exterior chimneys and chases may also have to be completed before walls are framed. In some cases, such as internal masonry fireplaces supporting roof structural members, it is necessary to have these constructed prior to wall framing in order to avoid interfering with this work.

The following items pertaining to the planning and coordination of trades prior to wall framing should be reviewed before starting any construction.

➜ Review plans and specifications carefully to identify any special items which have to be installed prior to wall framing.

➜ Order and arrange for delivery of these special items well in advance of wall framing to avoid delays.

➜ Coordinate with trades responsible for constructing fireplaces, chimneys and chases to maximize productivity and minimize conflicts.

By carefully planning ahead, proper installation without delays and trade conflicts is possible. Failure to plan ahead may require that some special items are substituted with less suitable items, or altogether omitted from the house.

added. This second top plate usually laps the first plate at the corners and partition intersections and, when nailed in place, provides an additional tie to the framed walls. Where the second top plate does not lap the plate immediately underneath at corner and partition intersections, these may be tied with 0.036 in. (0.91 mm) galvanized steel plates at least 3 in. (75 mm) wide and 6 in. (150 mm) long, nailed with at least three 2 1/2 in. (63 mm) nails to each wall.

Interior partitions supporting floor, ceiling or roof loads are called loadbearing walls; others are called non-loadbearing or simply partitions. Interior loadbearing walls are framed in the same way as exterior walls. Studs are usually 2 x 4 in. (38 x 89 mm)

lumber spaced at 16 in. (400 mm) on centre. This spacing may be changed to 12 in. (300 mm) or 24 in. (600 mm) depending on the loads supported and the type and thickness of the wall finish used. (See Table 20.)

Partitions can be built with 2 x 3 in. (38 x 64 mm) or 2 x 4 in. (38 x 89 mm) studs spaced at 16 or 24 in. (400 or 600 mm) on centre depending on the type and thickness of the wall finish used. Where a partition does not contain a swinging door, 2 x 4 in. (38 x 89 mm) studs at 16 in. (400 mm) on centre are sometimes used with the wide face of the stud parallel to the wall. This is usually done only for partitions enclosing clothes closets or cupboards to save space. Since there is no vertical load to be supported by

Multiple stud arrangements at exterior corner. In the two-stud arrangement, a plasterboard clip is used at the corner for support.

Three stud   Two stud

gypsum board clip

insulation

corner studs

bottom plate

subfloor

end joist

sill plate

foundation

43

Multiple stud arrangements at the intersection of an interior partition with an exterior wall: (A) two studs used; (B) bracing or blocking is used; (C) the partition is attached to exterior wall after drywall has been installed; (D) insulation must be installed before sheathing is applied.

A

B

C

D

polyethylene strip
partition stud
insulation in spaces between blocking
spaced blocking
bottom plate
subfloor

end joist
sill plate
foundation

44

Horizontal nailing support for interior finish. Nailing support provided by 2 in. (38 mm) lumber nailed to top plates with 3 in. (76 mm) nails at 12 in. (300 mm) on centre.

ceiling joist

2" x 6" (38 x 140 mm) nailing support

polyethylene air/vapour barrier strip (may also be installed between top plates - not required between floors)

plate

stud

45

End-wall framing and nailing support for interior finish using platform construction method.

- stud
- bottom plate
- subfloor
- floor joist
- wood nailing support for interior finish
- end joist
- plate

46

partitions, single studs may be used at door openings. The top of the opening may be bridged with a single piece of 2 in. (38 mm) lumber the same width as the studs. These members provide a nailing support for wall finish, door frames and trim.

Multiple-stud post made up of at least three studs, or the equivalent, is generally used at exterior corners and intersections to secure a good tie between adjoining walls and to provide nailing support for the interior finish and exterior sheathing. Corners and intersections, however, must be framed with at least two studs.

Figures 43 and 44 illustrate commonly used exterior corners and partition intersections.

Nailing support for the edges of the ceiling finish is required at the junction of the wall and ceiling where partitions run parallel to the ceiling joists. Figures 45 and 46 illustrate the types of nailing support commonly used.

BALLOON FRAMING

In balloon-framed construction, both the studs and first-floor joists rest on the foundation sill plate (Fig. 47) and the centre beam or bearing wall. Studs are toenailed to these supports with four 2 1/2 in. (63 mm) nails; the joists in turn are nailed to the studs with two 3 in. (76 mm) nails. When lumber subfloor is laid diagonally, blocking is required between the joists at the wall lines to support the ends of the boards.

Second-floor joists bear on a 1 x 4 in. (19 x 89 mm) ribbon that has been let into the studs, and the joist are nailed to the studs. The end joists parallel to the exterior walls on both first and second floors are similarly nailed to the studs.

When framing the floor, blocking should be inserted between joists at the wall to support the ends of diagonal subfloor boards. As the spaces between the studs are not interrupted

Wall framing using balloon construction method.

- second-floor joist
- fire stop
- 1" x 4" (19 x 89 mm) ribbon let-in
- stud
- insulate prior to application of sheathing or sheathing membrane
- first-floor joist
- fire stop
- foundation sill plate (anchored)

alternative corner

47

HEALTHY HOUSING INSIGHT

Minimizing Waste in Wall Framing

The amount of waste generated during wall framing may be significantly reduced through proper planning, and appropriate practices. Consider the following items when planning and building walls:

→ Use kiln-dried lumber and store it properly to reduce warped and twisted pieces.

→ Use precision-trimmed studs which are pre-cut to the right length for a standard wall height.

→ If a standard height wall is not desired, select a height which makes the most use of wall studs.

→ Space studs at 24 in. (600 mm) on centres wherever possible.

→ Order lumber for lintels that is a multiple of the lintel length. (A 4 ft. 6 in. (1.5 m) lintel using two members is more economically created with a 10 ft. (3.3 m) length, rather than cutting from two 8 ft. (2.6 m) lengths).

→ Cut all lumber in one location to make best use of end cuts.

by wall plates (as in platform framing), fire stops are required at floor
and ceiling levels to eliminate continuous passages in the wall and thus
resist the spread of fire. Lumber blocking 1 1/2 in. (38 mm) thick is commonly
used for this purpose. Fire stops,
however, are not required where the
wall space is filled with insulation.

SIZING WALL STUDS

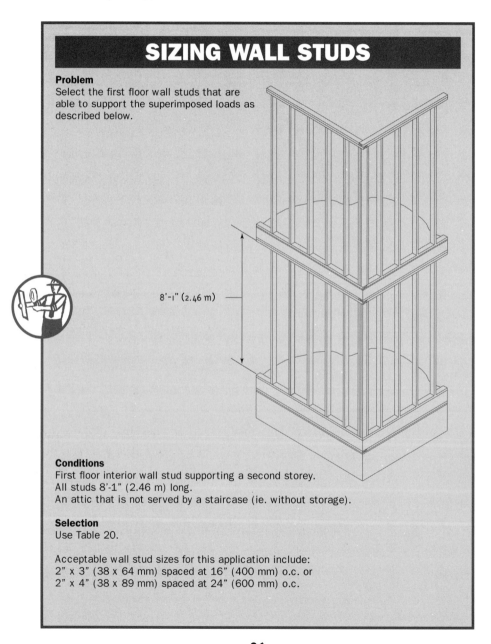

Problem
Select the first floor wall studs that are
able to support the superimposed loads as
described below.

8'-1" (2.46 m)

Conditions
First floor interior wall stud supporting a second storey.
All studs 8'-1" (2.46 m) long.
An attic that is not served by a staircase (ie. without storage).

Selection
Use Table 20.

Acceptable wall stud sizes for this application include:
2" x 3" (38 x 64 mm) spaced at 16" (400 mm) o.c. or
2" x 4" (38 x 89 mm) spaced at 24" (600 mm) o.c.

86

CEILING AND ROOF FRAMING

There are two basic types of roofs — pitched and flat — and each type has many variations.

The slope of a roof is expressed as a ratio of rise-to-run with the vertical component, or rise, always being shown first. There are two conventions for expressing the slope of a roof: imperial and metric.

The imperial convention is based on the use of a framing square, and the run is always expressed as 12, based on 12 inches to a foot. For example, a roof with a slope of 45° is expressed as a 12/12 pitch. A roof with a 4/12 pitch has a rise of 4 inches for every 12 inches of run.

Using the metric convention, for slopes less than 45°, the first number should always be shown as one. A ratio of 1:5, for instance, indicates a rise of 1 mm for every 5 mm of hori-zontal dimension, or 1 m for every 5 m. For slopes steeper than 45°, the second number (that is, the horizontal component) should always be one to facilitate easy verification. A ratio of 5:1 expresses a rise of 5 mm for a hori-zontal dimension of 1 mm, or 5 m for each 1 m. The use of mixed units, such as 1 mm in 10 m, should be avoided.

Expressed as a ratio, the stan-dard slope reference of 4 in 12 (or 400 mm in 1200 mm) becomes 1:3; simi-larly, 3 in 12 becomes 1:4. In special cases, where a high degree of accuracy is required, angular expressions of slope are acceptable.

For purposes of definition, flat roofs might be classed as those having less than 1:6 slope. Pitched roofs vary in slope from 1:6 to 1:1 or more (for example, 2:1), depending on the roof covering and the use of attic space.

Roof framing using lightweight roof trusses.

metal plate connector

roof truss

48

L-shape trussed roof.

See isometric below

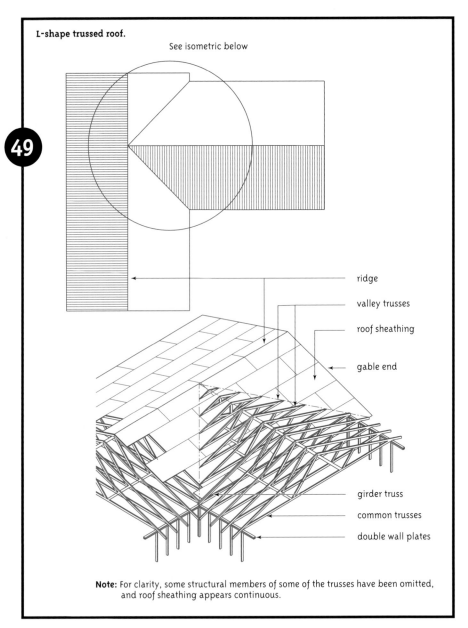

49

ridge

valley trusses

roof sheathing

gable end

girder truss

common trusses

double wall plates

Note: For clarity, some structural members of some of the trusses have been omitted, and roof sheathing appears continuous.

The dimensions of roof joists and rafters for the various grades and species of lumber and for the different live loads encountered are given in Tables 29 to 32.

PITCHED ROOFS

Roof trusses are most often pre-assembled, although they can be constructed on site. Pitched roofs can also be stick-built, although this is a

Types of prefabricated roof trusses.

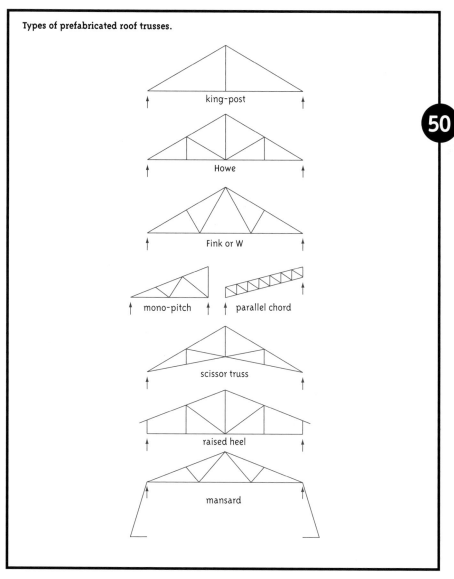

king-post

Howe

Fink or W

mono-pitch   parallel chord

scissor truss

raised heel

mansard

50

time-consuming process. Of the pitched roofs, the gable roof is the simplest to construct, especially with the use of lightweight roof trusses (Fig. 48). Other configurations, such as the hip roof and L-shape roof, though more complex, can also be framed with trusses (Fig. 49).

Pre-assembled Roof Trusses

Pre-assembled roof trusses offer many advantages in that they save material and speed up the process of enclosing the house. They provide, in one step, a surface for the roof sheathing, a surface for the ceiling finish material and a space for insulation. Ventilation

Temporary bracing of roof trusses

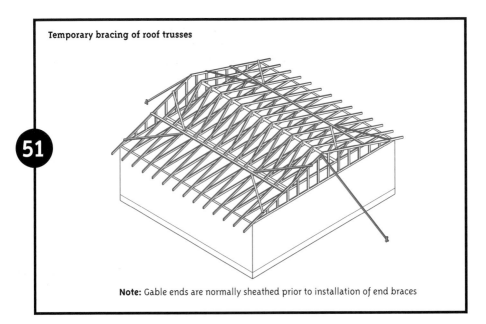

51

Note: Gable ends are normally sheathed prior to installation of end braces

of the attic space is easily accomplished through the eaves or gables or both, and at or along the ridge. In most cases, trusses are designed to span from exterior wall to exterior wall with no intermediate loadbearing walls to support the roof loads (Fig. 50). Thus, the entire house may be used as one large workroom during construction. This increases the flexibility of interior planning, because partitions can be placed without regard to structural requirements. Additional flexibility and speed is gained with pre-assembled components and add-on features such as garage roof trusses, porch roofs, simulated mansards and window canopies, which can also be supplied by the truss manufacturer.

Metal-plate-connected trusses can be delivered to the construction site and placed on a flat, clean portion of the site. Trusses under a 20 ft. (6 m) span are usually installed by hand.

Trusses longer than 20 ft. (6 m) require special lifting techniques to avoid damage.

The trusses must be lifted into position with care to prevent excessive lateral bending. The first to be put in place is the gable truss, which is braced to the ground and wall. Each additional truss is lifted into position, generally 24 in. (600 mm) on centre, toenailed to the top plates and temporarily braced (Fig. 51). When all trusses are plumbed and properly positioned, they are braced permanently (Fig. 52). The stiffness of the roof is increased after the sheathing has been applied.

Site Assembly of Pitched Roofs

For on-site construction, the simplest roof is the gable roof (Fig 53A). All rafters are cut to the same length and pattern, and erection is straightforward. A variation of the gable roof may include dormers for additional light, head room and ventilation (Fig. 53B and Fig. 53C). However, openable windows and fixed skylights that can be fitted on a slope between rafters will provide ventilation and light without the complexity and cost of framing a dormer. In the hip roof design, shown in Figure 53D, common rafters are fastened to the ridge board while hip rafters supply the support for the jack rafters.

Important considerations in framing a liveable attic space are insulation and proper air and vapour barrier sealing; these techniques are

Permanent bracing of roof trusses: (A) permanent bracing of top chord plane; **(B)** and **(C)** permanent lateral bracing to web member or bottom chord plane.

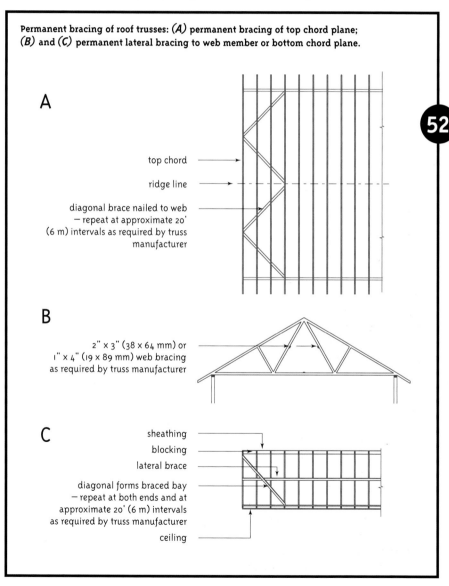

A

52

top chord

ridge line

diagonal brace nailed to web
— repeat at approximate 20'
(6 m) intervals as required by truss
manufacturer

B

2" x 3" (38 x 64 mm) or
1" x 4" (19 x 89 mm) web bracing
as required by truss manufacturer

C

sheathing

blocking

lateral brace

diagonal forms braced bay
— repeat at both ends and at
approximate 20' (6 m) intervals
as required by truss manufacturer

ceiling

dealt with in the chapters on *Thermal Insulation* and *Vapour and Air Barriers*. The choice of framing members for structural strength, based on Tables 24 to 27, may not provide sufficient depth for insulation and necessary ventilation space. Larger size members or a modified framing technique will be needed to meet current standards.

Ceiling Joists are used to support the ceiling finish and to act as ties between exterior walls and, in some cases, opposing rafters. They may also provide support for roof loads transferred to them by dwarf walls (knee walls) used as intermediate support for rafters, in which case they need to be appropriately increased in size. (See Table 28 for ceiling joist spans.) When the joists also support floor loads, their size should be determined by the floor joist tables. (See Tables 15 and 16.)

In pitched-roof framing, the ceiling joists are nailed in place after the interior and exterior wall framing is complete but before the rafters are erected, because the thrust of the rafters will otherwise tend to push out the outside walls. Ceiling joists are generally used to tie the lower ends of the rafters in pitched roofs that slope 1:3 or more. To prevent the rafter ends from moving outward, the ceiling joist is nailed to the side of each pair of rafters (Fig. 54). The joists are lapped and nailed together or spliced at the centre loadbearing wall, thus providing a continuous tie across opposing rafters. The number of nails used in the connections depends upon the roof slope, rafter spacing, snow load and width of the house. (See Table 19 for nailing practice.)

The additional roof load imposed by dwarf walls that run at right angles to the ceiling joists (Fig. 55) should be taken into account when the size of the joists are determined. An increase in the depth of the joists to the next standard depth will usually provide the additional strength required where the roof slope is more than 1:4. When the slope is 1:4 or less, the size of the ceiling joists is determined from span tables for roof joists (Tables 24 and 25.)

Since hip rafters are about 2 in. (51 mm) deeper than the common or jack rafters, they reduce the space along the end walls to the extent that in low-slope roofs, there may not be enough room to install the outside ceiling joist at normal spacing from the wall. In this case, doubled joists are used and positioned to suit the available space (Fig. 56). Tail joists are then added and toenailed to the outside wall plate and end-nailed to the doubled joist. The spacing of these tail joists is usually the same as the spacing of the main ceiling joists.

Rafters are cut to length with the proper angle cut at the ridge and eaves and with notches (known as birdmouths) provided for the wall or rafter plates. The heel or lower part of the rafters should bear directly over the exterior wall. Depending on the plan of the roof and the shape of the outside walls, the rafters are placed:
- directly on the wall plates (Fig. 54);
- on a rafter plate nailed to the top of the ceiling joists (Fig. 55), or
- on a loadbearing wall supported on the exterior wall plate (Fig. 57).

Types of pitched roofs: *(A)* gable; *(B)* gable dormer; *(C)* shed dormer; *(D)* hip.

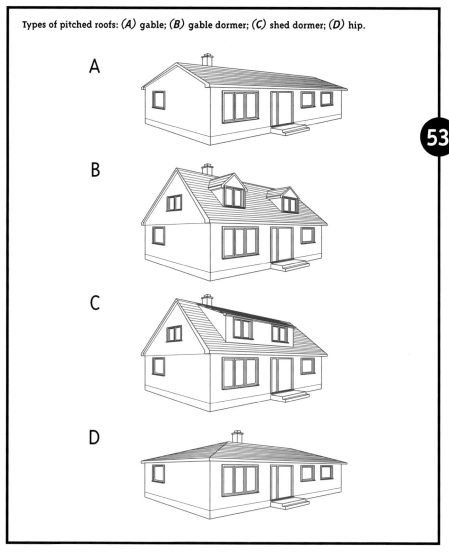

A

B

C

D

53

The last method is used where a portion of the outside wall is set back. In this case, the ceiling joists extend beyond the exterior wall and are nailed to the side of the rafters. This provides lateral support for the bearing wall and resists outward and downward movement of the ends of the rafters.

A ridge board (Fig. 54) or a ridge beam (Fig. 55) is used to ensure a level ridge line and for ease in erecting and aligning the rafters. Rafters are erected in pairs and nailed to the ridge board or beam. The lower ends are toenailed to the wall plate. Each pair of rafters is usually located directly opposite each other. However, they may be offset at the ridge by their own thickness. This offsetting is

(A) ceiling and roof framing with ridge board: (1) each rafter toenailed to ridge board with four 2 1/4 in. (57 mm) nails or end-nailed with three 3 1/4 in. (82 mm) nails; (2) 1 x 4 in. (19 x 89 mm) strip nailed to top of collar tie at their centre with two 2 1/4 in. (57 mm) nails when the braces are more than 8 ft. (2.4 m) long; (3) ceiling joists butted with splice plate over centre bearing partition. Joists also nailed to each part of rafters (see Table 27 for nailing practice); (4) collar tie used as intermediate support for rafters nailed to each pair of rafters with three 3 in. (76 mm) nails at each end; (5) ceiling joists toenailed to top wall plate with two 3 1/4 in. (82 mm) nails, one each side; (6) rafter nailed to plate with three 3 1/4 in. (82 mm) nails;

(B) jack rafter nailed to hip rafter with two 3 1/4 in. (82 mm) nails.

54

A
Gable Roof

- ridge board
- rafter
- collar brace
- collar tie
- gable end stud
- ceiling joist
- top wall plate

1
2
3
4
5
6

B
Hip Roof

- hip rafter
- jack rafter
- ceiling joists
- top plate
- corner post

Rafter heel supported on a rafter plate nailed to top of each ceiling joist with two 4 in. (101 mm) nails.

2" x 6" (38 x 140 mm) ridge beam

2" x 4" (38 x 89 mm) rafter plate

rafter

55

exterior wall

knee wall with 2" x 4" (38 x 89 mm) top and bottom plate and 2" x 4" (38 x 89 mm) studs in line with each ceiling joist and rafter

2" x 4" (38 x 89 mm) strut at 4' (1.2 m) o.c.

ceiling joists lapped directly above interior loadbearing wall

Doubled ceiling joists and tail joists used where hip rafter reduces clear space near the end wall.

2" x 6" (38 x 140 mm) jack rafter

2" x 8" (38 x 184 mm) hip rafter

56

ceiling joist

2" x 6" (38 x 140 mm) double ceiling joist

normal location for ceiling joist if space is available

2" x 4" (38 x 89 mm) tail joist

end wall framing top plate

required to maintain vertical alignment of the rafters when the lower ends are tied to ceiling joists that have been lapped (rather than butted together) at the centre loadbearing wall (Fig. 55).

A roof which slopes less than 1:3 should be vertically supported at the peak. This can be accomplished by providing a 2 x 6 in. (38 x 140 mm) ridge beam, supported at 4 ft. (1.2 m) intervals by 2 x 4 in. (38 x 89 mm) vertical struts (Fig. 55). A loadbearing wall may be used instead of the ridge beam. Since these methods of support reduce the outward thrust of the roof, continuous ties between the lower ends of opposing rafters are not necessary. Ridge beams are also required for steeper pitched roofs when the outside ends of the rafters cannot be tied together to resist thrust.

Intermediate Support for Rafters is generally installed between the ridge and exterior walls to reduce the span of the rafters. This reduces the size of the rafters which are required as the span is taken from this intermediate point to the ridge or eave support.

For rafters in roofs which slope 1:3 or more, intermediate support is generally provided by a 2 x 4 in. (38 x 89 mm) collar brace nailed to the side of each pair of rafters. Since these

Rafter heel supported on loadbearing wall. Ceiling joists project beyond the wall line and are nailed to the rafters (see Table 19 for nailing practice). Roof struts 2 x 4 in. (38 x 89 mm) used as intermediate support for rafters. Struts are nailed to the side of the rafter with three 3 1/4 in. (82 mm) nails and toenailed to bearing wall with two 3 1/4 in. (82 mm) nails.

57

3/4" (19 mm) thick ridge board

intermediate support 2" x 4" (38 x 89 mm) struts to be set not less than 45° to the horizontal

studs in loadbearing wall located directly under each rafter

2" (38 mm) thick splice plate

interior bearing wall

roof rafters notched and bearing directly on top plate of exterior wall

2" x 4" (38 x 89 mm) continuous nailer and soffit supports

ceiling joists bearing on double plate

wall sheathing

exterior wall

braces are in compression and subject to buckling, they should be supported against lateral deflection when more than 8 ft. (2.4 m) long. This can be done by nailing a 1 x 4 in. (19 x 89) mm continuous member at right angles to the collar braces near their centre with three 3 in. (76) mm nails at each end (Fig. 54).

Intermediate support for rafters in roofs which slope less than 1:3 is usually provided by a dwarf bearing wall (Fig. 55) built in the same way as a loadbearing partition, except that a single top plate may be used where the rafters are positioned directly over the studs.

Struts may also be used as intermediate supports for rafters in pitched roofs. A 2 x 4 in. (38 x 89 mm) strut (Fig. 57) is nailed to the side of each rafter and supported on a loadbearing partition. The angle of the struts should not be less than 45° to the horizontal.

Rafters which run at right angles to the ceiling joists may be supported at an intermediate point by a dwarf wall sitting on a beam placed between the ceiling joists. The underside of the beam is raised at least 1 in. (25 mm) above the ceiling finish by blocks inserted under the ends of the beam at the exterior walls and centre loadbearing partition. The space thus formed prevents the beam from damaging the ceiling finish when deflected at its centre by the roof loads.

A beam similarly installed may also be used as intermediate support for hip and valley rafters. In this case,

PLANNING AHEAD

Roof Covering Loads

The tables for sizing roof members assume that a conventional roof covering, such as asphalt shingles, cedar shakes or lightweight metal roofing, is being installed. Some roof coverings, such as terra cotta tile, are much heavier and hence the roof members must be sized accordingly. The following points should be considered when sizing roof framing members supporting heavier than normal roof coverings.

→ Obtain the unit weight (pounds per square foot or kilograms per square metre) from the manufacturer, and add this to the local snow load. Use this adjusted snow load to size roof framing members. If the adjusted snow load exceeds that found in the tables, consult with a competent structural designer.

→ If trusses are being used, notify the truss manufacturer of the additional load due to the heavier roof covering so that these may be sized properly.

→ Carefully observe all requirements for bracing and strapping that may be required to properly install and support the roof covering.

a roof strut is used to transfer the load from the hip or valley rafter to the beam.

Where intermediate support is required for a few rafters in the end section on a hip-type roof, a simple form of support can be provided by a beam (sometimes called a "strongback") consisting of two 2 x 4 in. (38 x 89 mm) members nailed together, set on edge and nailed to the bottom of the rafters. This beam is in turn supported at points along its length by 2 x 4 in. (38 x 89 mm) struts radiating from a common point of support on the centre loadbearing wall. The angle of any strut should not be less than 45° to the horizontal. The ends are cut to fit the selected angle and securely nailed in place.

Hip and Valley Rafters should be about 2 in. (50 mm) deeper than the common rafters (Figs. 54B, 56 and 58).

This additional depth provides full contact with the angle-cut of the jack rafters. In hip roofs, the jack rafters are nailed to the hip rafters and wall plate. Where a valley occurs, the jack rafters are nailed to the valley rafter and ridge.

Dormers, such as small gable dormers, are framed so that the rafters at each side are doubled to support the side studs and valley rafters. The top end of the valley rafters are supported by a header (Fig. 59). The most common method of construction is to install the roof sheathing before the dormer is framed, and then saw the sheathing flush with the framing members around the opening. A bottom plate added on top of the sheathing supports the side studs enclosing the dormer and also serves as a nailing base for the wall sheathing. If future expansion is contemplated or additional rooms are to be built in the attic, consideration should be given to framing the roof to accept future dormers when the house is built.

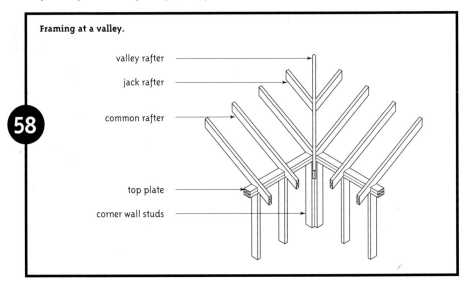

Framing at a valley.

valley rafter

jack rafter

58

common rafter

top plate

corner wall studs

Typical dormer framing. After roof sheathing is applied, blocking is added between side studs at roof line to provide nailing support for wall sheathing.

double header

jack rafter

double rafter

valley rafter

side stud

Note: size of window to allow for proper flashing, detailing and finishing of roofing

roof sheathing applied prior to construction of dormer

59

Wide projection at gable end supported by "lookout" rafters.

ridge beam

rafter

top plate of gable end wall

blocking between lookouts to support roof sheathing and inner edge of soffit covering

lookouts at 24" (600 mm) o.c.

ceiling joist

top plate

header or rough fascia

fascia board at eave and gable end

corner studs

blocking cut away to show top plate

60

Narrow projection at gable end. Rake rafter supported by ridge beam, rafter header, blocking and roof sheathing.

blocking spaced at 24" (600 mm) o.c. supporting soffit covering

ridge beam

rafter

3/4" (19 mm) nailing strip to support edge of soffit

ceiling joist

roof sheathing

gable wall sheathing taken up to underside of roof sheathing

top plate

studs

rake rafter

corner studs

rough fascia supports heel of rake rafter

61

Gable-end Framing and Projections

After the roof-framing members are up, the gable-end studs are cut to fit and nailed in place. Studs in unfinished attics may be placed with the wide face parallel to the wall. The ends of the studs are then cut to fit the angle of the rafter and are toenailed to the wall plate and to the underside of the rafter with four 2 1/2 in. (63 mm) nails at each end (Fig. 60).

Construction of the roof projections commonly used at the gable ends is shown in Figures 60 and 61. As with eave projections, the soffit is covered with 1/4 in. (6 mm) sanded plywood or pre-finished aluminum or vinyl sheets, and fascia board is added to the outside framing member.

Roofs which project less than 12 in. (300 mm) over the gable-end wall usually terminate with a framing member sometimes called the rake rafter (Fig. 61). A 1 in. (19 mm) nailing strip is fastened to the rafter located above the gable-end wall. Blocking spaced at 24 in. (600 mm) on centre is used to support the soffit covering. This blocking is toenailed to the nailing strip and end-nailed to the rake rafter. The soffit covering is then installed and nailed to these supports. A fascia board is added in the manner previously described.

Gable-end projections extending more than 12 in. (300 mm) beyond

HEALTHY HOUSING INSIGHT

Attic Rooms

The *Healthy Housing* principle of affordability and economic viability may be promoted by considering future conversion of the attic into habitable space. Through proper planning, it may be converted into a high quality living space, deferring initial construction costs until resources are available and needs arise.

Consider these features when planning attic rooms.

Truss attic space

Roof trusses are structurally more efficient than framed roofs; however, the webs do not permit future conversions of the attic into habitable space.

ridge beam required with knee walls

select roof framing system to accommodate insulation

collar tie (optional)

recommended 1:1 minimum roof slope

size ceiling joists as floor joists

optional knee wall recommended minimum height 5'-6" (1.65 m)

➡ Plan stairwells in the house so that they may be extended to the attic space, or determine an appropriate future location for outside stairs.

➡ Size ceiling joists as floor joists, and use insulation which may be transferred to the roof assembly during conversion. Ensure that the roof assembly will accommodate sufficient insulation with an air space above.

Continued on page 102

Continued from page 101 ➜ A roof slope of 1:1 or steeper is recommended, particularly if a knee wall is not provided. If a knee wall is provided, check local by-laws regarding height restrictions of the building.

➜ Rough in or plan for future services such as electricity, plumbing, heating, ventilation, and telephone.

With the addition of elements such as dormers and skylights, properly planned attics may be converted into high quality living space, easily and economically.

the wall should be supported by framing members called "lookouts" (Fig. 60). The gable-end studs are placed with the narrow face parallel to the sheathing, and a top wall plate is added. The lookout members, usually the same size as the rafters, are spaced at 24 in. (600 mm) on centre. The ends are supported by end-nailing to the first rafter and to the header, and toenailing to the wall plate. Blocking is then fitted between the lookouts at the wall line to support the roof sheathing and inner edge of the soffit covering. The soffit covering is nailed to these supports, and a fascia is added as previously described. The length of lookout members should be about twice the width of the roof overhang. A double rafter is used to support the inner ends of the lookout members when they project into the roof more than one and one-half rafter spacing.

FLAT ROOFS

Flat roofs are generally less practical and less durable than pitched roofs, especially in heavy snowfall areas. They are sometimes used to cover extensions of the main house and in combination with upper floor decks. Carports and garages are frequently covered with a flat roof.

In flat-roof construction where rafters also serve as ceiling joists, the term "roof joist" is used. The size of these roof joists is established on the basis of both roof and ceiling loads. (See Tables 24 and 25.) Rafters chosen for structural adequacy may not, however, provide adequate depth for insulation and ventilation of the roof space. In such cases, wider lumber or engineered wood products should be used.

Roof joists for flat roofs are usually laid level, with roof sheathing and a roof covering on top. The underside of the roof joists is used to support the ceiling. A slope of at least 1:50 should be provided for roof drainage by sloping each joist with a ledger strip on the underside of the joist at the bearing wall, or by adding a tapered strip to the top of the joists. The house design may call for an overhang of the roof beyond the wall or for a parapet wall carried above the roof. Insulation may be added just above the ceiling. In this case, the space above the insulation should be ventilated not only to help prevent condensation in the winter, but also to help remove hot air in the summer. Alternatively, rigid insulation may be installed on top of the roof sheathing and the roof covering placed on the insulation. In this case, the space above the ceiling is not ventilated. Figure 62A shows a simple type of flat

Two flat-roof designs. Rafters may also serve as ceiling joists.

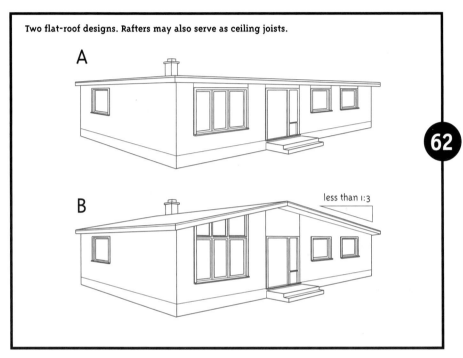

A

B

less than 1:3

62

Typical construction of flat roof with overhang.

Note: dashed lines indicate alternative framing layout

roof joist

lookout rafter

header

exterior wall plate

rafter header

63

roof in which the bottoms of the roof joists are level, eliminating the need for separate ceiling joists.

When an overhang is called for on all sides of the house, lookout rafters are ordinarily used (Fig. 63). These lookout rafters, which are usually twice as long as the overhang, are toenailed to the wall plate and end-nailed to the first roof joist. If the lookout rafters project into the ceiling area more than one and one-half joist space, two roof joists are nailed together to form a header. One outside rafter header is then added and end-nailed to the lookout rafters and roof joists.

This serves as a nailing support for the roof sheathing, fascia board and soffit covering. Such overhangs are generally from 16 to 24 in. (400 to 600 mm) but do not exceed 4 ft. (1.2 m).

Sloped roofs, as shown in Figure 62B, may have a ceiling finish attached to the roof joists with the ceiling following the pitch of the roof to form a "cathedral" ceiling. The roof joists are supported on a ridge beam in this case.

Note: Insulation is generally placed between the roof-ceiling joists. A ventilated space of at least 2 1/2 in. (63 mm) must be provided between the top of the insulation and the underside of the roof sheathing. This can be achieved by placing 2 x 2 in. (38 x 38 mm) cross purlins over the top of, and at right angles to, the roof-ceiling joists. The 2 x 2 in. (38 x 38 mm) members may be shimmed to provide the required roof slope. Figure 126 shows a cross-section of the completed roof.

ROOF SPACE VENTILATION

For both pitched and flat roofs, it is important to provide adequate ventilation of the roof space above the insulation. Even where air and vapour barriers are used, some moisture will leak around pipes and other openings and through the vapour barrier itself. If water vapour is allowed to accumulate in attic spaces and under flat roofs, during cold weather it is likely to condense in a cold spot in sufficient quantity to cause damage. Since most types of roof membranes are highly resistant to vapour transmission, the most practical way of removing vapour which enters the roof space is by ventilation.

During cold weather, heat loss through the ceiling insulation combined with exposure to sun may provide enough heat to melt the snow on the roof, but not on the eaves. Water from the melting snow can then freeze and form ice dams at the eave-strough and roof overhang. This may cause water to back up at the eaves, penetrate through the roof and leak into the walls and ceilings. Similar dams may form in roof valleys. A well-insulated ceiling and adequate ventilation will keep attic temperatures low and help prevent snow on the roof from melting. The installation of appropriate eave protection and valley flashings will also prevent potential water damage.

A common method of providing ventilation is to install louvered openings or continuous screened slots in the soffit at the eaves of gable and hip

HEALTHY HOUSING INSIGHT

Alternative Roof Framing Systems

A number of alternative roof framing systems are available which fulfill the Healthy Housing objective of resource efficiency. These manufactured alternatives use less material, and, due to their advanced engineering, can make use of waste material from less desirable, fast-growing tree species.

wood I-joists with vented webs

roof beams supporting stress skin panels

parallel chord trusses with metal webs

wood roof truss with raised heel

Parallel chord trusses provide longer spans than commonly available in dimensional lumber, and permit the placement of high levels of insulation while providing adequate ventilation of the roof cavity. This advantage is also available through conventional trusses when a raised heel is incorporated. This permits full depth placement of insulation over the exterior wall plates without restricting attic ventilation.

A novel approach to traditional post-and-beam construction involves using beams from timber, glulam or structural composite lumber to support stress skin panels. These structural panels comprise a sandwich of roof sheathing, insulation and an interior panel finish or nailing surface.

A common consideration for all of these alternatives is the need to plan accurately and to adhere to the final plan during construction. Unlike conventional framing approaches, these efficient alternatives are manufactured with precision, and there is much less flexibility for field changes or adjustments.

roofs (Fig. 64). Air movement through such openings depends primarily on wind. These are most effective when combined with vents located high on the roof such as ridge vents (Fig. 65A) or gable end vents (Fig. 65B).

Flat roofs insulated between the roof joists are difficult to ventilate unless there is clearance above the insulation, and the joist spaces are interconnected to permit free circulation of ventilating air (see Figs. 126 and 127). These common techniques are not applicable where fine snow can be wind-driven through such vent openings and deposited on the roof insulation. In such situations, local building practices should be followed.

SIZE OF VENTS

The size of roof vents, expressed as net or free area of the vent openings, depends on the slope and construction of the roof being ventilated.

For roofs with a slope of 1 in 6, or steeper, the minimum net area of ventilators for attic roof spaces is 1/300 of the insulated ceiling area. For example, a ceiling area of 1000 sq. ft. (100 m²) requires vents totaling at least 3.33 sq. ft. (0.33 m²) in net area. The area provided should be increased to allow for restrictions such as louvers, wire cloth or screens.

For roofs with a slope of less than 1 in 6, and for roofs constructed with roof joists (flat roofs and cathedral ceilings), the minimum unobstructed vent area is 1/150 of the insulated ceiling area. Flat, mild sloping and cathedral ceilings require at least twice as much roof vent area as steeper roofs with attics.

For all types of roofs, vents should be distributed uniformly on opposite sides of the building, where possible, with at least 25 percent of the openings located at the top of the space, and at least 25 percent of the openings located at the bottom of the space.

When planning roof ventilation, it is important to ensure that at least 2 1/2 in. (63 mm) of space is provided

Soffit roof ventilators.

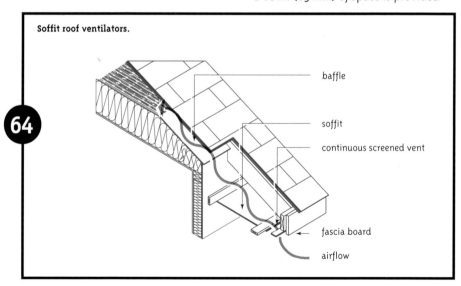

baffle

soffit

continuous screened vent

fascia board

airflow

64

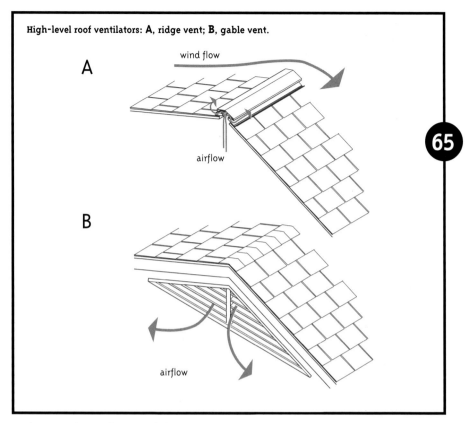

High-level roof ventilators: **A**, ridge vent; **B**, gable vent.

65

between the insulation and the underside of roof sheathing. Vents and ceiling insulation should be installed so that air flow through vents and roof spaces is not restricted.

Vents must not allow the entry of rain, snow or insects. Corrosion-resistant metal or plastic materials should be used for vents and to screen ventilator openings.

Where an access hatch to the attic or roof space is required, ensure that it is fitted with a tightly sealed and insulated door or cover, especially where the access hatch is located within the heated part of the dwelling. Access hatches located on the exterior of the building, often also serving as a gable end vent, are becoming a popular alternative to traditional locations such as ceilings above closets.

RELATED PUBLICATIONS

Habitable Attics: New Potential for an Old Idea
Canada Mortgage and Housing Corporation

SIZING CEILING JOISTS

Problem

Select the minimum ceiling joist that is acceptable for the conditions described below.

span = 14'-2" (4.3 m)

spacing = 16" (400 mm)

Conditions

Attic is inaccessible, without storage.
Ceiling supports insulation and drywall interior finish.
Span is 14'-2" (4.3 m)
Ceiling joist spacing is 16" (400 mm)
Commercial designation and grade specified is SPF No. 2 or better

Selection

Use Table 28.

For this application select:
2" x 6" (38 x 140 mm) ceiling joist

SIZING ROOF RAFTERS

Problem
Select the smallest dimension rafter that is able to span the roof as described below.

Rafter span = 15'-6" (4.7 m)

3

1

Conditions
Building location is: Ottawa, Ontario.
specified roof snow load is 36 lbs/ft² (1.72 kPa).
Roof slope is 1 in 3.
Rafter span is 15'-6" (4.7 m).
Commercial designation and grade specified is SPF No. 2 or better
Shingle roofing to be used.
Lower ends of the rafter are restrained.

Selection
Use Table 26.

Acceptable rafters include:
2" x 8" (38 x 184 mm) at 12" o.c. (300 mm o.c.)
2" x 10" (38 x 235 mm) at 24" o.c. (600 mm o.c.)

SIZING ROOF JOISTS

Problem
Select the roof joists that are able to span the roof as described below.

Roof joist span = 13'-9" (4.19 m)

Conditions
Building location is: Ottawa, Ontario.
Specified roof snow load is 36 lbs/ft² (1.72 kPa).
Roof slope is 1 in 3.
Roof joist span is 13'-9" (4.19 m).
Commercial designation and grade specified is SPF No. 2 or better
Shingle roofing to be used.
Lower ends of the roof joists are restrained.

Selection
Use Table 24.

Acceptable roof joists include:
2" x10" (38 x 235 mm) at 16" o.c. (400 mm o.c.)
2" x 12" (38 x 286 mm) at 24" o.c. (600 mm o.c.)

FLASHING

Flashing is provided, where necessary, to prevent the entry of water through joints between materials. Proper installation of flashing is important, as is the selection of the most suitable materials for each specific location.

The minimum recommended weights and types of materials for flashing are shown in Table 31.

Aluminum flashing should be isolated from masonry or concrete or coated with an impervious membrane to reduce the possibility of corrosion.

Flashing should be used at the junction of roofs and walls, roofs and chimneys, over window and door openings, in roof valleys and in other critical areas.

A typical example of construction requiring flashing is at the intersection of two types of materials, as shown in Figure 66. The stucco is separated from the wood siding below by a wood drip cap. To prevent the water from entering the wall, pre-formed flashing is installed over the drip cap to form a drip at the outside edge. The flashing should extend at least 2 in. (50 mm) above this drip cap and under the sheathing membrane. This type of flashing is also used over the heads of windows and doors unless they are well protected by a roof overhang. Where the vertical distance between the top of the trim and the underside of the overhang is more than one-quarter of the overhang's horizontal projection, flashing should always be used.

The heads and sills of openings in masonry-veneered, wood-frame walls should be flashed. Head flashing should extend from the front edge of the lintel, up and over the lintel and on up under the sheathing paper. Where a jointed masonry sill is used, the flashing should extend from the outer edge under the masonry sill up to the underside of the wood sill.

Flashing should also be used at the junction of roof surfaces and walls. If built-up roofing is used, a cant strip should be provided to avoid a right-angle bend in the membrane and consequent puncturing. The built-up roofing is carried at least 6 in. (150 mm) up the wall of the house over the cant strip and sheathing. The sheathing paper is then lapped 4 in. (100 mm) over the edge of the roofing. When the siding is placed on the wall, a clearance of at least 2 in. (50 mm) should be allowed between the siding and the roof to keep the siding well clear of water draining down the roof surface (Fig. 67).

Where stack-vents penetrate the roof, they should be flashed to prevent moisture entry.

Flashing should be used where two roof lines intersect to form a valley. Depending on the shingling method used, valleys are referred to as open or closed. Open valleys are commonly flashed with one layer of sheet metal at least 24 in. (600 mm) wide or with two layers of roll roofing. When roll roofing is used, the bottom layer may be Type S or Type M mineral surface material (mineral surface down), at least 18 in. (450 mm) wide.

Typical flashing between two different materials.

66

A

stucco

stud

stucco lath

sheathing

lap wall sheathing membrane over metal flashing

metal flashing

drip cap

siding

B

stucco finish on metal lath

lap sheathing membrane over metal flashing

metal base trim and flashing

This layer is centred on the valley and fastened along the edges with nails spaced 16 to 18 in. (400 to 450 mm) apart. A 4 in. (100 mm) band of cement is then applied along the edges of the bottom layer, and a strip of Type M mineral surface roll roofing approximately 36 in. (914 mm) wide is placed over the first layer (mineral surface up). The top layer is fastened along the edges with only enough nails to hold it in place until the

(A) open valley and shingle flashing at side wall; (B) cricket flashing used with chimney that is more than 30 in. (750 mm) wide.

A

valley flashing

flashing

3" (75 mm) head lap in shingle step flashing

siding to have 2" (50 mm) minimum clearance above shingles

flashing

67

B

more than 30" (750 mm)

3" (75 mm) head lap in counterflashing

3" (75 mm) head lap in shingle step flashing

cricket or saddle

shingles are applied. The roof shingles are stopped on a line 4 to 6 in. (100 to 150 mm) from the centre of the valley, this distance being greater at the eaves than at the ridge (Fig. 67A).

Closed valleys are generally flashed with one layer of sheet metal, 0.006 in. thick. Each course of shingles is continued across the valley, ensuring that shingle nails are not placed within 3 in. (75 mm) of the valley centre line at the ridge or 5 in. (125 mm) at the eaves. Where rigid shingles are used, they are cut to fit the centre line of the valley, but these should not

be used with the closed valley method or roofs that slope less than 1:1.2.

Flashing squares (sometimes called "step-flashing" or "shingle flashing") should be used at the intersections of shingled roofs with walls or chimneys. This type of flashing is installed at the time the shingles are applied. One square is used at each course and is bent up along the wall under the sheathing membrane (Fig. 67A). The siding will cover the flashing along the wall, except for the clearance allowed. These squares should be large enough to give a good lap at the roof and wall line, and the head lap should be no less than 3 in. (75 mm). On the roof slopes behind a chimney, the flashing should extend both up the roof and up the chimney to a point equal in height to the counterflashing of the chimney, but in any case not less than 1 1/2 times the shingle exposure.

Counterflashing is used at the intersection of a roof with a masonry wall or chimney. This counterflashing should extend at least 6 in. (150 mm) up the side of the chimney or masonry veneer and be embedded at least 1 in. (25 mm) into the mortar joint. The counterflashing is fitted tightly against the masonry and lapped over the shingle flashing at least 4 in. (100 mm). Counterflashing is applied to all sides of the chimney where it penetrates the roof.

If the upper side of a chimney is more than 30 in. (750 mm) wide, a cricket or saddle should be installed (Fig. 67B). These are often made of sheet metal and should be placed over a wood-framing support constructed during roof-framing operations. The saddle should be suitably flashed at the roof and counterflashed at the chimney. Open joints and laps should be soldered or sealed, or a locked joint used. A saddle is not required, however, if the metal flashing is carried up both the roof and the chimney to a height at least equal to one-sixth the chimney width. This shingle flashing should never be less than 1 1/2 times the shingle exposure and the chimney counterflashing never less than 6 in. (150 mm).

ROOF SHEATHING AND COVERINGS

ROOF SHEATHING

Roof sheathing is applied over roof trusses or rafters and usually consists of plywood, oriented strandboard (OSB), structural wood panels or lumber. Sheathing provides a nailing base for the roof covering and laterally braces the roof framing.

Installing Roof Sheathing

When plywood or OSB is used for roof sheathing, it is laid with the face grain at right angles to the framing (Fig. 68). Sheathing-grade structural wood panels (SWP) is used for this purpose. To obtain a good tie across the roof framing, the end joints of the panels should be staggered on the framing members. The edges of the panels should be separated by at least an 1/8 in. (2 to 3 mm) to prevent buckling when minor expansion occurs during wet weather.

The thickness of the plywood, OSB or structural wood panel used for roof sheathing depends to some extent on the spacing of the rafters, roof joists or trusses and whether or not the edges of the sheets are supported. To prevent damage to the roof covering when thinner panels are used, the joints running across the framing should be supported by 2 x 2 in. (38 x 38 mm) blocking, nailed securely

Application of structural wood panel roof sheathing.

nails 12" (300 mm) o.c.

rafter

metal H-clip or blocking

ceiling joist

1/8" (2-3 mm) space

68

nails 6" (150 mm) o.c.

grain direction

double top plate

between the roof framing members, or by metal H-clips inserted between sheets. The latter method is widely used because the installation is simple and economical. Minimum thicknesses for plywood and other roof sheathing are shown in Table 32. Table 18 identifies the nail and staple requirements for roof sheathing. Staple fastening for 3/8 in. (9.5 mm) roof sheathing must be 1/16 in. thick, 1 1/2 in. long with a 3/8 in. crown (1.6 mm thick, 38.1 mm long with a 9.5 mm crown), and be driven with the crown parallel to the framing. (See Table 33.) Thicker roof sheathing, no less than 5/8 in. (15.5 mm), is required for built-up roofing on a flat roof where it is used as a walking deck. In these cases, Table 17 should be used to determine the minimum thickness for the sheathing.

Under materials requiring solid and continuous support, such as asphalt shingles and built-up roofing,

lumber sheathing must be laid closed (Fig. 69B). The boards are usually 3/4 in. (19 mm) thick, but this thickness may be reduced to 11/16 in. (17 mm) where supports are spaced at 16 in. (400 mm) on centre. Boards 8 in. (184 mm) or less wide are nailed to the framing members with two 2 in. (51 mm) nails per bearing. Those wider than 8 in. (184 mm) should be nailed with three 2 in. (51 mm) nails per bearing. Boards wider than 12 in. (286 mm) should not be used for roof sheathing. For a wood shingle roof, the roof boards may be spaced the same distance apart on centre as the shingle exposure. This method (Fig. 69A), commonly used in damp climates, permits freer movement of air around the boards and under shingles, thus reducing the possibility of decay.

Roof Sheathing Details

Where openings occur in the roof structure for interior chimneys, the

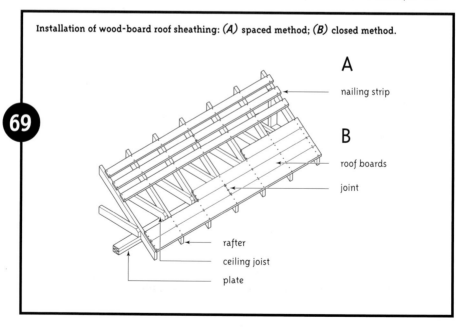

Installation of wood-board roof sheathing: (A) spaced method; (B) closed method.

A

nailing strip

B

roof boards

joint

rafter

ceiling joist

plate

69

roof sheathing and framing members should have a clearance of 2 in. (50 mm) from the finished masonry, or metal chimney, on all sides for fire protection (Fig. 70). This clearance may be reduced to 1/2 in. (12 mm) for exterior masonry chimneys. Roof sheathing should be securely nailed to

HEALTHY HOUSING INSIGHT

Roof Sheathing Options

There are a large number of roof sheathing options available in wood-frame construction. Some of these products are more resource efficient than others, depending on the roof application as well as the geographic location of the building. Consider the following points for the appropriate selection of roof sheathing materials.

Avoid Over Design

When it comes to roof sheathings, thicker is not necessarily better. The requirements in local building codes represent adequate strength and durability, with a factor of safety added on to ensure good performance, provided the material is properly installed. Avoiding the use of thicker sheathings saves money and forest resources.

Use Materials Made From Scrap Wood

All engineered wood products are not alike. Plywood sheathing is typically manufactured from higher grade species of mature trees. Waferboard and oriented strand board incorporate scrap wood and wood from less desirable, fast-growing tree species. Both types of engineered wood products provide adequate performance, but the latter group of roof sheathing products may be more resource efficient.

Consider Local Materials

In many areas, using local materials is more appropriate than importing materials. For example, using rough sawn boards as roof sheathing is preferred in many parts of Canada over engineered wood products. The selection of local materials encourages employment and reduces the use of energy associated with the transport of imported materials.

Select an Appropriate Roof Covering

The type of roof covering which is selected often determines the number of roof sheathing options available. When metal or wood shake roof coverings are used, spaced boards may serve as the roof sheathing, utilizing a fraction of the wood compared to sheet-type roof sheathings.

Keep in mind that no matter what type of roof sheathing option is selected, a key consideration is the quality of workmanship employed.

Roof sheathing detail at a valley and at a chimney opening.

chimney opening
(allow additional
2" (50 mm) around
the chimney

header

70

rafter

roof sheathing

valley

ridge board

ceiling joist

plate

stud

the rafters and headers around the opening.

Roof sheathing at valleys and hips should be fitted to give a tight joint and should be securely nailed to the valley or hip rafter (Fig. 70). This will give a solid and smooth base for flashing.

Flashing is discussed in detail in the chapters that follow. Refer to this discussion for more information.

ROOF COVERINGS

The roof covering is usually installed as soon as the roof framing and the sheathing has been completed and before any other interior or exterior finishing work starts. This sequence produces a weatherproof working space within the building early in the construction process so that other trades can begin their work. It also protects the lumber and interior panel products from excessive moisture.

Roof coverings should provide a long-life, waterproof finish that will protect the building and its contents from rain and snow. Many materials have withstood the test of time, and have proven satisfactory under various conditions.

Asphalt shingles are by far the most commonly used roof covering for pitched roofs. Galvanized steel or aluminum roofing is also common in some regions. At normal roof pitches, metal roofs will generally shed snow, a desirable characteristic in heavy snowfall areas. Roll roofing, wood shingles, handsplit shakes, sheet metal and concrete or clay tile among others are also used. For flat or low-pitched roofs, built-up roofing with a gravel topping or cap sheet is frequently used. The choice of materials may be influenced by cost, local code requirements or local preferences based upon past experience.

The minimum and maximum slopes for the different types of roof coverings are presented in Table 34.

The minimum slopes of roofs is 1:6 for asphalt shingles (using a low-slope application), 1:4 for wood shin-

HEALTHY HOUSING INSIGHT

Roof Covering Materials Selection

The quality and performance of roof covering materials is an extremely important aspect of wood-frame house construction, due to the costly water damage that may result from a leaky roof, and the considerable expense associated with roof replacement. There are several key considerations involved in selecting an appropriate roof covering material.

→ The source of the material may be renewable or non-renewable. Asphalt-based, metal, clay and concrete roof coverings use non-renewable materials. Wood products are generally renewable when harvested from a properly managed forest.

→ The material may be produced from recycled material, or it may be recyclable or non-recyclable. Generally, the use of recycled materials should be encouraged to conserve natural resources, whereas non-recyclable materials should be avoided.

→ The material may have a relatively short or long service life. This factor, balanced against initial cost, may significantly influence the final selection of a roof covering material.

The brief comparison of roof covering options which follows is presented in an ascending order of cost and useful service life.

The predominant roof covering used in wood-frame house construction is asphalt shingles. While these products are being recycled in some areas, for most areas they may be considered non-recyclable. Their useful service life ranges between 15 and 25 years.

Wood shingles obtained from properly managed forests are renewable and provide a useful service life comparable to asphalt shingles.

Metal roofing is non-renewable but recyclable, and depending on the type of metal used, may have a significantly longer service life in comparison with asphalt or wood shingles.

Clay and concrete tiles are non-renewable, but often completely reusable due to their stability and long service life. These types of roof coverings require greater structural support. Installation procedures are more difficult than conventional roofing.

gles, and 1:3 for handsplit shakes and asphalt shingles (using normal application). Built-up roof coverings are rarely used on roofs where the slope exceeds 1:4.

In order to avoid water damage caused by melting snow, which sometimes forms into ice dams at the eaves, shingle or shake-covered roofs must have additional protection. This protection usually consists of either Type S (smooth surface) or Type M roll roofing laid with the joints lapped at least 4 in. (100 mm) and cemented together. Placed over the roof sheathing, this protection sheet extends from

(A) Snow and ice dams. Ice dams often build up on the overhang of roofs and in eaves troughs, causing water from melting snow to back up under shingles at the eaves; (B) eave protection prevents water trapped by ice dams from entering the roof.

71

A
- melting snow
- trapped water
- ice dam
- water penetrates roof
- vapour barrier
- insulation
- eavestrough

B
- water carried to eavestrough
- eave protection to run 12" (300 mm) beyond inside face of stud line
- 12" (300 mm) minimum
- 36" (900 mm) minimum
- inside face of stud
- eavestrough
- insulation

the edge of the roof to a line at least 12 in. (300 mm) beyond the inside of the inner face of the exterior walls, thus preventing water penetration through joints in the roof sheathing (Fig. 71A and B). The eave protection must extend at least 36 in. (900 mm) up the roof slope.

Methods of flashing shingled roofs at valleys, chimneys and intersecting walls are described in the chapter on *Flashing*.

Asphalt Shingles on Slopes 1:3 or Greater

Asphalt strip shingles should be a minimum No. 210 grade. Square-butt strip shingles are usually 12 x 36 in. (310 x 915 mm) or 13 1/4 x 39 3/8 in. (335 x 1000 mm) in size, have three tabs and should be laid with 5 in. (130 mm) or 5 3/4 in. (145 mm) of their width exposed to the weather. Since there are approximately 21 to 26 strips in a bundle, a bundle will cover about 32 sq. ft. (3 m²).

Bundles should be piled flat for storage so that strips will not curl when the bundles are opened. Care should be taken in piling shingles on the roof; if too many are piled together, the load capacity of the framing may be exceeded.

The method of laying an asphalt-shingle roof is shown in Figure 72. Eave protection is first provided by one of the methods already described. A starter strip at least 12 in. (300 mm) wide is then placed along the eaves before the first course of shingles, so that it extends at least 1/2 in. (12 mm) beyond the eaves, rakes and fascia board to form a drip edge. Starter strips with metal drip edges can also

be used. This projection prevents water from backing up under the shingles by capillary action. A shingle strip laid with the tabs facing up the roof slope is often used for this purpose. Type M (mineral-surfaced) roll roofing may be used as a starter strip and when continued up the roof slope will also serve as eave protection. The starter strip is nailed along the bottom edge at 12 in. (300 mm) intervals. The first course of shingles is then laid with the butt edge in line with the bottom of the starter strip.

In shingle application, the exposure distance is important, and the exposure depends on the roof slope and the type and length of shingle used.

Several chalklines will help align the shingle courses so that tabs and tab notches will be in a straight line which creates a good appearance. Each shingle strip should be stapled or nailed. Four large-head roofing nails should be used on each strip and should be long enough to penetrate through or 1/2 in. (12 mm) into the roof sheathing. Good nailing is important. When a nail penetrates a crack or knothole, another nail should be driven alongside into sound wood. Cementing the tabs of strip shingles is recommended for all areas.

Plastic cement can be used for this purpose with a spot approximately 1 in. (25 mm) in diameter being placed under the centre of each tab. Most shingles are manufactured with an adhesive strip on the underside of the tabs. Interlocking and other special shingles should be laid according to the manufacturer's directions.

Asphalt Shingles on Low Slopes of 1:6 to 1:3

Additional precautions must be taken on low slopes to ensure a waterproof roof covering. Except for the first two courses, three thicknesses of shingles are used on the entire roof including hips and ridges. This is achieved by using an exposure of not more than one-third the full height of the shingle. A starter strip is first installed as described for higher-sloped roofs, but laid on a continuous band of cement not less than 8 in. (200 mm) wide. The first course of shingles is then cemented to the strip with a continuous band of cement that is 4 in. (100 mm) wider than the shingle exposure. For example, a 10 in. (250 mm) band of cement should be used when the shingle exposure is 6 in. (150 mm). The succeeding courses of shingles are laid on a band of cement 2 in. (50 mm) wider than the shingle expo-sure, so that an 8 in. (200 mm) band is used when the exposure is 6 in. (150 mm).

To avoid defacing the exposed surface of the shingles with cement, the band should be located between 1 and 2 in. (25 and 50 mm) above the butt edge of each succeeding course of shingles. Each shingle strip should be stapled or nailed in place with four nails.

If cold application cement is used, it should be applied at a rate of approximately 1 gal./100 sq. ft. (0.5 L/m²) of cemented area. Hot applica-tion cement is applied at a rate of approximately 0.2 lb./sq. ft. (1 kg/m²) of cemented area. The above tech-nique is necessary only for slopes lower than 1:4 since there are special low-slope shingles of sufficient length to maintain the three thicknesses necessary at this roof pitch.

Application of asphalt shingles.

roof sheathing

eave protection

roofing nail

tar seals

exposure

fascia board

starting course either solid strip or reversed shingles

72

Wood Shingles

Wood shingles commonly used for houses are No. 1 and No. 2 grade. Red or white cedar are the principal species of wood used for shingles, because their heartwoods have high decay resistance and low shrinkage. Pine and yellow cedar are also used for shingles. The width of wood shingles varies, but the maximum width is 14 in. (350 mm) with a minimum width of 3 in. (75 mm).

Figure 73 illustrates the proper method of laying a wood-shingle roof. As is the case for asphalt shingles, underlay and roofing felt is not usually required for wood shingles, but eave protection, as described previously, should be installed.

The first shingle course should be laid double with the upper shingles overlapping the joints in the course beneath and both rows extending about 1 in. (25 mm) beyond the fascia boards at the eaves. This precaution will prevent water from backing up underneath the shingles. Shingles should be laid 1/4 in. (6 mm) apart to allow for swelling when wet. The joints between shingles in one course should be offset at least 1 9/16 in. (40 mm) from the joint between shingles in the course below. The joints in succeeding courses should be spaced so that the joint in one course is not in line with the joints in the two previous courses laid.

Only two nails should be used for each shingle. The distance of the nails from the butt edge of the shingle being nailed should be the shingle exposure plus 1 9/16 in. (40 mm), with

Installation of wood shingles.

eave protection to run 12" (300 mm) beyond inside face of stud line

roof sheathing

two nails per shingle

13/16" (20 mm) edge distance to nails

wood shingles

exposure

1 9/16" (40 mm) lap

1/4" (6 mm) space between shingles

fascia board

first shingle course (double)

extend 1" (25 mm)

project shingles 1/2" (12 mm) for drip

73

an edge distance of about 13/16 in. (20 mm). For example, if the shingle exposure is to be 5 in. (125 mm), add 1 9/16 in. (40 mm), and thus the nail should be 6 9/16 in. (165 mm) from the butt edge of the shingle being nailed. Shingles are fastened with hot-dip galvanized or other corrosion-resistant shingle nails. Flat grain shingles wider than 8 in. (200 mm) are sometimes split and nailed as two shingles to avoid problems with cupping and warping.

Handsplit Shakes

Cedar handsplit shakes must not be less than 18 in. (450 mm) long and 4 in. (100 mm) wide. They must also be no wider than 13 3/4 in. (350 mm). The butt thickness should be between 3/8 and 1 1/4 in. (9 and 32 mm) (Fig. 74).

Shakes may be applied over spaced or closed roof sheathing. When spaced sheathing is used (Fig. 69A), 1 x 4 in. (19 x 89 mm) (or wider) strips are placed on centres equal to the weather exposure at which the shakes are to be laid, but never more than 10 in. (250 mm). In areas where wind-driven snow conditions prevail, closed roof sheathing is recommended.

Proper weather exposure is important. As a general rule, 7 1/2 in. (190 mm) exposure is recommended for 18 in. (450 mm) shakes, and a 10 in. (250 mm) exposure for 24 in. (600 mm) shakes. The minimum recommended roof pitch for handsplit shakes is 1:3.

A 36 in. (900 mm) strip of No. 15 roofing felt should be laid over the sheathing boards at the eave line. The beginning or starter course of shakes should be doubled; for extra texture, it can be tripled. The bottom course or courses can be 15 in. (380 mm) or 18 in.

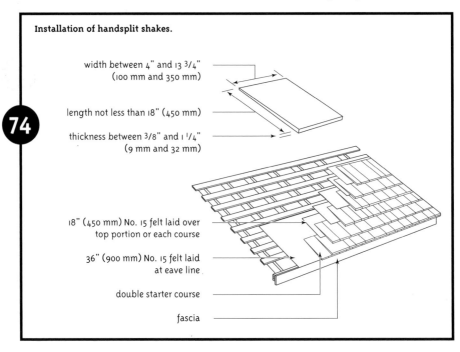

Installation of handsplit shakes.

width between 4" and 13 3/4" (100 mm and 350 mm)

length not less than 18" (450 mm)

74

thickness between 3/8" and 1 1/4" (9 mm and 32 mm)

18" (450 mm) No. 15 felt laid over top portion or each course

36" (900 mm) No. 15 felt laid at eave line

double starter course

fascia

(450 mm) shakes, the former being made expressly for this purpose.

After each course of shakes is applied, an 18 in. (450 mm) wide strip of No. 15 roofing felt should be laid over the top portion of the shakes, extending onto the sheathing. The bottom edge of the felt should be positioned above the butt at a distance equal to twice the weather exposure. For example, 24 in. (600 mm) shakes laid with 10 in. (250 mm) exposure would have felt applied 20 in. (500 mm) above the shake butts. Thus, the felt will cover the top 4 in. (100 mm) of the shakes and extend out about 15 in. (350 mm) onto the sheathing (Fig. 74).

Shakes should be spaced between 1/4 to 3/8 in. (6 to 9 mm) apart. Side joints should be offset no less than 1-9/16 in. (40 mm) over the adjacent courses. When straight split shakes are used, the "froe-end" (the end from which the shakes have been split and which is smoother) should be laid uppermost (towards the ridge).

Finish at Ridge and Hips

The most common type of finish is shown in Figure 75A. Asphalt shingle squares (one-third of a strip) are used over the ridge or hip and blind-nailed. Each shingle is lapped to provide the same coverage as the roofing shingles. It is good practice to the lay the ridge cap so as to provide the maximum

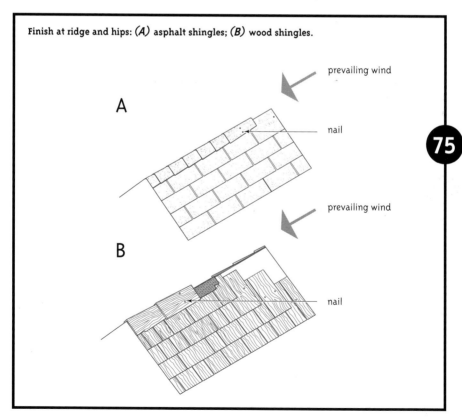

Finish at ridge and hips: (A) asphalt shingles; (B) wood shingles.

A

prevailing wind

nail

75

prevailing wind

B

nail

protection from the prevailing wind.

In the case of wood shingles, 6 in. (150 mm) wide shingles are alternatively lapped and blind-nailed (Fig. 75B). Flashing is sometimes used under a wood-shingle ridge.

Built-up Roofs

Built-up roof coverings are installed by roofing firms that specialize in this work. Roofs of this type may have three or more layers of roofing felt. Each layer is mopped down with tar or asphalt, the final surface being coated with the same material. The surface is then covered with gravel (embedded in the asphalt or tar) or with a cap sheet. This covering provides ballast and protection from the sun's ultraviolet radiation. It is important to note that coal tar products and asphalt products are not compatible and must not be used together.

The eave line of projecting roofs is usually finished with metal edging or flashing. A gravel stop or cant strip is used in conjunction with the flashing at the eaves when the roof is covered with gravel (Fig. 76A). Where built-up roofing is finished against another wall (except a masonry-clad wall), the roofing is mopped to the cant strip and turned up the wall at least 6 in. (150 mm). The wall sheathing paper and siding is then applied over the roof membrane. (Fig. 76B).

Built-up roof: (A) eave flashing and drip; (B) junction of built-up roof and wall covered with siding.

76

siding

sheathing membrane

2" (50 mm) minimum lap

membrane flashing

cant strip

roof sheathing

built-up roofing

metal gravel stop

fascia board

B

A

Where a built-up roof intersects a masonry-clad wall, the roof membrane is similarly returned up the face of the masonry. Counter-flashing is then added. This counter-flashing should be embedded into the mortar joints at least 1 in. (25 mm), extending down the wall about 6 in. (150 mm) and lapping over the flashing at least 4 in. (100 mm).

Single-ply membranes can also be used for flat roofs. They consist of

Details of sheet metal roofing.

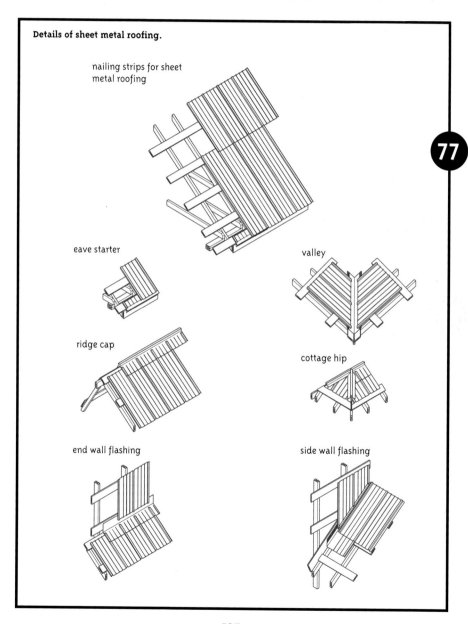

nailing strips for sheet metal roofing

eave starter

valley

ridge cap

cottage hip

end wall flashing

side wall flashing

77

various synthetic materials that are resistant to freeze-thaw cycling, ozone attack and ultraviolet degradation. They are relatively simple to lay, but are not often used on the small roofs that are typically part of wood-frame construction.

Sheet Metal Roofing

Sheet metal roofing is manufactured in 30 to 36 in. (762 mm to 914 mm) widths, depending on the profile of the corrugation, and in any lengths specified by the builder. It comes with the necessary accessories for treating the various details of the roof, such as hips, valleys, eave starters and edges (Fig. 77). The usual method of fastening the metal roof sheets is to lay 1 x 4 in. (19 x 89 mm) wood nailing strips across the rafters at no more than 16 in. (400 mm) on centre. For more positive attachment and better nailing, 2 x 4 in. (38 x 89 mm) purlins can be used. There must be a nailing strip underneath each end joint (Fig. 77). The choice of metal thickness, be it steel or aluminum, will depend on the local snow load, but it should not be less than 0.013 in. (0.33 mm) for galvanized steel, 0.018 in. (0.46 mm) for copper or zinc and 0.019 in. (0.48 mm) for aluminum. The required thicknesses for specific snow loads are given in tables provided by the manufacturer.

Concrete and Clay Tile Roofing

When considering the use of concrete or clay tile, it must be remembered that these materials are considerably heavier than other roofing systems, and thus the roof supporting structure of rafters or trusses must be designed to withstand the additional load. A professional engineer should be consulted to obtain a proper design. Simulated versions of tile roofing do not normally require a special structural design. Be sure to follow manufacturers' recommendations.

RELATED PUBLICATIONS

Construction and the Environment: How Home Builders and Renovators Can Help Build a Green Future
Canada Mortgage and Housing Corporation

Making a Molehill out of a Mountain (Video)
Canada Mortgage and Housing Corporation

CHECKING BACK

Adequate Sizing of Roof Framing Members

Depending on the type of roof covering materials being installed, it may be necessary to check the sizing of roof framing members. The typical sizes of roof framing members correspond to conventional roof covering materials such as asphalt shingles, cedar shakes or lightweight metal roofing. If clay or concrete roof coverings are being used, it will likely be necessary to resize roof framing members accordingly.

→ Check back to the chapter on *Ceiling and Roof Framing* to ensure that the roof framing members are adequately sized.

→ Check with the roof covering manufacturer for the higher loads imposed by heavyweight roof coverings, and use this data when sizing roof framing members.

HEALTHY HOUSING INSIGHT

Minimizing Waste in Roof Construction

Roof waste may be significantly reduced through proper planning and construction practices. Consider the following points when planning and building roofs.

→ Avoid ordering much more material than is required, unless arrangements for returning unused goods to suppliers have been made.

→ Where possible, make the lengths of roofs a multiple of 16 in. (400 mm) or 24 in. (600 mm) so that wasted roof sheathing is minimized.

→ Collect and store waste materials to promote complete recycling — avoid mixing waste construction materials. Separate materials individually for better recycling opportunities.

→ Use the short pieces of lumber from floor and wall framing as blocking or lookouts.

When using materials which are not recyclable, consider alternative uses. For example, waste clay roofing tile may be used as splash blocks for rain water leaders, or as creative landscape elements. Waste concrete roof coverings may be broken up and used along with granular materials as backfill. For more insights into managing construction waste, refer to *Applying the 4 Rs of Wood-Frame Construction* in the *Framing the House* chapter.

WALL SHEATHING AND EXTERIOR FINISHES

Wall sheathing is the outside covering used over the wall framework and is nailed directly to the wall framing members. Sheathing provides a nailing base for some types of siding and backing for others. It can also be used to brace the structure, although in most cases sufficient bracing is provided by the interior wall finish. Insulating sheathing materials will not normally provide the required temporary or permanent bracing. When such sheathing is used, let-in braces of wood or metal can be used as bracing if required. Sheathing must be applied to the gable ends and walls where the exterior cladding is a type that requires solid backing.

Several types of sheathing are used in present-day construction: fibreboard, gypsum board, plywood, oriented strand board, rigid insulation and lumber. Table 35 lists the various types of sheathing and the minimum thickness necessary to provide sufficient backing for exterior finishing materials.

TYPES AND INSTALLATION OF SHEATHING

Oriented Strand Board and Waferboard are structural panels made from thin, short wood wafers that are bonded together with a waterproof phenolic adhesive. While waferboard contains wafers that are randomly arranged, oriented strand board contains wafers that are narrower and that are oriented in the long direction of the panel. This gives the panel added strength and rigidity in the long direction. The designation O-1 or O-2 indicates an oriented panel, while an R-1 designation indicates a panel containing randomly arranged wafers.

The panels are formed into sheets 4 ft. (1.2 m) wide and usually 8 ft. (2.4 m) long. The minimum thickness that should be used is 5/16 in. (7.9 mm) for studs up to 2 ft. (600 mm) on centre and 1/4 in. (6.35 mm) for studs up to 16 in. (400 mm) on centre. oriented strand board and waferboard sheathing can be installed the same as plywood.

Panel-type sheathing, such as fibreboard, plywood, oriented strand board or waferboard, is often applied vertically. The panels are nailed to the wall framework before the wall is raised to position. This sequence helps the wall maintain its squareness, avoids the need for scaffolding, and closes the house in as soon as the framing is completed. Often the window openings are covered by the sheathing panels and are not cut until after the windows are delivered.

The sheathing panels can also be applied horizontally, in which case the vertical joints should be staggered wherever possible.

A space at least 1/8 in. (2 to 3 mm) wide should be left between the sheets to permit expansion without buckling. The panels are nailed to the framing at 6 in. (150 mm) on centre along the edges, and 12 in. (300 mm) along the intermediate supports (Fig. 78).

Plywood is usually sheathing grade, unsanded, laminated with a water-proof adhesive and may contain knots. The minimum thickness for exterior type plywood wall sheathing should be 5/16 in. (7.5 mm) for studs 24 in. (600 mm) on centre, and 1/4 in. (6 mm) for studs up to 16 in. (400 mm) on centre. Sheets are 4 ft. (1.2 m) wide and usually 8 ft. (2.4 m) long.

Fibreboard sheathing should be at least 7/16 in. (11.1 mm) thick for studs 24 in. (600 mm) on centre and 3/8 in. (9.5 mm) for studs 16 in. (400 mm) on centre. It is supplied in sheets 4 ft. (1.2 m) wide and generally 8 ft. (2.4 m) long, and is usually impregnated with an asphalt material to increase water resistance.

Gypsum board sheathing consists of a gypsum filler faced on both sides with treated paper. It should be at least 1/2 in. (12.7 mm) thick for studs 24 in. (600 mm) on centre and 3/8 in. (9.5 mm) thick for studs 16 in. (400 mm) on centre. It is supplied in sheets 4 ft. (1.2 m) wide and 8 ft. (2.4 m) long. The sheets are applied horizontally across the studs and nailed to the framing members.

Insulating sheathing is available in a number of types. One type is a semi-rigid glass-fibre panel with an exterior

Vertical and horizontal application of panel-type sheathing.

Vertical application

Horizontal application

window opening

78

3/8" (10 mm) minimum edge distance to nail

1/8" (2-3 mm) space between sheets

edge nail 6" (150 mm) o.c.

nail 12" (300 mm) o.c.

galvanised nails

1/8" (2-3 mm) space between sheets

edge nail 6" (150 mm) o.c.

nail 12" (300 mm) o.c.

foundation

Lumber sheathing application: *(A)* horizontal and diagonal; *(B)* started at foundation wall.

A

Horizontal application

joint

foundation

Diagonal application

stud

45°

B

sheathing

joist

foundation wall

79

vapour-permeable, waterproof membrane. The others are rigid panels of either expanded polystyrene, extruded polystyrene, polyurethane, isocyanurate or phenolic material. They come in different thicknesses, and the insulating value per unit thickness varies.

They are installed on the wall like any other panel sheathing but with special large-headed nails. A good reason for fastening this insulating sheathing before the wall is raised is its lightness and, for some types, its brittleness. Even a mild wind can make it difficult to install insulating sheathing on the vertical. Rigid glass fibre sheathing with vapour-permeable membrane can become an air barrier when the joints are sealed with contractor sheathing tape.

There are two methods of installing sheathing down to the foundation sill. Either the panel extends beyond the bottom wall plate by the required length and the missing part at the top plate is filled in, or longer panels of 9 ft. (2.74 m) length are used, where available, to cover the wall down to the sill area. It is advantageous to cover the header and sill with the same wall sheet because this reduces air infiltration.

Lumber sheathing, which should not be less than 11/16 in. (17 mm) thick, is used in boards 6 to 12 in. (140 to 286 mm) wide. It is milled in a shiplap, tongue-and-groove or square-edge pattern. The boards are nailed at each stud with two nails for the 6 to 8 in. (140 and 184 mm) widths and three for the 10 to 12 in. (235 and 286 mm) widths. End joints in the board must be placed over the centre of the studs with the joints staggered on different studs. Lumber sheathing may be put on either horizontally or diagonally (Fig. 79A) and is extended beyond the subfloor to cover the header joist and the sill plate (Fig. 79B). The angle cuts in the diagonal approach require more time and materials.

WALL SHEATHING MEMBRANE

Sheathing membrane (traditionally referred to as sheathing paper) should be water resistant but vapour permeable. New materials, such as spunbonded polyolefins and polypropylenes, are being used today that are not paper products. The sheathing membrane's function is to provide a second barrier to the entry of any wind and rain that might penetrate the cladding. It is also intended to

direct water, which does penetrate the cladding, over the flashing at the base of the wall. It must be permeable enough, however, to permit any water vapour to escape from the interior that may penetrate imperfections in the air and vapour barriers. One layer of sheathing membrane is generally used over wall sheathing and may be applied horizontally or vertically with 4 in. (100 mm) laps at the joints. At horizontal flashings, the upper sheet should be lapped over the lower sheet to direct moisture outward.

Where wall sheathing is not used, two layers of sheathing membrane are needed unless a large panel siding such as plywood is used. Both layers are applied vertically, with the joints lapped 4 in. (100 mm) at the studs. Both layers are stapled to the framing members, the top layer with staples spaced every 6 in. (150 mm) along the edges of the sheet to hold it securely in place.

EXTERIOR CLADDING

Because the type of exterior cladding used on the walls will greatly affect the appearance of the house and the amount of maintenance, it should be selected with care. Common types of cladding used are: metal, vinyl, hardboard or lumber siding; panel siding made of plywood, oriented strand board, waferboard or hardboard; wood shingles or shakes; stucco, and masonry cladding such as brick, both clay and concrete, concrete block and stone.

Most siding can be affected by moisture and should be kept 8 in.

PLANNING AHEAD

Sheathing Membranes and Air Barriers

Sheathing membranes are required beneath siding, stucco or masonry veneer. Membranes which are permitted for this application are intended to be of the breather type, permitting any humidity built up in the walls to vent to the outside. At the same time, these membranes are designed to resist bulk water from penetrating the exterior walls, generally caused by wind-driven rain.

Air barriers are required in all exterior components of the building envelope to prevent air leakage which can cause internal moisture damage and waste energy. In some cases, the requirements for the air barrier and the vapour barrier are met by using polyethylene located on the interior which is carefully sealed at joints and penetrations. In other cases, the air barrier may be a separate membrane applied to the exterior face of walls.

When combining the requirements for sheathing membranes and air barriers, the following points should be considered:

➜ Ensure that the air barrier membrane conforms to the requirements for sheathing membrane materials. It must allow water vapour (humidity) to escape from inside to outside.

➜ Install the air barrier membrane so that it is continuous and airtight. Typically, taping joints and sealing penetrations is required to provide an effective barrier to air leakage.

➜ When exterior insulating sheathing is used, products which incorporate an air barrier membrane may also be considered.

➜ In most cases, when a sheathing membrane is required, it makes sense to provide a material which also serves as an air barrier membrane.

➜ When in doubt, consult your local building department prior to construction for acceptable materials and methods.

It is important to resolve the type of air barrier and how it will be installed prior to the installation of wall sheathings and exterior finishes. Plan ahead carefully by referring to the requirements for air barriers in the *Vapour and Air Barriers* chapter.

(200 mm) off the ground and 2 in. (50 mm) from an adjoining roof surface. Methods of flashing over window and door openings and between different types of wall covering are described in the chapter on *Flashing*.

Metal and Vinyl Sidings

Metal and vinyl sidings are used extensively and are virtually maintenance free since they come with factory-finished surfaces. They are produced in different shapes and

HEALTHY HOUSING INSIGHT

Exterior Cladding Selection

Exterior cladding options are numerous because many new materials and systems are being continuously introduced. Appropriate choices for exterior cladding materials should take into consideration the following issues.

Durability and Maintenance

Exterior claddings should last the life of the building and be easy to maintain. Avoid exterior claddings with a poor performance record based on local experience. Also consider the time and cost associated with exterior claddings which require frequent maintenance.

Resource Efficiency

Materials may be renewable or non-renewable, new or recycled, recyclable or non-recyclable, and reusable or non-reusable. The use of non-recyclable and non-reusable materials is less desirable.

Compatibility and Adaptability

Exterior claddings should be compatible with the building system being constructed. For example, in wet regions of the country where wind-driven rain commonly occurs, exterior claddings which do not serve as rain screens should be avoided. Exterior claddings should also be adaptable if numerous changes to the building are foreseeable over its useful life. Typically, siding, panel and stucco type claddings are more adaptable than masonry veneer types.

In addition to these fundamental issues, the following points regarding the performance of entire wall systems may be considered.

➜ Walls represent among the most expensive elements to retrofit in a building, especially when window replacement is included. When using exterior claddings such as masonry veneer, ensure that better practices in terms of thermal insulation levels and window quality are followed, otherwise future retrofit costs will often prove prohibitive.

➜ Exterior claddings seldom significantly improve the energy efficiency of a building.

patterns, some of which simulate the appearance of wood bevel siding and vertical board and batten. They come in configurations designed for continuous interlocking between boards so that only the upper side of the board is nailed while the bottom edge is locked to the upper part of the board below (Fig. 80A). Interior and exterior corners, termination points of the soffit and gable ends as well as windows and doors, are all treated with specially designed trim pieces. The installation follows the same simple steps that are generally applicable to any kind of siding of the small 6 to 8 in. (150 to 200 mm) width.

Horizontal Application. The wall is prepared by applying the sheathing membrane as described. In wet and humid coastal climates, furring on the wall is recommended to provide a "rain screen" and a vented space to facilitate drying. A level line is established around the house for the starter strip that is normally placed a minimum of 6 to 8 in. (150 to 200 mm) above finished grade. All trim pieces for corners, windows, doors and openings and starter strips are fastened. The siding is then applied in successive courses to the underside of the soffit.

Laps of adjacent boards should be staggered more than 24 in. (600

Types of siding: *(A)* aluminum or vinyl; *(B)* bevel or feather-edge; *(C)* tongue-and-groove with V-joint; *(D)* drop siding; *(E)* board-on-board.

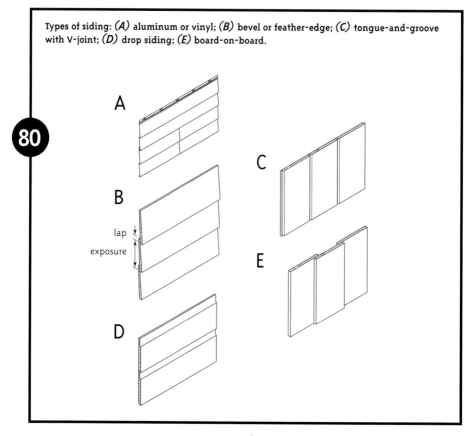

80

mm) apart and should all face in the same direction away from the general viewing angle.

An important point that must be remembered in each step of the installation is the need to let the siding, especially vinyl siding, expand and contract with temperature changes. Always follow the manufacturer's installation instructions when installing siding.

In the case of vinyl siding, the change in dimension could be from 1/4 to 1/2 in. (6 to 12 mm). If movement is restricted, buckling will occur. For this reason, the nails should be placed in the centre of the nail slot and not be hammered tight to the wall.

Vertical Application. The same general rules apply to vertical application as to horizontal. Using the vertical method, the starting point is a corner of the building with the appropriate corner trim. All other trim pieces also precede the installation of the siding.

Hardboard Siding

Hardboard horizontal siding comes with a primed or prefinished surface in a variety of colours. It often has plastic splines (Fig. 81) which function as locking devices between panels. It is installed in a similar manner to metal and vinyl siding. In some cases, manufacturers suggest installing the siding over furring. Follow the installation instructions from the manufacturer.

Lumber Siding

Lumber siding should be sound and free of knot holes, loose knots, checks or splits. Easy working qualities and freedom from warp are desirable features. The species most commonly used are cedars, pines and redwood. It has also become more common to use pressure-treated lumber for siding. Pressure-treated siding may be manufactured from pine or other species. The moisture content of the siding at the time of application should be the same as it will experi-

Horizontal hardboard siding.

sheathing
sheathing membrane
vertical furring strips
plastic spline
horizontal hardboard siding
metal starter strip
screen to prevent insects

81

ence in service, that is, about 12 to 18 percent, depending on the region's humidity and climate.

In wet, humid climates, such as the coastal regions of Canada, an air space is often formed behind the siding to prevent water penetration and to vent moisture away from the wall. This is done by mounting the siding on furring strips nailed on top of the sheathing paper to the studs behind. In these cases, a screen should be installed at the base of the wall to protect against insects and the top should be blocked to compartmentalize the wall.

Horizontal Application. Bevel or feather-edge siding (Fig. 80B) generally starts with the bottom course of boards furred out as shown in Figure 82B. A 1/4 in. (6 mm) thick furring strip is used for this purpose. Each succeeding course overlaps the upper edge of the lower course, the minimum lap being usually 1 in. (25 mm). Spacing for the siding should be carefully laid out before the board is applied. To determine the maximum board spacing (or exposure), the minimum lap should be deducted from the overall width of the siding. The number of board spaces between the soffit and the bottom of the first course at the foundation wall should be such that the maximum exposure will not be exceeded. This may mean that the boards will have less than the maximum exposure. Where possible, the bottom of the board that is placed over the top of the windows should coincide with the top of the window cap (Fig. 82A).

Bevel siding should have a butt thickness of at least 1/2 in. (12 mm) for widths of 8 in. (184 mm) or less and 9/16 in. (14.3 mm) for widths greater than 8 in. (184 mm). The top edge should not be less than 3/16 in. (5 mm) thick.

Drop (or matched) siding should be at least 9/16 in. (14.3 mm) thick and 8 in. (184 mm) or less in width. It comes in a variety of patterns with matched or shiplap edges. Figure 80D shows a common pattern for drop siding.

Where bevel or drop siding is used, the butt joints between boards in adjacent courses should be staggered as much as possible. Butt joints should be made over a stud. The siding should be carefully fitted and be in close contact with other members and adjacent pieces. Ends should be sealed. Loose-fitting joints allow water to get behind the siding which can cause paint deterioration around the joints and lead to decay at the ends of the boards. One method sometimes used to obtain a tight joint is to place a small bead of caulking compound or putty along the end of each board after it is nailed and then press the next board into the compound. The excess compound is struck off, leaving a smooth waterproof joint. Joints occurring elsewhere, such as at window or door trim, can be similarly treated.

Bevel and drop siding should be face-nailed to lumber sheathing or studs. The size of the nail depends on the thickness of the siding and the type of sheathing used. One method of nailing often used is to drive the nail through the siding just above the lap so that the nail misses the top edge of the piece of siding beneath. (See the nailing method detail in Figure 82.) This method permits each siding board to expand and contract as the moisture content changes. Thus, there is less tendency for the boards to split as may occur when both edges of the board are nailed. Since the amount of swelling or shrinking is proportional to the width of the wood siding, nailing above the lap is more important with wide boards than with narrow boards.

Installation of siding: *(A)* method of application; *(B)* starting course.

A

siding flush with top of flashing set first

metal flashing

sheathing membrane around window opening

scribe tight against window

detail: nailing method

butt joints made over centre of stud if sheathing omitted

foundation wall

B

stud

sheathing

siding

bottom plate

header

sill plate

$^1/_4$" (6 mm) furring strip

extend siding below blocking

8" (200 mm) minimum

parging

82

Vertical Application. Lumber siding that can be applied vertically includes: plain matched boards; patterned matched boards; square-edge boards covered at the joints with a batten strip, or square-edge boards spaced apart and covered with another board. Vertical siding is usually 9/16 in. (14.3 mm) thick. Boards should not be wider than 12 in. (286 mm). Vertical boards may be fastened to 9/16 in. (14.3 mm) lumber sheathing, 1/2 in. (12.5 mm) plywood or 1/2 in. (12.5 mm) oriented strand board or waferboard, 2 x 2 in. (38 x 38 mm) blocking fitted between the studs at 24 in. (600 mm) on centre or to horizontal furring strips. The furring may be 1 x 3 in. (19 x 64 mm) lumber where the framing is spaced not more than 16 in. (400 mm) on centre or 2 x 4 in. (19 x 89 mm) lumber where the framing is spaced not more than 24 in. (600 mm) on centre. Butt joints should be mitred to prevent the entry of water into the joint. When the spaced method (sometimes called "board-on-board") is used (Fig. 80E), the boards next to the wall are normally wider than the top boards and are fastened with one row of nails near the centre of each board. The top board is then applied so that it laps the edges of the first board at least 1 in. (25 mm). These top boards are fastened with two rows of nails driven slightly outside the edges of the boards underneath. This method of nailing permits the wider board to expand and contract without splitting.

The board and batten method uses square-edge boards which are ordinarily 8 in. (184 mm) or less in width. The boards are applied with the edges at least 1/4 in. (6 mm) apart and fastened with one row of nails near the centre of each board. To cover the joint, a narrow batten is used which laps the edges at least 1/2 in. (12 mm). This batten is fastened with one row of nails driven in the joint between the two boards, so that the boards may swell or shrink without splitting either the boards or the batten strip. Since the batten also serves to prevent the board edges from curling outward, the nailing should be secure and closely spaced.

Tongue-and-groove matched siding (Fig. 80C) is commonly 8 in. (184 mm) or less in width. The first board is face-nailed near the grooved edge and angle-nailed through the tongue. Each successive board is driven in closely and angle-nailed through the tongue. A nail set is used to finish off the nailing.

Nails cost little compared with the cost of the siding and labour, but the use of good nails is important. It is poor economy to buy siding that will last for years and then fasten it with nails that will rust badly within a short period. Corrosion-resistant nails, such as hot-dipped galvanized nails, will hold the siding permanently and will not disfigure the paint surface. Casing or siding nails are normally used for this purpose. Heads are driven flush with the face of the siding and later covered with paint. If finishing nails are used, the heads should be set below the surface and the hole filled with putty after the prime coat of paint is applied. The length of the nails depends on the thickness of the siding and the type of sheathing used. Nails should be long enough to penetrate at least 1 in. (25 mm) into the nailing support.

Plywood Panels

Exterior type plywood is also used as a wall covering. The plywood sheets are made with a plain or grooved surface and are usually applied vertically. The joints may be V-grooved or flush or may be covered with batten. Plywood is available with a resin-impregnated kraft paper laminated to the face. This provides a smooth, moisture-resistant surface which resists checking or splitting after painting.

The minimum thickness of plywood applied as sheathing is 1/4 in. (6 mm). It may be applied directly to unsheathed wall framing. The minimum thickness used is 1/4 in. (6 mm) for stud spacings of 16 in. (400 mm) on centre and 5/16 in. (8 mm) for spacing of supports up to 24 in. (600 mm) on centre. This assumes the face grain is installed at right angles to supports. Where the face grain is installed parallel to supports the minimum thickness is 5/16 in. (8 mm) and 7/16 in. (11 mm) for studs spaced at 16 in. (400 mm) and 24 in. (600 mm) respectively.

After the plywood panels are cut and fitted, all edges should be protected with a suitable paint or sealer before installation. A 1/8 in. (2 to 3 mm) space between the sides and ends of the panels and butted ends of the battens will permit expansion without bulging. Vertical joints are filled with caulking or covered with a batten. Horizontal joints are flashed or lapped at least 1 in. (25 mm).

The edges of plywood panels should be supported and fastened with corrosion-resistant nails, usually 2 in. (51 mm) long. The nails are spaced 6 in. (150 mm) along the edges and 12 in. (300 mm) at intermediate supports.

Hardboard Panels

Hardboard is also produced in sheets with a variety of finishes and may be applied over sheathing or to unsheathed walls. The minimum thickness of sheets should be at least 1/4 in. (6 mm) on supports that are not more than 16 in. (400 mm) on centre. It is fastened to the framing member or to sheathing with corrosion-resistant nails at least 2 in. (51 mm) long. Nails are spaced 6 in. (150 mm) along the edges and 12 in. (300 mm) along intermediate supports. A gap at least 1/8 in. (2 to 3 mm) should be provided between sheets.

Corner Treatment for Siding

The method of finishing siding at the corners may be influenced by the house design. Corner boards may be appropriate to some designs and mitred joints to others.

For lumber siding applied horizontally (Fig. 83), mitred corners are most common, but metal corners or corner boards may also be used.

Mitred corners (Fig. 83B) must fit tightly and smoothly for the full depth of the mitre. To maintain a tight fit at the mitre, it is important that the siding is properly seasoned before delivery and protected from rain when stored at the site. The ends are often set in caulking compound or putty when the siding is applied.

At interior corners, the siding is usually butted against a corner strip of 1 or 1 1/2 in. (25 or 38 mm) material, depending upon the thickness of the siding.

Metal corners (Fig. 83C), used as a substitute for mitred corners, are made of light-gauge metals such as aluminum or galvanized steel. The application of metal corners requires less skill than making good mitred corners or fitting siding to a corner board.

Corner boards (Fig. 83A and D) are generally used with drop siding, but may be used with other types of siding as well. The boards are made of 1 or 1 1/2 in. (25 or 38 mm) material, depending on the thickness of the siding. The corner boards are applied against the sheathing with the siding fitted tightly against the narrow edge of the corner boards. Joints between the siding and corner boards should be filled with caulking compound or putty when the siding is applied.

Plywood and hardboard are usually lapped at the corners or fitted to a corner board. Lumber siding applied vertically is lapped at the corners.

Wood Shingles and Machine-grooved Shakes

Wood shingles or machine-grooved shakes are sometimes used for wall covering. A large selection is available, including special wall shingles in

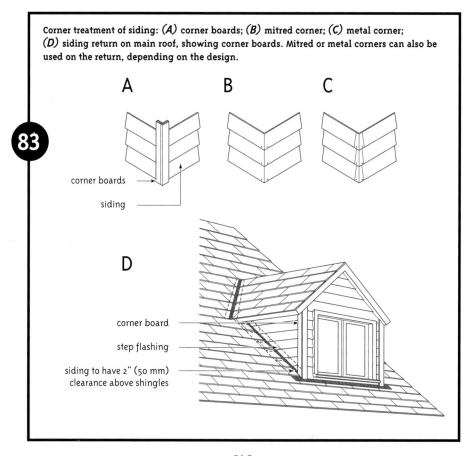

Corner treatment of siding: **(A)** corner boards; **(B)** mitred corner; **(C)** metal corner; **(D)** siding return on main roof, showing corner boards. Mitred or metal corners can also be used on the return, depending on the design.

83

A B C

corner boards

siding

D

corner board

step flashing

siding to have 2" (50 mm) clearance above shingles

lengths of 16, 18 and 24 in. (400, 450 and 600 mm), factory-painted or stained.

Shingles are usually separated into three grades. The first grade is composed of clear shingles, all heartwood, all edge grain. The second grade consists of shingles with clear butts and permits defects in the part of the shingle which is normally covered in use. The third grade includes shingles that have defects other than those permitted in the second grade. These shingles may be used for undercoursing.

Shingles are made in random widths varying in the first grade from 2 1/2 to 14 in. (65 to 350 mm); only a small proportion of the narrow width is permitted in the first grade. Shingles of a uniform width, known as dimension shingles, are also available. Widths of 4, 5 or 6 in. (100, 125 or 150 mm) may be specified. Table 36 shows the commonly used exposure and thickness of wood shingles and machine-grooved shakes. Lumber, oriented strand board, waferboard or plywood sheathing should be used under shingles or shakes.

When the single-course application is used, the joints in succeeding courses should be offset at least 1 9/16 in. (40 mm), and care taken that the joints in any two or three courses do not line up.

To obtain deep shadow lines, shingles can be laid in what is called double-coursing. This may be done by using a lower grade shingle under the shingle exposed to the weather. The exposed shingle butt extends about 1/2 in. (12 mm) below the butt of the undercourse. Where double-coursing

is used, wider exposure to the weather is possible. Joints in the outer course should be offset from joints in the undercourse by at least 1 9/16 in. (40 mm).

Shingles should be fastened with corrosion-resistant nails. Shingles up to 8 in. (200 mm) wide require only two nails. Those more than 8 in. (200 mm) wide require three. Nails should be driven about 13/16 in. (20 mm) from the edges and 1 in. (25 mm) above the exposure line for single-course application, and 2 in. (50 mm) for double coursing.

Stucco Finishes

Stucco generally consists of a mixture of Portland cement and well-graded sand, with hydrated lime added to make the mixture more plastic. An alternative stucco mixture calls for replacing the lime with masonry cement. Table 37 lists the proportions for the preparation of these two stucco mixes. Other proprietary stucco mixes are available. Their formulations will vary depending on the manufacturer of the mix.

Applied in three coats (two base coats and one finish coat), the stucco is held in place by stucco mesh or wire lath. A variety of finish coats are available, from standard coloured cement finishes to finely textured acrylic finishes. The "stone dash" finish is seldom used except in retrofit applications.

Stucco reinforcing of self-furring welded mesh, or fully primed or galvanized woven mesh, is stretched horizontally over sheathing paper, with the joints in the mesh lapped at least 2 in. (50 mm). External corners are reinforced either by extending the mesh from one side 6 in. (150 mm) around the adjacent corner, or by vertical strips of reinforcing that extend 6 in. (150 mm) on either side of the corner. Stucco must be no closer than 8 in. (200 mm) from finished grade except where it is applied over concrete or masonry.

A well-detailed layer of heavy-weight building paper, lapped 4 in. (100 mm) at the edges, must be applied. It is very important to apply flashings around penetrations in the walls. The building paper must be carefully applied around window openings and lapped correctly to ensure that water does not enter at the window flanges. Tar-saturated felts or papers should not be used beneath the stucco. The tar can bleed through the stucco causing unsightly discoloura-tion.

Galvanized steel fasteners should be used to hold the mesh in place. Suitable fasteners are 1/8 in. (3.2 mm) diameter nails with heads that are about 7/16 in. (11.1 mm) or alternative with 0.078 in. (1.98 mm) thick staples. Fasteners are spaced 6 in. (150 mm) vertically and 16 in. (400 mm) hori-zontally, or 4 in. (100 mm) vertically and 24 in. (600 mm) horizontally. Other fastening patterns may be used, provided there are at least two fasten-ers per square ft. (20 fasteners per square metre) of the wall surface. Where the sheathing is other than lumber, waferboard or plywood, the fasteners should penetrate the sheath-ing and go into the framing member (stud or plate) at least 1 in. (25 mm).

The base coat consists of two layers of stucco. The first layer (scratch coat) of stucco is applied to a thick-ness of 1/2 in. (12 mm) that completely embeds the wire lath or mesh. The scratch coat surface must be scored or raked to provide a bonding key for the second coat. Curing time will depend on outdoor temperature and weather conditions. It is not uncommon to allow 48 hours of cure time before the second coat is applied.

Just before putting on the second coat, the base is dampened to ensure a good bond between the coats. The second coat is applied at least 1/4 in. (6 mm) thick and firmly trowelled into the scored surface of the base.

A wide variety of finishes are available today, from standard white or coloured cement to modified and acrylic finishes. Acrylic finish coats are often applied over conventional Portland cement, with good results. It is important that the chosen product has good weatherability and is vapour permeable. In cases where a wall requires a fire rating, the base coat thickness will need to be check to ensure it is sufficiently thick.

For finish coats, the second coat should be moist-cured for at least 48 hours and then left to dry for five days, preferably longer, before the finish coat is applied. The base should be dampened to ensure a good bond and the finish applied to a depth of at least 1/8 in. (3 mm).

In dry warm weather, fresh stucco should be kept damp to ensure proper curing. In cold weather, each coat of stucco should be kept at a tempera-ture of at least 50°F (10°C) for 48 hours after application.

Masonry Veneer

If masonry veneer is used for the exterior cladding of above-grade walls, the foundation must include a supporting ledge or offset wide enough to allow a space of about 1 in. (25 mm) between the masonry and the sheathing paper (Fig. 84).

A base flashing should extend from the outside face of the wall over the top of the ledge and at least 6 in. (150 mm) up the wall behind the sheathing paper. Corrosion-resistant metal ties, nailed to the studs and embedded in the mortar joints between the masonry, should be used to tie the veneer to the framework. When fastened to every other stud these are usually spaced 32 in. (800 mm) apart horizontally and 16 in. (400

mm) vertically. Alternatively when fastened to every stud, they may be spaced 24 in. (600 mm) horizontally and 20 in. (500 mm) vertically, or 16 in. (400 mm) horizontally and 24 in. (600 mm) vertically, depending on the stud spacing.

Weep holes serve both a venting and a drainage function. They should be placed about 32 in. (800 mm) apart in the bottom course of the masonry veneer and above-grade windows and doors. This can be done by omitting the mortar from the vertical joints.

Masonry veneer should be at least 3 1/2 in. (90 mm) thick where there are raked joints and 2 3/4 in. (75 mm) thick where the joints are unraked.

If a brick veneer is used, the bricks selected should be hard, absorb

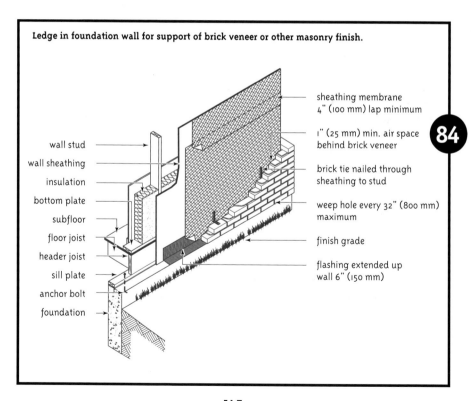

Ledge in foundation wall for support of brick veneer or other masonry finish.

sheathing membrane
4" (100 mm) lap minimum

1" (25 mm) min. air space
behind brick veneer

84

wall stud

wall sheathing

insulation

brick tie nailed through
sheathing to stud

bottom plate

weep hole every 32" (800 mm)
maximum

subfloor

floor joist

header joist

finish grade

sill plate

flashing extended up
wall 6" (150 mm)

anchor bolt

foundation

little water and be manufactured for exposure to the weather. Stone veneers should be selected from the materials known locally to be durable.

Brick or stone should be laid in a full bed of mortar. Care should be taken to avoid dropping mortar into the space between the veneer and sheathing paper, because this will block the cavity behind the veneer. Outside joints must be tooled to a smooth finish to provide maximum resistance to water penetration. Mortar mix proportions should conform to those shown in Table 5.

Masonry laid during cold weather should be protected from freezing until after the mortar has set. The temperature of the masonry and mortar should be maintained above 41°F (5°C) for at least 24 hours after installation.

PLANNING AHEAD

Painting and Staining

If an exterior finish requiring painting or staining is being installed, plan ahead to minimize work and potential problems.

→ Prepare for painting and staining as the exterior finish is being installed. If nails have to be countersunk and the holes filled prior to painting or staining, do this as the materials are being installed.

→ For difficult to access areas and decorative wood trims or mouldings, sealing and priming these before installation will ensure complete coverage and simplify the application of finish coats.

For more information on exterior finishes, refer to the chapter entitled *Painting*.

HEALTHY HOUSING INSIGHT

Minimizing Waste in Wall Sheathings and Claddings

The reduction of waste from wall sheathings and exterior claddings requires careful planning and proper construction practices. The following points should be considered when dealing with wall sheathings and exterior claddings.

➜ Only order the amount of material that is required. Before ordering materials, make suitable arrangements for returning unused goods to suppliers.

➜ Always store and handle materials carefully. Waste often results from damage which can be avoided. Keep materials covered with a tarp on site.

➜ Have one person cut all materials in one location to make better use of off-cuts.

➜ Use standard wall heights so that sheathing and panel materials do not have to be cut in length. Where possible, make the lengths of walls a multiple of 16 in. (400 mm) or 24 in. (600 mm) to better utilize off-cuts.

➜ A small amount of exterior cladding waste is practically unavoidable. Where services are available, collect and store waste materials for recycling.

For general insights into managing construction waste, refer to *Applying the 4 Rs of Wood-Frame Construction* in the *Framing the House* chapter.

WINDOWS AND DOORS

The appropriate selection and proper installation of windows and doors represents a very important aspect of wood-frame house construction. Windows and doors are often able to play a role in a number of systems within the building. Daylight, view, natural ventilation and means of egress are all affected by the windows and doors that are selected.

Poor quality windows and doors can lead to high energy bills and maintenance costs. Irrespective of their quality, window and door problems may also be caused by poor installation. Unlike paint and wallpaper, the cost of replacing poorly performing windows and doors is extremely high, and often quite disruptive. It is generally more cost effective to invest in good quality windows and doors, and to ensure that these are properly installed, rather than having to upgrade these components later.

There are several important factors to consider when selecting windows and doors. The energy efficiency of doors, and particularly windows, is a critical consideration. These components can account for a high fraction of a dwelling's heat loss. It is important to consider the size and swing of exterior doors, not only to comply with building code requirements, but also to accommodate the easy movement of people and furnishings into and out of the dwelling. The size and style of windows should be carefully considered since this will influence the appearance of the house as well as the natural ventilation and natural light which are provided. Durability and maintenance are two additional factors which apply to any exterior component of the dwelling, and especially to windows and doors. Finally, some thought should also be given to providing adequate resistance to forced entry through the type and location of windows and doors.

Light, View and Ventilation

Windows and doors with glazing can provide light and view for the occupants provided they are appropriately sized and located. Specific rooms call for unobstructed windows large enough to allow natural light. Normally, living and dining rooms require glazing to be no less than 10 percent of the area of the room. Other rooms such as bedrooms, dens and family rooms should have windows that represent at least 5 percent of the floor area of the room. These requirements promote healthful indoor spaces that consider the psychological well-being of the occupant.

Windows can also provide natural ventilation by allowing outside air to flow inside. Openable windows can eliminate the need for mechanical ventilation during the non-heating season. For most rooms where the window is used to provide natural ventilation, this requires an unobstructed, openable window area of at least 3 sq. ft. (0.28 m²) be installed. Bathrooms require a window at least 1 sq. ft. (0.09 m²) in area. Unfinished basements need openable windows that represent at least 0.2 percent of the basement floor area if non-heating season mechanical ventilation is to be eliminated.

While windows can provide benefits of light, view and ventilation they can also pose a fire hazard to adjacent properties. Because fire can spread from windows to adjacent houses, building codes place strict limits on the amount of glazing in walls that are close to property lines. Glazed openings are not permitted in walls that are within 4 ft. (1.2 m) from a property line. Walls more than 4 ft. (1.2 m) may contain limited glazed openings depending on the distance from the property line and the area of the wall facing the property line. Consult your local building department for specific requirements.

Means of Egress

Windows can play a part in the building's means of egress, allowing occupants to escape to the outdoors in case of emergency. These windows, typically located in bedrooms, should open to the outside without special hardware. They should also have an unobstructed open portion with no dimension less than 15 in. (380 mm) and with an open area of at least 3.8 sq. ft. (0.35 m2) as shown in Figure 85. For example, a window with an opening which measures 18 x 30 in. (450 x 750 mm) would conform to this requirement.

Windows intended to serve as egress windows should have a sill height no more than 39 in. (1.0 m) above the floor, and not be more than 23 ft. (7 m) above ground level. Access can be improved to windows high on walls and intended to serve as egress windows by using built-in furniture. The furniture can act as a step, allowing easy escape in fire situations.

Window Styles

There is a wide variety of windows available today categorized under several common styles. Each style has its own advantages and disadvantages which should be carefully considered when selecting windows.

Minimum dimensions for egress windows.

15" (380 mm) min.

3.8 ft² (0.35 m²) min. unobstructed area

85

Horizontal slider

Fixed windows are generally the least expensive, and usually offer the best level of energy efficiency and resistance to forced entry. They do not offer any natural ventilation and cannot serve as a means of egress from the dwelling in case of fire.

Single or double hung windows are a traditional style. Only one sash (usually the bottom unit) operates in single hung windows, while both sashes operate in double hung units. Prior to advances in window technology, these windows did not perform well in terms of ease of operation and air leakage. However, modern types have been developed to address these factors, and can also offer good resistance to forced entry.

Horizontal and vertical slider windows are easy to operate, and, because they do not project out from or into the dwelling, are safer since they do not act as obstacles. Their operation tends to make horizontal

sliders less airtight than casement, awning and tilt-and-turn windows since the weatherstripping is exposed to wear due to friction.

Casement and awning windows are among the more expensive styles. Due to their operation, these windows are very airtight and offer good resistance to forced entry. Casement windows are well suited to deflecting prevailing winds into the dwelling for natural ventilation and passive cooling. Awning windows have the advantage of shedding rain effectively when open.

Tilt-and-turn windows are the most flexible of all window styles. Some types can act like casement and awning windows. These windows can be very airtight when fitted with compression-type closing devices.

Before proceeding with a discussion of window performance and selection criteria, it is important to

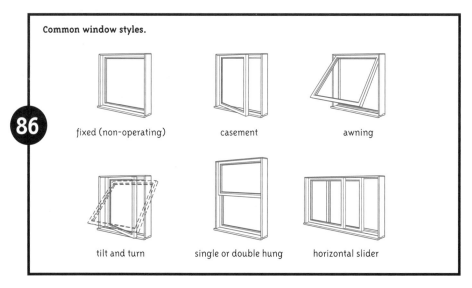

Common window styles.

fixed (non-operating)   casement   awning

tilt and turn   single or double hung   horizontal slider

86

Window terminology.

interior   exterior

edge seal or spacer
glazing
gas fill
low-emissivity coating

87

frame

sash

glazing unit
(sealed unit)

sill

drip

become familiar with some common window terms. These terms have been summarized in Figure 87.

Window Performance

Significant advances in window technology have been achieved through ongoing research and development by government and industry. These advances are available as options in most manufacturer's products. It is important to appreciate how these contribute to improved performance when making a selection.

Multi-pane Windows

In order to reduce the potential for condensation, windows that separate heated space from unheated space or the exterior must be at least double glazed. Each pane of glazing helps to increase the inside surface temperature of the innermost pane of glass,

thereby reducing the potential for condensation.

Condensation, a common homeowner complaint, can be reduced by installing good, energy efficient windows. Some condensation on windows is normal and should be expected, particularly around the edges of the glazing during cold weather. Nonetheless, multi-pane windows with thermally broken frames and good quality spacers can go a long way towards reducing the likelihood of condensation in today's houses.

Low-emissivity Coatings

A large proportion of the heat loss and gain through a window is due to radiation — a process where warmer objects radiate heat to cooler objects, as in the case of the sun warming the earth with its radiant energy. A low-emissivity (Low-E) coating is a thin metallic film deposited on glass which acts as a mirror to radiant heat, reflecting it back into the dwelling during cold weather, and back to the outdoors during hot weather. Low-emissivity coatings work to reduce heating and cooling bills. They provide a double-glazed window with about the same performance as a clear, triple-glazed window, but at less additional cost. An increasing proportion of window manufacturers are offering Low-E glazings as a standard feature due to their improved resistance to condensation on the inside glazing during cold weather.

Gas Fills

Another innovation in window technology is the replacement of air with inert gas fills between panes of glass in a sealed unit. Inert gases have a higher insulating value than air because they are heavier, resulting in lower convective and conductive heat losses between the panes of glass. Argon is the most commonly used gas due to its availability and low cost. Gas fills are a cost-effective upgrade over conventional air-filled glazings.

Edge Seals

The thermal efficiency of a sealed glazing unit can be significantly improved by using a low-conductivity edge seal or spacer between panes of glass. Traditionally, edge seals have been made of aluminum which conducts heat rapidly resulting in cold areas around the edges of glazing units. Plastic, silicone and glass fibre spacers are now used to reduce thermal bridging at the perimeter of sealed glazing units.

Frames with Thermal Breaks

Window frames made from metal, plastic or fibreglass can conduct a large amount of heat unless a thermal break made from an insulating material is provided. Without thermal breaks, window frames can become so cold that frost forms on the inside during extremely cold weather. This is less of a problem in wood windows, due to the relatively higher insulating value of wood, as well as in windows that have extruded frames filled with insulating materials. It is important to check the construction of windows to ensure that the frames are either well insulated or have a thermal break.

Energy Rating

The Energy Rating (ER) is a useful measure of the overall heating season performance of a window in a typical dwelling. The ER considers heat loss due to transmission and air leakage, along with solar heat gain, averaged over north, south, east and west exposures. The ER may be positive or negative. A positive ER indicates that on average, the window gains more heat from incoming solar energy than it loses over the heating season. Most ER ratings for windows are negative, as can be seen in Figure 88. Many manufacturers quote thermal resistance values for the centre of glazing in their windows. This is always higher than the effective thermal resistance of the window when the effects of the edge seal and window frame are taken into account. Typical effective thermal resistance values are provided in Figure 88 in both imperial (R) and metric (RSI) units. Numerous studies on cost-effective energy efficiency

Comparison of typical window thermal efficiencies.

Thermal Performance of a Typical Casement Window with Low Conductivity Edge Seal			
R (RSI) Energy Rating	Aluminum Frame with Thermal Break	Wood or Vinyl Frame	Fibreglass Frame
Double Glazed Clear with Air Fill	1.59 (.28)/-40.6	2.04 (.36)/-24.9	2.38 (.42)/-19.0
Double Glazed Low-E with Air Fill	1.99 (.35)/-32.7	2.67 (.47)/-17.1	3.12 (.55)/-11.5
Double Glazed Low-E with Argon	2.10 (.37)/-29.0	2.90 (.51)/-13.3	3.46 (.61)/-8.0
Triple Glazed Clear with Air Fill	1.99 (.35)/-32.7	2.84 (.50)/-11.8	3.18 (.56)/-10.8
Triple Glazed Low-E with Air Fill	2.21 (.39)/-27.9	3.41 (.60)/-9.5	3.86 (.68)/-6.2
Triple Glazed Low-E with Argon	2.33 (.41)/-25.2	3.69 (.65)/-6.8	4.25 (.75)/-5.4

88

improvements to new housing indicate that as a minimum, windows should have an ER of approximately -13 or higher. This translates into a double-glazed window with Low-E coating and argon gas fill. Higher efficiency windows are recommended in the colder regions of Canada.

Airtightness, Water Resistance and Wind Load Resistance

Windows in Canada are expected to conform to the CSA standard, *CAN/CSA-A440-M, Windows*. The standard includes a window classification system that rates windows according to their airtightness, water resistance and wind load resistance characteristics. Normally, the ratings achieved by each window are marked on the window. Windows installed in houses should be identified as meeting the A1 (airtightness), B1(water resistance), and C1 (wind load resistance) ratings of the CSA standard.

Window Selection

Windows are seldom selected solely on the basis of minimum building code requirements for light and natural ventilation. The contribution of windows to the external appearance of the dwelling, a pleasing view (or privacy), natural light and passive solar heating are often more important considerations. The style and operating characteristics of windows should be carefully considered within this context. The provision of effective natural ventilation does not require every window to be operable. The selective use of operating windows can reduce window costs, thereby permitting an investment in higher quality windows.

Durability and maintenance should be considered both for exterior and interior applications. Maintenance free finishes are highly recommended to reduce the need to paint windows. These are also highly advisable for two- and three-storey houses where access for maintenance is difficult. In areas such as bathrooms, water resistant interior finishes for windows are recommended. This avoids potential water damage to sashes and frames, reducing the need for continued maintenance.

Security is another consideration

in the location and type of windows. This aspect of window selection is further discussed in the *Healthy Housing Insight* later in this chapter.

Window Installation

Windows are normally installed after the house framing and roof covering are complete. Proper scheduling should ensure delivery of the windows at this stage. However, it may be necessary to accept earlier delivery and arrange for storage of the windows on site. It is recommended to store windows upright on a dry, level surface, in their original packaging, and leaving the temporary bracing in place. When stored outside, a vented

Typical window installation.

rough opening dimensions 1 " (25 mm) larger than outside of window frame to provide a minimum 1/2" (12.5 mm) space between the window frame and rough opening

lintel

fill air space with foam sealant to stop air leakage
or
insulate and air seal with common building materials

attach window with wood screws through sides of window frame only
or
nail through brick moulding on the outside

shims at jamb and sill junctions only

shim at junction of multiple units

jack stud

cripple stud

Note: Always refer to manufacturer's installation instructions prior to framing.

platform covered with a large tarpaulin is the preferred means of storage. Remember to label and store screens separately. If left on windows during construction, screens may be damaged or clogged with dust.

Prior to installation, it is important to review the manufacturer's installation instructions, and ensure that all of the proper tools, fasteners and materials are available. Windows must be installed plumb and level within the rough opening using shims to maintain the window true and the spaces around it even. Depending on the technique used to insulate and air seal the window breaching (the gap between the window and the rough opening), this may be addressed prior to, or after, installing the window. The most common technique now being employed involves applying polyurethane foam to insulate and air seal the breaching in one step.

This step may be performed when the house is being insulated and air sealed.

Exterior Doors

Exterior doors, like windows, contribute to the external appearance of a dwelling and are most often selected on the basis of style and finish. With the exception of custom doors, most exterior doors come as pre-hung manufactured units ready for installation within a rough opening. Exterior doors are typically manufactured in wood, steel, plastic and fibreglass. Wood doors are normally solid, while other types consist of inner and outer structural panels filled with insulation. These modern door types are generally more energy efficient. However, wood doors have proven performance and a traditional appearance which has maintained their popularity in the marketplace. Irrespective of the style and appearance of the door, a number of common considerations are worth noting.

Hardware, in particular locksets and hinges, are important items both in terms of functionality and durability. The main entry door to a dwelling will be locked and unlocked, opened and closed countless number of times over its useful life. Low-cost hardware may not prove the least costly in the long run.

Requirements for resistance to forced entry apply to door hardware under the National Building Code. Deadbolt locks in exterior doors to houses should have a cylinder with no fewer than five pins and a bolt throw of at least 1 in. (25 mm). Double doors should have heavy duty bolts top and bottom with an engagement of at least 5/8 in. (15 mm). Hinges need to be fastened to wood doors with wood screws not less than 1 in. (25 mm) long, and to wood frames penetrating at least 1 3/16 in. (30 mm) into solid wood. Refer to Figure 90.

Resistance to forced entry extends beyond door hardware to the framing for the door as well. Solid blocking should be provided on both sides of the door way at lock height between the jamb for the door and the structural framing so that the jambs resist spreading by force. Additional screws in the drywall around the door frame will also strengthen resistance to forced entry.

Door hardware requirements.

90

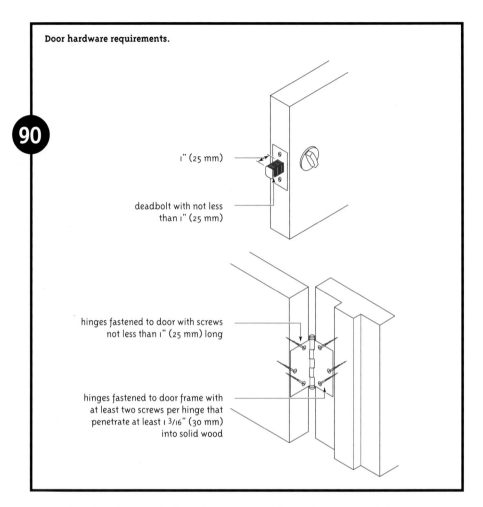

1" (25 mm)

deadbolt with not less
than 1" (25 mm)

hinges fastened to door with screws
not less than 1" (25 mm) long

hinges fastened to door frame with
at least two screws per hinge that
penetrate at least 1 3/16" (30 mm)
into solid wood

Weatherstripping is the primary line of defence against air leakage around doors, and should be carefully examined when selecting an exterior door. It should be effective, durable and easy to replace. Air leakage of items such as mail slots should also be considered.

Glazing in exterior doors should be thermally efficient, and depending on its size and location, may also have to be tempered glass for added safety. Generally, glass sidelights greater than 20 in. (500 mm) wide that could be mistaken for a door and glass in storm or sliding doors is required to be safety glass. Double-glazed sidelights are recommended, and when no glazing is provided, a door viewer should be considered for security purposes. Similar to windows, glazing in side doors near property lines, may be restricted depending on the distance to the property line.

The installation of pre-hung doors should always be carried out according to the manufacturer's installation instructions, otherwise

Pre-hung manufactured door.

head jamb

hinge jamb

lock jamb

pre-drilled lockset holes

hinge

threshold

91

warranties may be voided.

At present, practically all windows and doors are purchased and installed as complete manufactured systems. There may be cases, however, where a custom door or window may be desired, or an existing window in an older house may require improvement. In these cases, certain components may have to be milled prior to assembly and installation or retrofit. Refer to the next chapter entitled *Exterior Trim and Millwork* for further information on site-assembled windows and doors.

RELATED PUBLICATIONS

How to Lock Out Crime: Protecting Your Home Against Burglary
Canada Mortgage and Housing Corporation

HEALTHY HOUSING INSIGHT

Resistance to Forced Entry

A significant aspect of occupant health and well-being involves security within the dwelling through appropriate resistance to forced entry measures. The National Building Code provides minimum measures for doors and windows, however, a number of other issues relating to home security should also be considered. Forced entry remains a reality regardless of neighbourhood. The following points should be considered when designing and building the home.

Discouraging Forced Entry

➜ Window and door locations can either encourage or discourage attempts at forced entry. Basement windows located out of sight from the street and neighbouring homes are common forced entry points. As well, any windows which are accessible from the ground should be provided with secure locking hardware. Side and rear doors should not be located within recesses or behind any types of screens, such as lattice or planters.

➜ Landscaping should not shield or conceal doors and windows. Shrubs and hedges, planted in front of basement windows, provide convenient hiding places, unless they are very low to the ground.

➜ Outdoor lighting may be an unintentional aid to forced entry if high-intensity lights are focused away from the dwelling towards the street or neighbouring homes. The glare from these lights makes the areas adjacent to the home less visible. Direct light at the building or immediate surroundings. The installation of outdoor lighting with motion detectors at key locations is recommended.

➜ Indoor lighting controls allow for the automatic operation of lights to simulate an occupied home. These are recommended for households which experience frequent or lengthy absence.

➜ Home security systems are a more expensive and effective means of discouraging forced entry. Home security systems range from simple types installed by the homeowner, to sophisticated systems monitored by security companies.

A well-planned system of resistance to forced entry measures cannot guarantee complete home security; however, it will serve to effectively discourage the most common types of attempts at forced entry.

EXTERIOR TRIM AND MILLWORK

Exterior trim (that part of the exterior finish other than the wall covering) includes such items as window and door trim, soffits, rake or gable trim and fascia. Much of this material is cut, fitted and nailed into place on the job. Other materials or assemblies, such as louvres and shutters, are usually shop-manufactured.

The properties desired in materials used for trim are good painting and weathering characteristics, easy working qualities and maximum freedom from warp. Sealing the end joints or mitres of members exposed to moisture is recommended.

Fasteners used for trim, whether nails or screws, should be corrosion-resistant, that is, galvanized or aluminum. When finishing nails are used, they must be set and then puttied after the prime coat is applied. This method of fastening will generally prevent rust stains at nailheads. Fasteners must be compatible with the metal trim to avoid galvanic reaction between dissimilar metals, such as aluminum and steel.

EAVE PROJECTION

The eave overhang gives some protection to the side wall and connects the roof and wall. Soffits are usually closed in with pre-finished metal or vinyl panels or 1/4 in. (6 mm) sanded plywood nailed at 6 in. (150 mm) on centre along the edges and 12 in. (300 mm) at intermediate supports. The exterior finish is then butted up to the underside of the soffit. A fascia board added as a finished covering for the rafter header usually extends about 1/2 in. (12 mm) below the soffit covering to form a drip edge. The three general types of eave construction are shown in Figure 92.

A narrow eave projection (Fig. 92A) is sometimes used on roofs with a steep slope. Here the rafters are projected a short distance over the wall plate, and the ends are cut to suit the angle required for the rafter header and soffit covering. The soffit covering is nailed to the angled surface of the rafter. Where the soffit covering is less than 5 1/2 in. (140 mm) wide, a 1 in. (19 mm) board is generally used for this purpose, because the board does not require support along its edges.

When wider eave projections are used with a horizontal soffit, blocking is installed to support the soffit covering (Fig. 92B). A 1 in. thick (19 mm) nailing strip is placed on top of the sheathing along the wall and nailed to the framing. This strip supports the inner ends of the blocking and edges of the soffit covering. The blocking, which may consist of 2 x 2 in. (38 x 38 mm) material, is usually spaced at 24 in. (600 mm) on centre. It is toenailed to the nailing strip and end-nailed to the rafter header. The soffit covering and fascia board are then nailed in place.

Where the blocking provides partial support for the roof overhang (Fig. 57), 2 x 4 in. (38 x 89 mm) material is used. The members are securely nailed to the side of each rafter and butted against a 2 x 4 in. (38 x 89 mm)

Roof projection at eaves: **(A)** narrow eave projection; **(B)** wide eave projection with horizontal soffit; **(C)** wide eave projection with sloped soffit.

92

A

rafter
ceiling joist
top plate
sheathing membrane
wall sheathing
wall studs
siding

roof sheathing
continuous rafter header
fascia board
1" (19 mm) soffit board
intermittent soffit vents

B

rafter
ceiling joist
top plate
sheathing membrane
wall sheathing
wall studs
siding

roof sheathing
continuous 1" (19 mm) nailing strip
continuous rafter header
fascia board
blocking for soffit
vented soffit

C

rafter
ceiling joist
top plate
sheathing membrane
wall sheathing
wall studs
siding

roof sheathing
continuous rafter header
fascia board
plywood, OSB, waferboard soffit
intermittent soffit vents

Eave and gable-end intersections: (A) eave soffit is terminated at the wall line and gable-end soffit is continued to the fascia board at the eave; (B) eave soffit is sloped on same plane as gable-end soffit; (C) eave soffit carried out to the rake rafter and gable-end soffit is returned down to meet the eave soffit; (D) soffit and fascia detail using aluminum.

93

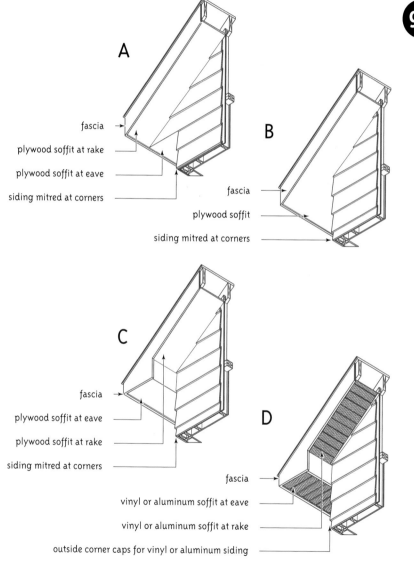

A

fascia

plywood soffit at rake

plywood soffit at eave

siding mitred at corners

B

fascia

plywood soffit

siding mitred at corners

C

fascia

plywood soffit at eave

plywood soffit at rake

siding mitred at corners

D

fascia

vinyl or aluminum soffit at eave

vinyl or aluminum soffit at rake

outside corner caps for vinyl or aluminum siding

nailing strip placed along the wall over the sheathing. This type of support is usually confined to overhangs of not more than 4 ft. (1.2 m).

Sloped soffits which follow the line of the projected rafter (Fig. 92C) are sometimes used instead of horizontal soffits. In this case, the soffit covering is nailed to the underside of the rafter. The outer edge of the soffit covering is nailed to the rafter header and the inner edge to 2 x 2 in. (38 x 38 mm) blocking placed between the rafters.

EAVE AND GABLE-END INTERSECTIONS

Eave and gable-end intersections depend largely on how the eave projection is finished. Figure 93 (A through C) shows three types of commonly used intersections. Figure 94D shows an example of an aluminum soffit. Aluminum can be used for all three types of intersections shown.

Where a sloped soffit is used at the eave projection, the soffit of the gable-end projection is carried through on the same plane as the eave soffit (Fig. 93B).

Where a horizontal soffit is used at the eave projection, the eave soffit may be carried through to the rake rafter (Fig. 93C). In this case, the soffit of the gable-end projection is terminated at the side wall and returned down to intersect the eave soffit. The fascia board at the gable end is increased in width at the eave to close in the end of the eave soffit.

Another type of intersection sometimes used with a horizontal eave

soffit has the eave soffit terminating at the side wall (Fig. 93A). The gable-end sheathing and siding is continued out of the edge of the eaves and serves as a covering for the end of the soffit. The gable-end soffit is carried down beyond the side wall and terminates at the eave.

WINDOW FRAMES AND SASHES

Windows are used in a house principally to provide light and air, but they are also an important part of architectural design. Windows are available in many types, each having its own advantages. The principal opening types are vertical sliding, horizontal sliding, casement and awning. Window frames and sashes may be made of wood, metal, fibreglass or plastic or a combination of these materials.

All windows should shed water and snow and be easy to reglaze if damaged. Construction of sash and frame must normally meet recognized window standards. Normally windows need to meet standards for air infiltration, water tightness and wind load resistance. In living areas of the house, the glass area should be about 10 percent of the floor area. In bedroom areas, this can be reduced to about 5 percent, but each bedroom should have at least one window that is openable from the inside without the use of tools or special knowledge, adequately sized for emergency exit. In kitchens, bathrooms and unfinished basements, no windows are required if electric lighting and mechanical ventilation are provided.

Excessive areas of glazing should be avoided, as much more heat is lost through windows than through an equivalent area of insulated wall. Generally, a total glass area of about 12 percent of the floor area of the house is adequate. On the other hand, energy-efficient windows with unshaded southern exposure can contribute positively to the heating of the house, especially when combined with heavy drapes or insulated shutters that can be closed on cloudy days and at night. For thermal insulation, new high performance windows are available in most locations in Canada.

Insulating glass units made of spaced sheets of glass are available for insertion in window sashes or frames. These windows with multiple glazings, selective coating and charged with argon or krypton can significantly reduce energy costs.

Double glazing (one sheet of glass fixed in the sash and one removable sheet) can also be used. Both types of double-glazing insulate better than single glazing and are less subject to condensation problems. Window units consisting of an inner and outer sash also give similar insulating values.

Where the total house air leakage has been reduced by good, airtight construction, interior humidity levels may be higher. Double glazing or storms in winter are a minimum requirement if excessive condensation on the window panes is to be avoided.

Good windows will be less effective if their installation does not produce a near-perfect air seal around the perimeter. Since it is not practical

to obtain an airtight fit where the sash contacts the frame, weatherstripping is often used at these points to reduce air infiltration. Most manufacturers make complete window units with the sash fitted and glazed, with weatherstripping, operating balances and hardware installed. Units combining screens and storm sash are also available.

Wood window sashes and frames should be treated to resist decay or be made of a wood species that is decay resistant, ensuring a longer life.

The exterior trim is usually attached to the window frame when the window is fabricated. To provide space for adjustment, the framework around the opening is usually slightly larger than the window. Wedges and shims are used to adjust the frame in the opening, and when in position, the window frame is nailed through the wedges to the wall framing. The exterior trim is also nailed to the studs and lintel. The space around the window frame is later filled with insulation. Figure 94 shows a typical window frame installation.

EXTERIOR DOOR FRAMES AND DOORS

Exterior door frames generally consist of 1 3/8 in. (35 mm) thick side and head jambs and a 1 3/4 in. (44 mm) sill. While a hardwood sill is more durable, a sill made of softwood with metal threshold may also be used. Frames are rabbetted to form stops for the main door. Stops for a screen or combination door are provided by the edge of the jamb and the exterior trim.

The door sill should bear solidly on the floor framing (Fig. 95), and the frame should be well nailed to the opening framework. This is usually done by adjusting the frame with wedges and then nailing through the trim and wedges into the studs. Exterior doors should be weatherstripped at the top, bottom and sides. For improved resistance to forced entry, the jamb of the door frame at the lock height should be shimmed on both sides immediately above and below the lock location. In addition, blocking should join the studs of the door opening with the adjacent studs.

Main doors should not be less than 1 3/4 in. (44 mm) thick. They should be at least 32 in. (810 mm)

wide and 6 ft. 6 in. (1.98 m) high. Wood storm doors should be 1 3/8 in. (35 mm) thick and metal doors at least 1 in. (25 mm) thick. Additional screws in the drywall around the door frame will also provide greater strength to resist forced entry.

Exterior doors are generally either the flush or panel type. For methods of hanging doors and installing hardware, see the chapter on *Interior Doors, Frames and Trim.*

Flush doors are made with structural wood panels or other suitable facings applied over a light framework and core. A core built of solid pieces of wood is called a solid core; a core built as a grillage is called a hollow core. Solid-core construction is generally preferred for exterior doors, particularly in cold climates, because

Typical window frame installation.

shim space filled with insulation, compressible gasket or urethane foam

interior window trim

94

main air/vapour barrier joined with sealant to wood jamb extension or to air/vapour barrier window wrap

window sill

shims as per manufacturers instructions

sheathing membrane

exterior siding

caulking

exterior window trim

window jamb

caulking

Section through door frame at sill.

space filled with insulation, compressible gasket or urethane foam

door jamb

sloped door sill

sheathing membrane

sheathing membrane

siding

95

caulking

exterior door trim

check for storm door

3/4" (19 mm) board

caulking

concrete stoop

this method of construction minimizes warping from differences in humidity or temperature on opposite sides of the door. Glazed panels may be inserted into solid-core doors.

Panel doors consist of stiles (solid vertical members), rails (solid cross members), and panels (thinner parts filling the spaces between stile sand rails). Many types containing various wood or glass panels are available. Metal or wood-faced doors whose cores are filled with rigid insulation are becoming more common. They should be used whenever a separate storm door is not provided.

Sliding doors, either fully or partially glazed, are sometimes used for access to patios or garden areas. All glazed areas in doors should be double-glazed safety glass. Trans-

parent glass in doors and sidelights, which could be mistaken for unobstructed passageways, should be safety glass, such as tempered or wired glass.

House doors that lead to garages should provide a gas-tight barrier to prevent automobile exhaust fumes from entering the home. These doors should be tight-fitting, weatherstripped, and provided with a self-closing device.

HEALTHY HOUSING INSIGHT

Maintenance and Durability Considerations

The maintenance and durability of exterior trim and millwork are important considerations when planning and constructing the dwelling. The following factors should be carefully examined prior to construction.

➜ The maintenance costs of exterior trim and millwork can often exceed the cost of the originally installed materials over the useful life of the building. In general, any type of painted finish, and especially those applied on site, will demand frequent refinishing.

➜ When maintenance is labour intensive and required frequently, it is often not performed properly. This situation is commonly encountered in the entry level and fixed income, elderly housing markets. The durability of these building elements may suffer severely as a consequence.

As a general rule, maintenance-free and durable finishes on exterior trim and millwork are recommended. Many appropriate materials meeting these criteria are available. The slightly higher premiums associated with these alternatives have been proven to be cost-effective investments.

STAIRS

Stairways should be designed, arranged and installed to afford safety, adequate headroom, and space for the passage of furniture. In general, there are two types of stairs in a house, those between finished areas usually referred to as main stairs, and those which lead to areas used only for storage, laundry and heating equipment, such as unfinished basements or attics. The main stairs, built to provide ease and comfort, are often a feature of design, while stairs to unfinished basements and attics are usually somewhat steeper and narrower and are built of less expensive materials. If the basement or attic is to be used as a living space, however, the stair dimensions should be similar to those of the main stairs. Stairs may be built in place or built as units in a shop and set in place.

Stair Design Terminology

The following are terms often used in stair design (Figs. 96 to 99):

Baluster: Vertical member in a guard placed between the handrail and the tread in the open portion of a stairway, landing or balcony (Fig. 96D).

Effective Depth: The portion remaining after the stringer has been cut out or ploughed to fit the treads and risers (Fig. 97).

Guard: Protective barrier, with or without openings, placed alongside the open portion of a stairway, landing or balcony.

Handrail: A rail running parallel to and on at least one side of the stairs, to be grasped when ascending or descending.

Headroom: The vertical distance from the outer edge of the nosing line to the underside of the ceiling above (Fig. 97).

Landing: A flat platform incorporated in a stairway, at least as wide and as long as the width of the stairs. Normally used to change direction of the stairs at right angles and to avoid the use of winders.

Newel: The main post for the handrail at the start and finish of the stairs, and the stiffening post at changes of direction and landings.

Nosing: The projection of the tread beyond the face of the riser (Fig. 97).

Rise: The vertical height of a step (Fig. 97).

Riser: Closed Riser: The vertical board under a tread.

   Open Riser: The vertical board under the tread is omitted and the tread is supported on the stringers only.

Run: The net depth of the tread measured from riser to riser (Fig. 97).

Stringer: The member supporting the treads and risers.

   Cut-out (Open): A stringer cut out to fit the treads and risers (Figs. 98B and C). Ploughed (housed): A stringer grooved to receive the exact profile of the treads and risers (Fig. 96C).

Total Rise: The distance measured vertically from finish floor to finish floor.

Total Run: The distance measured horizontally from finish floor on one level to finish floor on another.
Tread: The horizontal plane of a step.

Winder: A radiating or wedge-shaped tread converging on a centre point at an angle of 30°.

96

Parts of stairs: (*A*) risers and treads tongued and grooved together; (*B*) risers and treads connected with angle blocks; (*C*) housed stringers; (*D*) cut-out stringer (open) showing balusters and mitre-nosing return.

A

tread
nosing
riser
space for wedges
angle block

B

glued angle block
nail or screw
nail or screw

C

ploughed out for stairs and wedges

D

tread return
moulding
balusters placed in tread
stringer

Elevation

riser
nosing
mitre nosing return
baluster ends covered
mitre cut
stringer

Plan

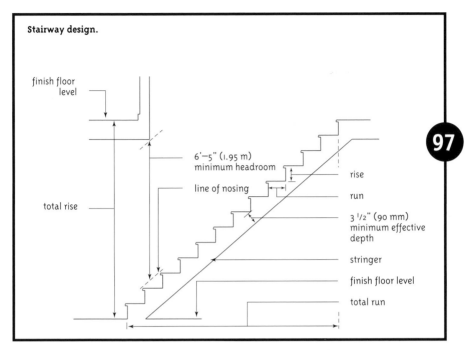

Stairway design.

finish floor level

6'–5" (1.95 m) minimum headroom

line of nosing

total rise

rise

run

3 1/2" (90 mm) minimum effective depth

stringer

finish floor level

total run

97

Ratio of Rise-to-run

The relation between the rise and the run should conform to well-established rules. Experience has shown that a rise of 7 to 7 1/2 in. (180 to 190 mm) with a run of about 9 3/4 to 10 1/4 in. (250 to 265 mm) combines both comfort and safety. These dimensions are commonly used for main stairs.

Although the dimensions presented above may be considered desirable, space does not always permit their use. If such is the case, the following limitations should be observed: all stairs should have a maximum rise of 7 7/8 in. (200 mm), a minimum run of 8 1/4 in. (210 mm), and a minimum tread width of 9 1/4 in. (235 mm). As well, stairs should have a rise no less than 5 in. (125 mm), a run or tread width no more than 14 in. (355 mm). These dimensions apply to stairs serving only one dwelling unit.

Stairway Design

Stairways may have a straight, continuous run without an intermediate landing, or they may consist of two or more runs with changes in direction. In the best and safest practice, a landing is introduced at any change in direction, but the turn may be made with radiating treads called winders. The length or width of any landing must not be less than the width of the stairs. Stairs must be at least 34 in. (860 mm) wide measured face to face of wall.

The diagrams in Figure 99 show different types of stairway designs. If winders are necessary because of cramped space, they must form an angle of 30°, so that three treads would be necessary for the maximum 90° turn permitted. Only one set of such winders is permitted between floor levels.

98

Basement stairs: *(A)* ploughed stringers; *(B)* cut-out stringers; *(C)* cut- out stringers with finish member nailed to the outside of the stringer.

A

stair tread nosing slightly chamfered

ploughed stringer

B

stair tread (supported on cut-out)

cut-out stringer

C

1" (25 mm) thick finished member on outside of stringer

stair tread (supported stringer)

cut-out stringer

Once the location, the width of the stairway and any landings, if required, have been determined, the next step is to fix the tread rise and the tread run. To fix the tread rise, the exact distance between the finish floors of the two storeys under consideration is divided by 7 1/4 in. (184 mm), a comfortable riser height. This calculation gives the number of risers needed over the total rise. Round up the number that results from this calculation to the next whole number. The tread width is determined by dividing the required number of treads into the total run of the stairs.

For example, if the total rise is 8 ft. 11 in. or 107 in. (2718 mm) and if each riser is set at 7 1/4 in. (184 mm), then 14.8 risers are needed (i.e., 107/7.25 = 14.8). Rounding up, 15 risers will be required each at 7.13 in. (181 mm) (i.e., 107/15 = 7.13).

It is important to remember that the minimum headroom for a stairway must be 6 ft. 5 in. (1.95 m) (Fig. 97).

Stringers

The treads and risers are supported on stringers which must always be solidly supported, firmly fixed, and properly positioned. The stringers may be either cut out (Figs. 96D and 98B

Types of stair designs.

width

total run

total rise

long L

wide L

narrow U

double L with winders and landing

wide U

99

and C) or ploughed (Fig. 96C) to fit the outline of the treads and risers.

Stringers should not be less than 1 in. (25 mm) thick when they are supported along their length or 1 1/2 in.

(38 mm) when supported only at the top and bottom. The overall depth should be at least 9 1/4 in. (235 mm), and when the stringer is cut out to fit the treads and risers, the portion

remaining should not be less than 3 1/2 in. (90 mm) deep. A third stringer should be used when the width of the stairs is more than 35 in. (900 mm). This may be increased to 48 in. (1200 mm) where risers support the front of the treads. Treads should be at least 1 1/2 in. (38 mm) thick when used with open risers. This thickness can be reduced to 1 in. (25 mm) where the stringers are not more than 29 in. (750 mm) apart or where the tread is supported by a closed riser attached to the treads.

The wall stringer may be ploughed out to the exact profile of the tread and riser with sufficient space at the back to take wedges (Fig. 96C). The top of the riser may be connected to the bottom of the tread by angle-blocks glued to both surfaces, screws being added to reinforce the joint. The bottom of the riser is attached to the back of the tread with screws (Fig. 96B). Another method is to tongue the top of the riser into the front of the tread and the back of the tread into the bottom of the next riser (Fig. 96A). The wall stringer is nailed to the wall, the nails being located behind the treads and risers. The treads and risers are fitted together and forced into the wall-stringer nosing, where they are set tight by driving and gluing wood wedges behind them. The wall stringer thus shows above the profiles of the treads and risers as a finish against the wall and is often made continuous with the baseboard of the upper and lower floors.

If the outside stringer is an open stringer, it may be cut out to fit the risers and treads. The edges of the risers are mitred with the corresponding edges of the stringer, and the nosing of the tread may be returned on its outside edge along the face of the stringer (Fig. 96D).

Newels, Handrails and Guards

Handrails run parallel to stairs and are designed to be grasped when ascending or descending, while guards surround openings to protect against falling over the edge. All stairways of three or more risers should have a handrail from floor to floor, and on both sides if the stair is 43 in. (1100 mm) or wider. For stairways that rise between enclosing walls, the rail is attached to the wall with brackets into solid framing members. For stairs that are open on one or both sides, handrails are usually supported by balusters and end against newel posts. Handrails should be set between 32 and 38 in. (800 and 965 mm) above the tread at the nosing line, with at least 1 5/8 in. (40 mm) clearance from the wall, and be built so that there is no obstruction that could break a handhold.

Guards should be placed around openings at landings and balconies that are more than 24 in. (600 mm) above the adjacent level, and alongside the open portions of stairways. They should never be less than 35 in. (900 mm) high around openings and above the stair nosings along the open sides of stairways. Where one or both sides of a stairway are open, the guard is also the handrail. Guards for exterior balconies or landings, porches or decks that are more than 5 ft. 11 in. (1800 mm) above finished ground level must be at least 42 in. (1070 mm) high. Spacing between balusters for all guards should not permit a 4 in. (100 mm) sphere from passing through.

Basement Stairs

Ploughed stringers (Fig. 98A) are commonly used supports for treads on basement stairs, but the tread may be supported on cut-out stringers (Fig. 98B). Another method sometimes used is cut-out stringers nailed to a finish member (Fig. 98C).

Exterior Steps and Stoops

Proportioning of risers and treads in laying out porch steps or approaches to terraces should be as carefully considered as it is in the design of interior stairways. The riser-to-tread ratio should not exceed those for main stairs referred to previously.

Outside steps and stoops need good support. If they are supported independently, their foundation should extend below the frost penetration line and be carried down to undisturbed ground. Outside steps and stoops leading to entrances often consist of precast units which are designed to be highly resistant to moisture, frost and impact damage. If concrete steps and stoops are made on site, the concrete should be 5 to 8 percent air-entrained and have a minimum of 3600 psi (25 MPa) compressive strength.

FRAMING DETAILS FOR PLUMBING, HEATING, VENTILATING AND WIRING

One advantage of wood-frame construction is that the space between the framing members in wood-frame walls, floors and roofs provides a safe and economical location to conceal the greater part of the heating, plumbing and electrical distribution system.

Most of the electrical wiring and many plumbing pipes and heating and ventilating ducts run parallel to the joists and studs and can easily be concealed in the space between the members. Where it is necessary to run pipes or wires at right angles to the joists and studs, the wood members may be notched or drilled. Within

certain limitations, the structural strength of a framing member is not seriously reduced by these notches or holes.

CUTTING THE FRAMING MEMBERS

Notching of Roof, Ceiling or Floor Joists. Notches made in the top at the end of the joists should be within one-half the joist depth from the edge of the bearing. The depth of the notch should be no more than one-third of the joist depth (Fig. 100B).

If notches are necessary elsewhere in the span (Fig. 100A), this should be

Example of notch limitations: (*A*) notch located away from support; (*B*) when applied to an 8 in. (184 mm) joist the depth of the notch at the support would be 2 3/8 in.(61 mm) maximum and the length of the notch would not extend more than 3 5/8 in. (92 mm) from the joist support.

100

A

joist size increased by depth of notch

effective depth of joist

B

maximum 1/3 of joist depth

maximum 1/2 of joist depth

never notch the underside of a joist

CHECKING BACK

Framing Layouts for Plumbing, Heating and Electrical

When planning for plumbing, heating and electrical services in the dwelling, it is important to consider how the installation of these items may be affected by the layout of framing members. Check back to the **Accommodating Ductwork and Piping** note in the **Floor Framing** chapter for some helpful guidelines.

There may also be some special items such as large, one-piece tub and shower enclosures or hot tubs that may have to be located prior to the construction of walls. Check back to the Installing **Special Items Prior to Wall Framing** note in the **Wall Framing** chapter.

considered when deciding the size of joist to use, so that the size of joist can be increased by the depth of the notch. The bottom edge of joists should not be notched, since this may cause a joist to split when it deflects under load.

Drilled Holes in Joists. Normally, holes drilled in joists should not be

larger than one-quarter the joist depth or closer than 2 in. (50 mm) to either edge (Fig. 101).

Notching and Drilling of Studs. Loadbearing wall studs that have been notched or drilled to more than one-third of their depth must be reinforced, usually with 2 in. (38 mm) lumber nailed to the side of the studs

Maximum size of holes drilled in joists.

joist

pipe

maximum diameter of hole ¼ of joist depth

2" (50 mm) minimum distance

101

102

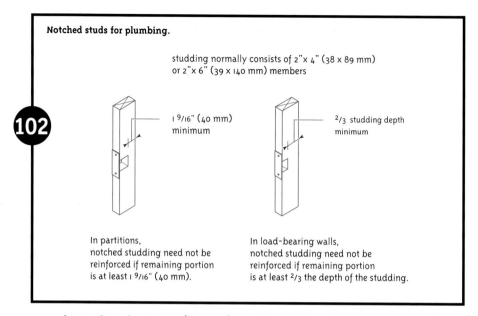

Notched studs for plumbing.

studding normally consists of 2"x 4" (38 x 89 mm)
or 2"x 6" (39 x 140 mm) members

1 9/16" (40 mm) minimum

2/3 studding depth minimum

In partitions, notched studding need not be reinforced if remaining portion is at least 1 9/16" (40 mm).

In load-bearing walls, notched studding need not be reinforced if remaining portion is at least 2/3 the depth of the studding.

and extending about 24 in. (600 mm) each side of the notch or hole. Similar reinforcing is used when notched partition studs have less than 1 9/16 in. (40 mm) of solid wood remaining. (Fig. 102).

Notching and Drilling of Top Plates. In loadbearing walls, top plates are also reinforced with 2 in. (38 mm) lumber when the solid wood remaining in the plates is less than 2 in. (50 mm) in width. If the required reinforcing must be placed on the face of the plate or stud, sheet metal is normally used so that the wall finish may readily be applied over it.

FRAMING DETAILS FOR PLUMBING SYSTEMS

The installation of the plumbing system usually begins after the framing. This initial work is called "rough-ing-in." It includes putting in the plumbing vents and drains and all the hot and cold water piping which will be enclosed in the walls and ceilings and under the basement floor. Piping in outside walls should be insulated. Since the bathtub must be put in before the wall finish can be applied, bathtub installation is usually included in roughing-in. Plumbing fixtures and accessories are not connected until the installation of the interior finish has been completed. The design and installation of the entire plumbing system is usually regulated by provincial or municipal codes. (See Figures 103, 104 and 105 for details of a typical plumbing system installation.)

When 3 in. (75 mm) copper or plastic piping is used, the stack wall may be made of 2 x 4 in. (38 x 89 mm) material. Sealing the area around the pipe is necessary to prevent air leakage into the attic space (Fig. 106).

Kitchen and bathroom in proximity for minimum pipe length.

kitchen sink and laundry tub drainage connected to this combined soil and vent stack

bathtub

103

toilet

cleanout

soil stack cleanout

floor drain in front of laundry tubs in basement

washbasin or vanity

use 6" (140 mm) stud wall when soil stack continues to upper floors

waste disposal piping system buried under concrete slab and directed outside the building to the sanitary sewer

cleanout

exterior face of building

Washbasin and bathtub fixtures.

washbasin mounted on brackets to blocking or stud wall

end profile of bathtub

washbasin

overflow

exposed drainage piping usually chrome plated or brass

outlet

104

drainage piping from washbasin connected to soil stack

subflooring cut to receive overflow piping

holes drilled in bottom plate and subflooring to receive hot and cold water piping

drainage piping from trap connected to soil stack

Where soil stacks or large pipes must run horizontally at right angles to the joists, it will be necessary to frame out the joists. To do this, headers are installed between the joists (Fig. 107). Alternatively, services are suspended and enclosed in a bulkhead.

177

Toilet fixture.

105

drainage piping from washbasin

bottom plate and subflooring cut to receive soil stack

toilet

toilet flange secured to subfloor

drainage piping from bathtub

soil stack

Venting for plumbing.

106

vent pipes extend through to the open air above the roof

rubber boot

use 6" (140 mm) stud partitions when soil stack continues to a higher floor

washbasin

In partitions, holes may be drilled in studs providing the remaining portion totals at least 1 1/2" (40 mm) otherwise studding must be suitably reinforced.

toilet

bathtub

soil stack and vent pipe

cleanout at basement level

In loadbearing walls, the remaining portion must be at least 2/3 the depth of the studs; otherwise studding must be suitably reinforced.

Framing for soil-stack pipes.

- drainage piping from wash basin
- floor joists
- soil stack
- header joist
- floor flange
- drainage piping from toilet
- drainage piping from bathtub

107

HEALTHY HOUSING INSIGHT

Water Efficient Fixtures and Appliances

Water conservation is one of the most important aspects of resource efficiency for healthy housing. The use of water-conserving fixtures and appliances not only saves this vital resource, but

Continued on page 180

Continued from page 179

reduces the energy needed for providing potable water and treating waste water. This is especially important in rural areas which rely on wells.

In recent years, manufacturers of water fixtures and water-consuming appliances have introduced water-conserving technologies in response to requirements in present day codes. However, there are fixtures which use significantly less water than the maximum amount permitted in codes, and there are also dramatic differences between appliances such as clothes and dish washers.

The critical fixtures and appliances to consider are typically toilets, showerheads and clothes washers. These account for most of the water used in a typical household. Low consumption toilets (sometimes referred to as Ultra Low-Flush, ULF, Ultra and Lite by manufacturers) use the least amount of water. Water-saving showerheads can use about half the water of conventional types. Clothes and dish washing machines which use between one-half to one-third as much water as conventional types are also available.

In the summer months, lawn watering can account for an abnormally high level of water consumption. If lawns are still preferred over alternative landscaping options, then hardy strains of grass and in-ground irrigation systems should be considered.

FRAMING DETAILS FOR HEATING SYSTEMS

There are many ways to heat a house. Heating systems range from the multi-controlled electric or hot-water heating systems to the relatively simple single space heater. In Canada, natural gas, oil and electricity are the most commonly used energy sources.

The three prevalent heating systems are: forced warm air, electric baseboards and forced flow hot-water heating. Other less frequently used systems are: air, ground or water source heat pumps with electric resistance back-up, heat pumps with natural gas back-up, and solid fuel-burning (wood or coal) furnaces.

Figure 108 illustrates a typical heating layout, while Figure 109 shows an isometric view of a typical heating system.

All types of heating systems may be safely and easily installed in wood-frame houses. Certain clearances, however, must be maintained between parts of the system and combustible material. Installers of heating equipment should be aware of local regulations before starting work.

For a warm-air heating system, the ducts for supply and return air are usually located between studs in walls and between joists in floors. When planning the house, locating joists, beams and studs to suit the requirements of the duct system must be considered.

Provision must be made for

controlled ventilation when planning the heat distribution system of the house. Assuming good airtight construction, the ventilation system must be designed to exhaust house air (primarily from bathrooms and kitchen but also from other rooms) and draw in outside air so that the air quality of the house is maintained.

Warm-air and Ventilation Systems

Normally, wall studs and joists are located so that they do not have to be cut to install heating ducts. When ducts must pass up through a wall to heat the room above, the top and bottom plates must be removed at these points, and the ducts are then fitted between the studs.

When a partition is supported on doubled floor joists and a heating duct is to go in the partition, the joists are ordinarily spaced apart, with blocking, to allow room for the duct. This eliminates the need to cut framing members unnecessarily or to use intricate duct angles.

Return air grilles, usually located on inside walls near the floor level, can be connected to a duct or an enclosed stud space. At this point, the bottom plate and subfloor is cut to make a passage for the duct or air space. Blocks are nailed between the joists to support the ends of boards if diagonal subflooring has been used. Sometimes, the studs have to be cut to accommodate large return air grilles.

Basement plan showing typical heating layout.

bedrooms

dining room

basement

up to toe space in kitchen counter

108

return air duct

copper tubing carried in concrete floor and connected to burner

oil feed and vent pipes

oil storage tank

living room

entrance hall

bathroom

bedroom

basement

Where this occurs, a lintel is used to support the studs that have been cut, and the opening is framed in the same way as the door opening shown in Figure 42. When enclosed, the space between the floor joists may be used as a return air duct and other return air ducts connected to the same joist space. Non-combustible material, such as metal, should be used to line the joist space within 24 in. (600 mm)

of the furnace, under floor registers, and at the bottom of vertical ducts.

Warm-air registers are usually placed in the floor close to the outside walls, preferably under the windows. These registers are fitted with vanes to direct the warm air over the wide area of the outside walls. Where possible, ducts leading to these registers are located between joists with a shaped "boot" connecting the duct and regis-

Isometric view of typical heating unit.

baseboard return air grille

return air — one or two joist spaces with bottom and end boxed-in with sheet metal

wiring from relay control box extended to thermostatic wall control outlet generally located 4' (1.2 m) off first floor level

generally 3" (75 mm) clearance required from wood members

furnace wiring extended to emergency switch box normally fixed to underside of floor joists at bottom of basement stairs

smoke pipe

barometric damper

relay control box

heating unit

conduit fastened to heating unit

warm air supply

extended plenum

warm air take-off

floor joists

plenum

strap supports

wiring

copper tubing from burner unit looped and taken in concrete slab to oil storage tank

109

ter. Then, only the subfloor and floor covering need to be cut. Diagonal subflooring must be supported by blocking at this point.

In houses with a crawl space, a warm-air furnace can either be put in a special compartment on the floor of the house, hung under the floor or mounted on a concrete base in the crawl space beneath the house. In the first two cases, the joists will have to be designed to carry the weight of the furnace.

Ventilation is often coupled to the warm air heating system of the house, using the heating ducts to also distribute ventilation air. In some cases, particularly for houses without forced air heating systems, dedicated, whole-house ventilation systems are used. These systems often require ducts that are smaller than those required for used for heating purposes. They are accommodated by the framing in a manner similar to the warm air systems.

Hot-water Systems

Where the heating system requires only small pipes for a supply-and-return system, pre-planning the structural framing layout to accommodate the pipes is not normally necessary.

Baseboard-type convectors are usually selected and located under windows along outside walls. In this manner, warm air rising through the convector blankets the outside walls. Virtually no cutting of the studs or joists is required with this type of installation as the baseboard type of convector is positioned on the surface of the wall.

Electric Baseboard Heating Systems

Because it is easy to conceal wiring in walls and floors, the accommodation of this type of electric heating system requires little or no planning in the structural framing. As with hot-water and warm-air systems, electric heating units are usually located along outside walls, so that the air warmed by the heating elements blankets the walls. Because the heating elements are mounted on the surface of the wall, there is no need to cut the wall studs. Radiant heating with the heating elements located in the ceiling is also used.

With hot-water systems and electric systems which use baseboard radiators, it is important, especially in a well-constructed, well-sealed house, to provide for room-air replacement and not rely entirely on natural convection and infiltration. If measures for air circulation are not implemented, humidity levels may rise to the point where condensation will occur.

FRAMING DETAILS FOR WIRING

Wiring a house for electrical services is usually started after the house has been closed in, that is, after the exterior wall sheathing and roof have been completed.

This initial phase of wiring, also termed roughing-in, includes the installation of wiring and the boxes for the switches, lights and outlets. Figure 110 presents some typical electrical equipment.

HEALTHY HOUSING INSIGHT

Heating Energy and Equipment Choice

There exists a large and growing number of heating energy and equipment options. All of these options may not be available in a given area. Some choices are also more appropriate than others.

Energy Source

Most heating energy sources are non-renewable. Wood and solar energy are notable exceptions. Utilize these renewable sources to the greatest extent possible before tapping into a non-renewable energy source. Be aware that in terms of cost, electricity is the highest priced energy source in most parts of Canada, whereas fossil fuels are significantly less expensive. Wood remains the fuel of choice in many rural areas.

Equipment Type and Efficiency

Heating system options are numerous, but essentially these fall into two categories: central heating (furnaces and boilers), and unitary heating (individually controlled baseboard heaters, wall heaters, fireplaces, and woodstoves). Central heating systems have the advantage of being combined with domestic water heating so that only a single piece of equipment needs to be purchased and maintained. Forced-air systems can easily incorporate air conditioning and ventilation, but cannot easily provide individual temperature control to each room or zone in the dwelling. Alternatively, when central hot water (hydronic) heating is employed, selected zones may be individually controlled, and the heating of floors in basements and bathrooms becomes possible. Unitary heating is useful in isolated or seasonal areas of the dwelling. Both hydronic and unitary heating systems require a separate ventilation system.

Affordability and Adaptability

Heating systems with low initial costs are not necessarily more affordable. Low efficiency equipment and high priced fuels can prove less affordable than heating system options with higher initial costs but lower operating costs. This is especially critical to entry level homebuyers and fixed-income households. The adaptability of heating systems also deserves consideration. Hot water heating has proven to be one of the most durable and flexible options available. Forced-air systems are less flexible and will require special treatment such as fire dampers when dwellings are converted from single family to multi-unit.

Carefully research and plan any heating energy and equipment choices.

Typical electrical equipment.

octagonal boxes for use
with fixture or junction
outlets

use approved boxes for
switches and outlets
in the house

standard plug-type
fuse

110

duplex wall outlet
and plate

toggle switch and plate

circuit breaker

Roughing-in is done before applying the inside finish and ordinarily before placing the insulation in walls or ceilings. Lighting fixtures, switches, outlets and cover plates are installed after the interior finish and painting operations.

The design and installation of the entire wiring system is usually regulated by a provincial electrical code. All provincial codes are closely modelled on the Canadian Electrical Code published by the Canadian Standards Association. The provincial codes usually require installation to be done by a licensed electrician. Owners are advised to check with the local authority before doing any wiring.

Figures 111 and 112 show the typical arrangement of electrical service entrance equipment. The details of drilling structural members for wiring are shown in Figure 113.

Box Location

The location of switches and outlets is important. The wiring plans should be studied carefully to ensure that everything is included. Today's house uses electricity for a multitude of purposes from radios and televisions to major appliances that require their own circuit. The location of outlets for all these purposes should be carefully planned.

The amperage of the electrical service and the number of circuits and outlets installed should also take into account future needs; after the house is finished, alterations and additions are expensive. To accom-

Typical arrangement of service entrance.

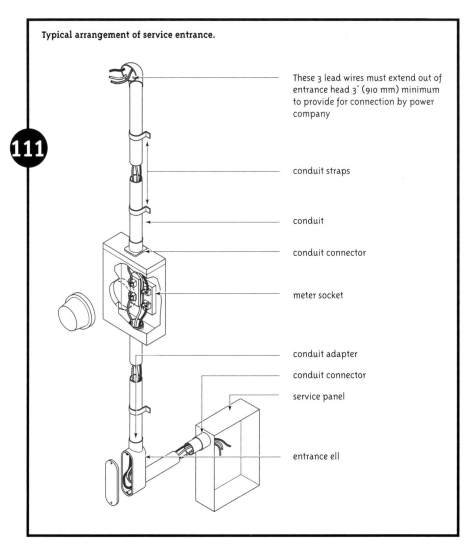

These 3 lead wires must extend out of entrance head 3' (910 mm) minimum to provide for connection by power company

conduit straps

conduit

conduit connector

meter socket

conduit adapter

conduit connector

service panel

entrance ell

modate the multitude of electrical appliances in a modern house, electrical services are usually 200 amps.

When planning the location of outlets and fans, remember that electrical boxes on insulated ceilings and exterior walls can be a major source of air leakage. At all times these should be carefully sealed.

SWITCHES

Switches are commonly located just inside the door of a room so that they may be easily reached upon opening the door. Switches may service a wall outlet for a table or a floor lamp as well as the usual ceiling or wall lights. It is common practice to locate the switch boxes about 4 ft. 6 in. (1.4 m) above the floor.

Service entrance equipment.

pot head

overhead wires

112

service mast

meter base and meter on exterior

3-wire 120 – 240V.
for details of entrance wiring
see Fig. 92

15' (4.6 m) above grade
9' (2.75 m) minimum on
low building

grounding wire

main breaker

distribution panel

1/2" (11 mm) plywood back-up
panel fixed to foundation wall

Note: Capacity 100 to 200 Amps.
The service wires are brought to
the main breaker located in the
basement through a rigid
conduit. The main breaker and
distribution panel containing
fuses for the branch circuits are
mounted on a plywood
back-up panel.

floor joists

water supply pipe fixed to
back-up strip

combination service
entrance panel

water meter

ground wire clamped below
shut-off valve

finished basement floor

Note: Ground wire from main entrance
panel must be clamped to the
water service entrance pipe below
shut-off valve as shown (metallic
pipe only).

Note: Service equipment must be grounded

Drilling of structural members for wiring.

blocking

caulking sealant or rubber grommet

truss chord

air/vapour barrier

drywall ceiling finish

surface mounted receptacle

pendant fitting recommended to reduce heat build-up

double studs at door opening

switch box to door framing with two 4" (100 mm) nails

wires stapled as shown

metal protection plate fixed to edge of stud member when required

1 1/4" (30 mm)

holes drilled to receive wires

Note: When holes are drilled closer than 1 1/4" (30 mm) to the edge of a stud, metal protection plates are required.

holes drilled in double top plate

to ceiling fixture

4'-6" (1400 mm)

holes drilled in studs to receive wires

outlet boxes fixed to studs with two 4" (100 mm) nails

holes drilled in bottom plate and joists

to service panel

113

Multiple-control switches are convenient in many locations so that lights may be controlled from more than one switch. A living room light could have a switch near the outside entrance door and another at inner doors leading to the kitchen or to a bedroom hallway. In two-storey houses, three-way switches should be provided at the bottom and at the top of the stairway to control stairway lighting. Three-way switches can control light from more than one location. Basement stair lights should also be controlled by three-way switches at the head and ft. of the stairs, particularly if there is living accommodation in the basement, or if there is an outside exit from the basement.

RELATED PUBLICATIONS

Canadian Plumbing Code
National Research Council of Canada
Canadian Electrical Code
Canadian Standards Association, CAN3-C22
Complying with the Ventilation Requirements of the 1995 National Building Code
Canada Mortgage and Housing Corporation

HEALTHY HOUSING INSIGHT

Energy Efficient Lighting and Appliances

Appliances and lighting represent a significant proportion of energy consumption in the typical household. Appropriate choices of appliances and lighting can cost effectively reduce the amount of energy consumed.

Appliances

➜ When purchasing appliances, always refer to the EnerGuide rating. Select appliances that are closest to the lowest rating available for the type of appliance being considered.

➜ For water-consuming appliances such as clothes and dish washers, check the amount of water these require — water conserving appliances also save energy.

Electric Lighting

➜ A large number of electric lighting options are available, but these vary considerably in their energy efficiency.

Continued on page 190

Continued from page 189

➜ Incandescent lighting is the least efficient, and should be reserved for lighting which is only used occasionally. Tungsten-halogen lighting is an efficient alternative to incandescent lighting.

➜ Fluorescent lighting is preferred where lighting will be used extensively. Compact fluorescent and energy-saving fluorescent lamps are the most efficient alternatives.

➜ Exterior lighting with photocell controls is recommended since the photocell prevents the lights from operating until dark. This avoids wasting energy when occupants forget to shut off outdoor lights.

Natural light

➜ The size and arrangement of windows and skylights can promote good natural light and reduce the use of electric lighting.

➜ Natural light and passive solar heating are entirely compatible, and represent cost-effective means of reducing energy consumption.

Having made appropriate choices for appliances and lighting, recognize that the cleaning and maintenance of appliances, light fixtures and windows are important factors in realizing the full potential of these investments in energy efficiency.

CHIMNEYS AND FIREPLACES

Chimneys and fireplaces can be of masonry construction supported on a suitable foundation. Lightweight, factory-built chimneys and fireplaces requiring no foundation are becoming more common. A chimney must be capable of producing sufficient draft to maintain the fire and carry off the products of combustion.

Since an ordinary fireplace has a very low heating efficiency, its chief value is decorative. Its efficiency can be increased, however, by use of a factory-made metal unit incorporated in the fireplace structure. In addition to direct heat from the fire, the room is also heated by air circulating through the unit. To be most effective, the unit should have draft-tight doors and a separate air supply directly from the exterior to aid combustion.

The inefficiencies of wood burning and the air leakage characteristics of fireplaces are somewhat offset when wood stoves are used. The fire safety requirements for wood stoves are similar to those for fireplaces.

Both the chimney and the fireplace must be carefully built to be free of fire hazards. Where possible, chimneys and fireplaces should not be located on outside walls. When located entirely within the house, they offer substantial advantages:

- heat that would otherwise be lost up the chimney and outdoors stays in the house;
- there will be less deterioration of the masonry from condensation of flue gases;
- if located near south-facing windows and of masonry construction, they will contribute to the thermal inertia of the house by storing solar energy gained during the day, and releasing it to the house during the night; and
- due to its warmer temperature, the chimney will have a better draft and thus exhaust flue gases more efficiently.

CHIMNEYS

Masonry chimneys must be built on a concrete footing, properly proportioned to support the load. Because a chimney may contain more than one flue, the minimum dimensions depend on the number of flues, and their arrangement and size. The wall thickness of a masonry chimney should not be less than 3 in. (75 mm) of solid masonry units.

The flue is a vertical shaft through which smoke and gases are carried to open air. A single flue may serve one or more appliances located on the same floor, for example, a furnace and water heater. In this case, both connections to the flue should be located one above the other to ensure a good draft. As well, installing a certified chimney liner is recommended. The size of the flue, and the placement of multiple connections, depends on the capacities of the appliances connected to it. A fireplace must always have a separate flue.

The flue lining for masonry fireplaces usually consists of rectangular glazed clay pipe in sections, which are about 24 in. (600 mm) long and installed when the surrounding masonry is being placed. Care should be taken to set the linings close and flush on top of each other with full mortar beds. If more than one flue is used in a chimney, flues should be separated from each other by at least 3 in. (75 mm) of solid masonry or concrete, or 3 1/2 in. (90 mm) of fire brick where fire-brick liners are used (Fig. 114). The linings usually start about 8 in. (200 mm) below the flue pipe connection and extend 2 to 4 in. (50 to 100 mm) above the chimney cap.

The top of masonry chimneys should be capped to keep water away from masonry joints. Concrete is generally used for this purpose. The top of the cap should be sloped away from the flue lining and extend beyond the chimney wall at least 1 in. (25 mm) to form a drip edge.

Most factory-built metal chimneys are fabricated in sections and connected during installation. They are comparatively light in weight, and can be supported by special anchors that are attached to the floor joists when the chimney is erected. Two precautions to be observed in the use of a factory-built chimney are:

• make sure the model has been tested and approved by the Underwriters' Laboratories of Canada; and

• ensure that it is installed in strict accordance with the manufacturer's instructions and the conditions of approval set out by the Underwriters' Laboratories of Canada.

The chimney flue should be carried high enough above the roof to avoid downdrafts caused by wind turbulence. The height should never be less than 3 ft. (900 mm) above the

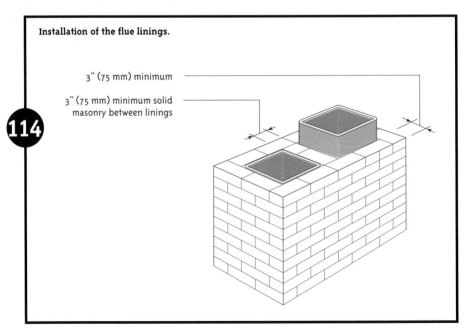

Installation of the flue linings.

3" (75 mm) minimum

3" (75 mm) minimum solid masonry between linings

114

highest point where the chimney inter-sects the roof and should extend at least 2 ft. (600 mm) above the ridge or any other roof surface within 10 ft. (3 m) of the chimney (Fig. 115).

A metal cleanout opening and door shall be provided near the bottom of the flue so that soot can easily be removed from the chimney.

Chimneys may be used to vent gas-burning equipment provided the lining complies with gas appliance installation codes. Alternatively, the equipment may be vented through special gas vents approved for this purpose.

FIREPLACES

A fireplace that draws properly can be assured by applying proper principles of design. Fireplaces must have an external air supply to improve combustion. The fireplace flue should have a liner. Its size depends on the size of the fireplace opening. One rule commonly used is to take one-tenth of the area of the fireplace opening to find the minimum size of the flue; however, the outside dimension of the flue should never be less than 8 x 12 in. (200 x 300 mm). The terminology and locations of the various parts of a fire-place are illustrated in Figure 116.

Chimney height above the ridge.

concrete cap

flue lining

36" (900 mm) minimum

24" (600 mm) minimum if chimney is less than 10' (3 m) from ridge

ridge

shingles

115

Other design principles commonly used in the construction of a fireplace with a single face are:
- the front of the fireplace should be wider than the back and the upper part of the back should tilt forward to meet the throat for better burning performance;
- the back, which should rise one-half the height of the opening before sloping forward, is usually about two-thirds of the opening in width;

- a smoke shelf, to reduce back drafts, is formed by projecting the throat forward as much as possible. The throat should be as wide and shallow as possible, but in total area it must equal the area of the flue; and
- the sides of the fireplace above the throat are drawn together to form the flue, which usually starts over the centre of the width of the fireplace; the slope, however, should not exceed 45° to the vertical.

Terms used in fireplace construction.

116

wall finish
mantel shelf
mantel
front hearth

flue lining
smoke chamber
smoke shelf
damper
throat
fire brick
ash dump
back hearth
ashpit

cleanout door

The lining of the fire box must be built with materials having a high resistance to heat. A steel liner designed for this purpose or 2 in. (50 mm) of fire brick meet this requirement. When fire brick is used, it should be laid with fire-clay mortar or high-temperature cement.

If a 2 in. (50 mm) fire-brick liner is used, the back and sides of the fireplace should be at least 8 in. (190 mm) thick including the thickness of the masonry liner. Portions of the back exposed to the outside may be 5 1/2 in. (140 mm) thick. Where a steel fireplace liner with an air circulating chamber surrounding the fire box is used, the back and side may be solid masonry units 3 1/2 in. (90 mm) thick or 8 in. (190 mm) hollow units.

The damper is a large valve set in the throat of the fireplace which can be adjusted from the front to regulate the draft. Many types of damper units are available. By choosing one with a correctly proportioned throat passage, the risk of failure in the function of the fireplace is reduced. The damper should be capable of being fully closed, and should be as tight-fitting as possible in the closed position to minimize heat losses up the chimney when the fireplace is not in use.

The hearth may be set even with the floor, or raised above the floor level. It consists of two parts: the front or finish hearth, and the back hearth under the fire. Because the back hearth must withstand more heat, it is usually built of fire brick. The front hearth is simply a precaution against flying sparks and is usually built of 4 in. (100 mm) reinforced concrete finished with ceramic tile. The front hearth should extend at least 16 in. (400 mm) in front of the fireplace opening and 8 in. (200 mm) on each side.

At the back of the fireplace, it is customary, but not essential, to have an ash dump through which ashes can be dropped into an ash pit. A cleanout door to the ash pit can be provided in the basement for periodic removal of ashes.

If a factory-built fireplace is used (Fig. 117), the same precautions should be observed as indicated for the use of factory-built chimneys.

In all cases, fireplaces chimneys should be as straight as possible to properly vent the fireplace.

A popular alternative for wood-burning fireplaces is now available through a wide variety of gas burning appliances (both natural gas and propane). Some of these are purely decorative and manufactured for installation into existing masonry fireplaces. However, gas fireplaces with higher combustion efficiencies and fans for distribution of the heat are also available. Ensure that these are installed according to the manufacturer's installation instructions and conform to all applicable requirements of the natural gas or propane appliance installation code.

Factory-built fireplace.

117

metal fire stop spacer

prefabricated
chimney flue

wood framing from
ceiling to hearth

prefabricated fireplace

wood mantel

non-combustible
hearth finish

HEALTHY HOUSING INSIGHT

Woodburning Appliance Selection

Woodburning appliances can provide effective and affordable home heating using a renewable energy resource. It is important to select appropriate appliances which function safely, cleanly and efficiently.

Woodburning Appliance Considerations

➜ When selecting any woodburning appliance, in addition to Underwriters' Laboratory certification, check that the appliance is also EPA certified. The U.S. Environmental Protection Agency was the first jurisdiction in North America to establish emission standards for woodburning appliances in response to concerns over air pollution from the burning of wood fuels. EPA certification ensures that the appliance is clean burning, and that as a result, it is also highly efficient.

➜ Locate the appliance in an area of the home where its immediate heating output is needed and welcome. Rooms where occupants spend a great deal of time, such as family rooms or living rooms, will benefit most from a woodstove or fireplace. Selecting appliances with glass doors affords a welcome view of the fire. Woodburning appliances are also useful in areas such as unheated sunrooms and workshops.

➜ Distribute the heat to other parts of the home using a forced-air heating system or a ventilation system with a recirculating mode of operation.

➜ Only use the type of chimney which has been certified for use with the appliance. Follow the manufacturer's certified installation instructions and have the completed installation inspected by the local fire department prior to closing it in.

➜ Use wood that has been harvested from managed woodlots. Avoid supporting sources of firewood which do not observe sustainable resource management of the forests. Wood that has been drying for at least two years is the best and cleanest burning fuel. Hardwoods are generally preferred to softwoods because they tend to burn longer. However, any suitable, well-seasoned species will burn properly in a properly installed wood heating system.

THERMAL INSULATION

The effectiveness of a building assembly such as a wall or ceiling in resisting the flow of heat is measured as its thermal resistance or R-value (RSI value). Although most materials have some resistance to the flow of heat, the materials used for structure, cladding and finish generally have relatively low resistance. Insulation is, therefore, added to reduce the loss of heat from the house. Wood-frame construction is quite easy to insulate since it incorporates many cavities which can be readily filled with relatively inexpensive types of insulation. The cavities or air spaces themselves have appreciable resistance to heat flow, but it is greatly increased by placing insulation in the space.

In the past, due to low energy prices, it was not common to completely fill wall stud spaces with insulation, or to insulate attics to a depth greater than that of the truss bottom chords or ceiling joists. Neither was it common to insulate foundation walls. Now, however, higher energy prices and our increasing realization of the need for energy conservation make it apparent that insulation should at least fill all available cavities within the building shell and that perhaps the shell construction should be altered to accommodate even more insulation. It has also become more apparent that uninsulated foundation walls are a major source of heat loss.

TYPES OF INSULATION

Insulation is manufactured from a variety of materials and in a variety of forms. These forms can be grouped into four basic types.

Batts

Batts consist of fibres of glass or steel mill slag spun together with a binding agent into a blanket-like strip of convenient length and width to fit standard framing spaces and in a range of thicknesses. This type is called "friction fit" because it is made slightly wider than the standard stud space so that it is held in place by friction.

It is often necessary to use insulation batts in cavities which are not as deep as the batts are thick. For example, 6 in. (150 mm) batts might be used in a wall built with 2 x 6 in. (38 x 140 mm) studs. The resulting compression has an insignificant impact on the thermal resistance of the batts.

Loose Fill

Many types of insulation are made in loose form for pouring or blowing into place. Common materials include glass and mineral wool fibre, and cellulose fibre.

Rigid

Rigid insulation is manufactured in sheets or boards using materials such as wood fibre, and expanded or extruded foamed plastic.

Semi-rigid

Semi-rigid insulation boards are relatively flexible compared to rigid insulation products, and are not as easily damaged by impact or bending. Typically, these are formed from glass and mineral wool fibres.

Foamed-in-place

Processes are available for spraying or injecting under pressure materials such as polyurethane and isocyanurate in a foamed liquid state. The foam sets into a rigid mass within minutes of installation. Because this foaming operation is, in effect, the last stage of manufacturing the product, and it occurs at the building site, the installer must be highly skilled and very conscientious to provide a product of uniform quality and consistency. Ensure that the products being installed are approved for use in houses. It is recommended that a qualified contractor perform the installation.

Amount of Insulation

The amount of insulation required for various parts of houses can be found in the 1995 National Energy Code for Houses (NECH). The amount of insulation is related to the severity of the climate as categorized in zones for each province, and the cost of space heating fuel. The zones in each province are established using the degree-day method. Degree-days are calculated for a given location by accumulating the differences between 64°F (18°C) and the mean temperature for every day in the year when the mean temperature is below 64°F (18°C). Degree-day values for a number of locations in Canada are listed in the National Building Code.

It should be recognized that the R-values (RSI values) required in the NECH are minimum effective thermal resistance values. *Effective thermal resistance* values are different than *nominal thermal resistance* values in that the former take into account thermal bridging through framing members, whereas the latter relate to the sum of installed insulation R-values (RSI values). The minimum required effective thermal resistance value in the NECH are indeed minimums. In many cases, it is worth considering higher R-values (RSI values) when building a new house. It is much easier to incorporate extra insulation when building, than to add it afterwards.

All walls, floors and ceilings which separate heated space from unheated space or the outside air should be insulated. Foundation walls separating heated basements or crawl spaces from the outside air or soil should also be insulated to at least 24 in. (600 mm) below grade level on the inside of the basement, or full height on the outside. Methods of insulating these different areas are given in the following sections. The figures illustrate a number of possible methods of insulating building elements. It is not intended to imply that these are the only acceptable methods. Specific materials, thicknesses and spacings are shown in the illustrations in order to correlate these with their effective thermal resistance values. In most cases, the material, thickness or spacing illustrated is only one of a number of equally acceptable alternatives. However, if elements other than those

CHECKING BACK

Foundation and Framing Detailing

The selection of the type and amount of insulation cannot be made without due consideration of appropriate foundation and framing details. Check back to the parts of this publication, mentioned below, to ensure that the required amount of insulation can be accommodated within the structure of the home.

→ Review the Foundations section in *Footings, Foundations and Slabs.*

→ Review the chapters entitled, *Floor Framing, Wall Framing and Ceiling and Roof Framing.*

Concrete wall with rigid insulation on outer face.

base flashing

R-12 (RSI 2.1) batt insulation

vapour barrier

sill plate

1/2" (12 mm) cement parging on wire lath nailed to sill plate and concrete

2" (50 mm) type 4 extruded polystyrene, or type 2 expanded polystyrene, or rigid glass fibre insulation bonded to concrete

granular backfill around insulation to protect against damage due to frost heave

8" (200 mm) concrete wall

Effective Thermal Resistance R-11.2 (RSI 1.97)

118

illustrated here, or listed in tables in the NECH are used, the effective thermal resistance of the assembly must be recalculated according to the method shown in the NECH.

INSULATION OF FOUNDATIONS

Foundation walls enclosing heated space should be insulated full height.

When insulation is applied on the outer surface of a wall or a slab perimeter, it should be of a type not susceptible to water damage, such as expanded or extruded polystyrene or insulation capable of draining water, such as high density, rigid glass fibre insulation. In addition, the insulation should be protected above grade with 1/2 in. (12 mm) cement parging on wire lath applied to the exposed face and edge (Fig. 118).

Where insulation is applied to the inner surface of foundation walls, the below-grade portions of the insulation and any associated wood strapping must be protected by a moisture

Concrete wall insulated with batts — horizontal strapping.

R-20 (RSI 3.5) batt insulation between joists

vapour barrier

119

R-12 (RSI 2.1) batt insulation

vapour barrier

1/2" (12.7 mm) gypsum board

moisture barrier (below grade only)

2" x 4" 38 x 89 mm) strapping at 24" (600 mm) on centre

keep framing members away from the foundation wall by standing off strapping, or using rigid insulation as a spacer

caulking

8" (200 mm) concrete wall

Note: Wall strapping may also be installed vertically as in conventional stud walls. Horizontal strapping allows for easier installation of plumbing and wiring

Effective Thermal Resistance
R-12.0 (RSI 2.11)

barrier in the form of a minimum 2 mil (0.05 mm) polyethylene film or two coats of bitumen applied to the inner surface of the wall to grade height. If the insulation is a type which will not readily absorb water (for example, expanded polystyrene), no damp-proofing is required behind the insulation, but associated wood strapping should be protected by, for instance, partial wrapping in polyethylene. However, in order to allow any moisture which does enter the wall to escape, neither the inner nor the outer surface of the above-grade portion of the wall should be dampproofed (Fig. 119).

Rigid board-type insulation should be bonded to the wall with cement grout or synthetic adhesive applied in bands forming a grid pattern. This pattern of bonding is recommended to limit warm moist air movement behind the insulation since this can cause condensation and ice build-up between the wall and the insulation. If a protein-based adhesive is used to bond the insulation to the wall, the adhesive should contain a preservative.

Due to its high potential for contributing to the rapid spread of fire, any plastic insulation applied to the inside of basement walls must not be exposed, but should be protected with an acceptable finish. Other types of insulation must also be covered to protect them from damage. Where fire protection covering is required, insulation should be held in place by mechanical fastening to framing members at least at the top and bottom of the insulation and around all openings.

Insulation is normally placed between the studs of preserved wood foundations. Preferably, the cavity should be filled to prevent air pockets and the possibility of convection loops being set up within the cavity.

Normal weight concrete, that is, concrete with a density of about 150 lb./cu. ft. (2400 kg/m^3) is normally used in basement construction. Lightweight concrete may be used to achieve higher thermal resistance but should have a 28-day compressive strength of at least 2000 psi (15 MPa).

In the following illustrations, the insulation is shown extending the full height of the basement wall. With hollow core concrete block walls, convection currents may occur if the wall is not insulated over its full height. The bottom edge of the insulation should be sealed by caulking and, in the case of batt-type insulation, by solid blocking.

INSULATION OF FLOORS

Floors over unheated crawl spaces or over heated or unheated garages should be insulated.

Where there is no finished ceiling on the underside of the floor, some material must be added to support the insulation. For friction-fit type batts or for rigid insulation (Fig. 120), wire lath or "chicken wire" tacked to the bottom of the joists may be the most economical method. For loose fill-type insulation (Fig. 121), the support must be provided by a material which is solid (to prevent the insulation from falling through) but permeable (to avoid trapping water vapour which

Floor over unheated crawl space insulated with friction-fit batts.

- 5/8" (15.5 mm) T and G plywood subfloor
- 1/8" (3 mm) floor tile
- R-31 (RSI 5.46) friction fit insulation
- 2" x 8" (38 x 184 mm) joists at 16" (400 mm) on centre
- wire lath (or other suitable material)

120

Note: Joist sizing is for example only

Effective Thermal Resistance R-24.3 (RSI 4.28)

Floor over unheated crawl space insulated with loose-fill insulation.

- carpet
- carpet underlay
- 3/4" (18.5 mm) T and G plywood subfloor
- 2" x 8" (38 x 184 mm) joists at 16" (400 mm) on centre
- R-31 (RSI 5.46) glass fibre loose-fill insulation
- 7/16" (11 mm) insulating fibreboard sheathing

121

Note: Joist sizing is for example only

Effective Thermal resistance R-27 (RSI 4.91)

happens to penetrate the vapour barrier).

The vapour barrier must be installed on the upper or warm side of the insulation. No additional vapour barrier need be installed where a plywood subfloor with tight-fitting or sealed joints is used, because it is generally a good air barrier and a very good vapour barrier.

The insulation must be tightly fitted around cross bridging or blocking between joists. This requires particular care with batt and rigid insulation. It is also important not to omit insulation in small spaces such as between blocked double joists or between a wall and the first joist. In such cases, the insulation should be cut slightly oversize and carefully installed to avoid bunching and excessive compression.

When the insulation is installed only at the bottom of the joist space, the area at the ends of the joist must be carefully considered. The area of the joist header is, in effect, a wall and should be insulated accordingly. Also a well-sealed air barrier must be provided around the perimeter and beneath the insulation to minimize the possibility of cold air leaking into the joist space and "short-circuiting" the insulation.

Insulating a floor over unheated space reduces the heat loss through it, but may not prevent it from feeling cold. Filling the floor cavity with a sprayed-in-place foam type or blown-in-place blanket type insulation is an effective alternative to providing radiant floor heating. The use of carpeting or rugs may also improve the comfort of floors over unheated spaces.

INSULATION OF WALLS

With normal 2 x 4 in. (38 x 89 mm) stud framing, the maximum effective thermal resistance that can be achieved by filling the cavity with batt-type insulation and using normal finishing, sheathing and cladding materials is approximately R-12 (RSI 2.1). By careful selection of the sheathing and cladding, this can be extended to about R-13 (RSI 2.3). This assembly, while suitable for seasonal buildings, does not meet current code requirements. Going beyond this level requires special measures. One such

A 2 x 6 in. (38 x 140 mm) wall.

½" (12.7 mm) gypsum board

polyethylene air/vapour barrier

R-20 (RSI 3.52) insulation batts

2" x 6" (38 x 140 mm) framing at 16" (400 mm) on centre

sheathing membrane

7/16" (11 mm) fibreboard sheathing

1" (19 mm) bevel wood siding

Effective Thermal Resistance R-17.8 (RSI 3.13)

122

approach is to use deeper studs, such as 2 x 6 in. (38 x 140 mm), in order to accommodate thicker batt insulation (Fig. 122). Insulation products with higher thermal resistance values are a simple alternative for enhancing the efficiency of the wall assembly (Fig. 123). Another approach is to use 2 x 4 in. (38 x 89 mm) studs with the cavities filled with batt insulation, and

A 2 x 6 in. (38 x 140 mm) wall with higher efficiency insulation.

1/2" (12.7 mm) gypsum board

vapour barrier

R-22 (RSI 3.87) insulation batts

2" x 6" (38 x 140 mm) framing at 16" (400 mm) on centre

1/2" (12.7 mm) gypsum sheathing

sheathing membrane (air barrier)

4" (100 mm) clay brick

1" (25 mm) air space

Effective Thermal Resistance
R-19.1 (RSI 3.37)

123

A 2 x 4 in. (38 x 89 mm) wall with exterior insulation.

1/2 " (12.7 mm) gypsum board

vapour barrier

R-12 (RSI 2.11) insulation batts

2" x 4" (38 x 89 mm) framing at 16" (400 mm) on centre

1 1/2" (38 mm) expanded polystyrene nailed to studs

sheathing membrane (air barrier)

horizontal metal siding with fibreboard backing nailed through polystyrene to studs

Effective Thermal Resistance
R-16.7 (RSI 2.94)

124

rigid insulation applied to the outside either in place of, or in addition to, the normal sheathing (Fig. 124). This latter method has the merit of providing a significant proportion of the wall's thermal resistance in a form which is continuous over the framing, thus reducing heat loss through the framing members.

Some types of semi-rigid insulation come with a spunbonded polyolefin sheet attached to one surface. This material is vapour permeable but air impermeable, and can constitute a good air barrier if the joints between the sheets are taped. Materials such as spunbonded polyolefin or perforated polyethylene are available in 4 and 9 ft. (1.2 and 2.7 m) rolls, and can be applied to the exterior of any wall assembly to create an effective air barrier.

Other types of insulation, such as rigid plastics, have low water vapour permeance and are also air and water impermeable. If they are placed with the joints butted and caulked, they could also form a good air barrier.

The use of a sheathing membrane on top of the insulating sheathing is required as a rain-shedding device, unless the joints in the sheathing are sealed or designed to shed water.

Loose-fill insulation is not permitted for walls since the cavity must be closed in before the insulation is installed, and this makes it difficult to ensure complete filling of the cavity. In addition, loose fill insulation may settle and create a space at the top of the cavity when disturbed by vibration. However, a number of blown-in blanket systems (BIBS) of insulation are permitted which inject loose-fill insulation in conjunction with a binder, such as latex, to provide a semi-rigid, blanket-like wall insulation.

Except where unavoidable, electrical and mechanical facilities such as boxes, pipes and ducts should not be installed in exterior walls. Where this cannot be avoided, insulation should be fitted tightly around the item in question and between the item and the outside surface in a manner which will minimize compression of the insulation.

Insulation for small spaces at intersections, corners and around openings should be cut only slightly oversize and carefully installed to avoid bunching and excessive compression.

Walls between dwelling units and garages should be insulated to the same degree as exterior walls whether the garage is heated or not, since garages are often left open for extended periods.

INSULATION OF TRUSS OR RAFTER-TYPE ROOF-CEILINGS

The thicker batts now available for insulating roofs are made in widths equal to the full centre-to-centre distance of standard roof framing. The lower portion is slightly compressed when installed between the framing, but the upper portion retains its width and covers the tops of the framing, thus reducing heat loss through the framing.

Eave details to avoid blocking ventilation: *(A)* suggested detail with ordinary truss heel joint; *(B)* alternative design with raised truss heel joint.

A

air ventilation baffle

mesh screen

125

B

baffle

1" (25 mm) minimum

mesh screen

Loose-fill insulation can also be used to cover the framing and, unlike the standardized batts, offers the advantage that only the amount desired need be installed. On the other hand, care must be exercised to ensure it is installed at the correct density or settling may occur. Loose-fill insulation must also be prevented from spilling onto eave vents and from being displaced by wind entering the vents. Baffles such as those shown in Figure 125 must be used to avoid blocking air circulation.

Batt and rigid type insulation should be installed so that it fits tightly against framing members. Care should be taken to ensure that air circulation to and from eave vents is not blocked.

INSULATION OF JOIST-TYPE ROOF-CEILINGS

When the ceiling finish is applied directly to its bottom surface, a roof framing member is called a joist rather than a rafter. This type of construction is found in flat roofs and some "cathedral" or sloping ceilings. When such roofs are insulated between the ceiling and the sheathing, condensation problems can occur because the space between the insulation and the sheathing is divided into small compartments which are difficult to ventilate. Thus, any moisture which

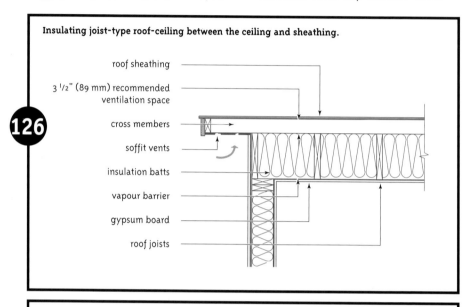

126

Insulating joist-type roof-ceiling between the ceiling and sheathing.

roof sheathing

3 ¹/₂" (89 mm) recommended ventilation space

cross members

soffit vents

insulation batts

vapour barrier

gypsum board

roof joists

127

Alternative method of insulating joist-type roof-ceiling between the ceiling and sheathing. This method can be used where the slope is at least 1:6, the joists run in the same direction as the slope, and the ventilation space is continuous from eave to ridge and is vented in both directions.

holes in web to cross ventilate betwen joists

2 ¹/₂" (63 mm) minimum ventilation space

roof sheathing

wood I-joist

baffle

fascia

soffit vent

insulation

air/vapour barrier

ceiling

Insulation of nominally flat joist-type roof-ceiling above the sheathing.

1 1/2" (40 mm) crushed stone or gravel

built-up roofing membrane

5" (127 mm) type 4 expanded polystyrene insulation

128

vapour barrier (only required for vapour permeable insulation)

3/8" (9.5 mm) plywood sheathing (not used as a walking deck

roof joist

1/2" (12.7 mm) gypsum board ceiling

Effective Thermal Resistance R-26.6 (RSI 4.68)

leaks through imperfections in the air/vapour barrier is not dissipated but accumulates and condenses. Measures to prevent this are shown in Figures 126 and 127.

Another approach to avoid condensation problems in joist-type roof-ceilings is to place the insulation above the sheathing, as is commonly done with flat roofs (Fig. 128).

RELATED PUBLICATIONS

Model National Energy Code of Canada for Houses
National Research Council of Canada

CHBA Builders' Manual
Canadian Home Builders Association

HEALTHY HOUSING INSIGHT

Insulation Selection

There are many insulation products available, and the number is growing as manufacturers seek to provide better performing and easier to install products. Some important factors to consider when selecting insulation products are summarized below.

→ **Occupant Health:** Never use insulation products which may adversely affect the health of the house occupants. This may occur when insulation is left exposed, or particulates enter ductwork.

→ **Energy Efficiency:** The energy efficiency of insulation products may vary significantly on a unit of thickness basis. For example, glass fibre insulation batts for installation in 2 x 6 in. (38 x 140 mm) cavities can vary from R-19 to R-22 (RSI 3.3 to 3.9). Obtain the highest thermal efficiency where possible.

→ **Resource Efficiency:** Where possible, use insulation materials made from industrial by-products or recycled waste. Most glass and mineral fibre products as well as cellulose products meet these criteria. Appropriate selection of insulation materials is an important step toward greater resource efficiency in house construction.

→ **Environmental Responsibility:** Avoid using insulation products which use processes or chemicals that degrade the environment. For example, some foam insulations use blowing agents which cause damage to the ozone layer. Also, some products produce toxic effluents during the manufacturing process. Research insulation products carefully to ensure that your purchasing power is promoting environmental responsibility.

→ **Affordability:** The stability and longevity of insulation products ensures that their stated thermal performance is sustained over the useful life of the house. Using innovative products should be balanced against proven performance, since the heating costs of housing can significantly affect its affordability, particularly for fixed-income households.

Insulation is a passive, energy-conserving element in the house which should be selected with careful consideration.

VAPOUR AND AIR BARRIERS

Many normal activities which take place within a house, such as cooking, dishwashing, laundering and bathing, generate considerable amounts of water vapour which are absorbed by the air in the house, increasing its humidity. If, during cold weather, this water vapour is allowed to pass into the outer shell of the building, the low temperature within the thickness of the shell can cause the water vapour to condense back into liquid or frost. Since wetting of the structure, cladding and insulation is obviously undesirable, some means must be used to contain the water vapour within the dwelling. This is the function of the building component which has traditionally been called the "vapour barrier."

Two mechanisms tend to drive water vapour through the building shell: vapour pressure and air movement.

In the winter, there is more water vapour in the air inside the house than in the outside air. As a result, the difference in vapour pressure tends to force the water vapour to diffuse through the materials making up the shell. Most building materials are, to some degree, permeable to the passage of water vapour, but those classified as vapour barriers (such as polyethylene) have very low permeability and thus are very resistant to this diffusion mechanism.

The second mechanism by which water vapour is forced through the building shell is air movement. There are often differences in air pressure from inside to outside the house created by a stack effect, the operation of fans, or the action of the wind. When the air pressure inside is greater than that outside, air will tend to flow outwards through any holes or cracks in the building envelope, carrying with it the water vapour it contains. It has been recognized that this air movement plays a much greater role in the transmission of water vapour than the diffusion mechanism. The most important aspect of an air barrier is continuity — an air barrier is only as good as it is continuous. Many materials, such as drywall, qualify as an air barrier even though they do not perform as well as a vapour barrier.

Common practice uses polyethylene to perform both functions of an air and vapour barrier. This combination is workable, although it does not overcome the difficulty of creating a continuous air barrier. Certain spots on the envelope, such as headers, openings, services, vent stacks, chimneys, electrical, plumbing and mechanical system penetrations, and unusual framing details, are hard to seal well.

However, once it is well understood that there should not be a direct path from the house interior to the outside through the wall cavity, additional precautions and measures can supplement the function of the material chosen to be the air/vapour barrier. The air barrier must be able to resist wind pressures which occasionally become very strong. Vapour pressure, on the other hand, is not as forceful and can be easily resisted.

PLACEMENT

While the air barrier can be placed at any point on the building envelope, the vapour barrier must be placed on the warm side of the structure. When air and vapour barriers are combined in the same material, the warm side is again the correct location. A slight deviation from this rule is permitted with extra thick walls. In this case, one-third of the total thermal resistance or R-value (RSI value) can be located inside of the air/vapour barrier.

The preferable method is to use polyethylene film. The film is available in large, room-height sheets which can be applied with a minimum of joints, thus reducing the chance of openings through which air can move.

Any joints which do occur should be lapped over two adjacent framing members. The National Building Code requires that when polyethylene is used as an air barrier, or as a vapour barrier where a high resistance to vapour movement is required, such as in wall constructions that incorporate exterior cladding or sheathing having a low water vapour permeance, it must be a minimum thickness of 6 mil (0.15 mm), and comply with applicable material standards (Fig. 129).

It is very important to avoid storing polyethylene in any manner which may lead to sustained exposure to sunlight. Ultraviolet radiation can significantly degrade the integrity of polyethylene, so it should be stored in an opaque container away from direct sunlight and high temperatures.

Two methods of applying an air/vapour barrier.

129

6 mil (0.15 mm) polyethylene

staples

plate

stud

continuous bead of acoustical sealant

A

Staple polyethylene to studs and plate and lap all seams by at least 4" (100 mm)

B

Place a bead of acoustical sealant over top of polyethylene at seam ensuring that the sealant is continuous and in line with the stud and plate

The ceiling air vapour barrier should overlap on the wall air vapour barrier, and both should be continuous on top of and behind intersecting interior partitions. Since interior partitions are usually framed before the insulation and air vapour barrier are installed, this latter condition is usually achieved by covering the top and ends of the interior partitions during construction with strips of air vapour barrier at least 18 in. (450 mm) wide which are subsequently lapped onto the main air vapour barrier. It is often necessary to use the tops of interior partitions as a walking surface when installing roof framing. In such cases, in order to avoid damage to the air vapour barrier strips and to provide better footing, they are installed between the two top plates (Fig. 130). In the case of non-load-bearing partitions, the upper plate can consist of 1 in. (19 mm) lumber since its only function is to protect the air vapour barrier.

The air vapour barrier should overlap and be stapled to door and window framing, and be taped to any wires or pipes which penetrate it. It

must also be continuous behind electrical boxes located in the exterior walls. This can be achieved by wrapping the box with a piece of 6 mil (0.15 mm) polyethylene and taping or caulking, or both, the polyethylene to the wires entering the box. This piece of polyethylene can then be lapped onto the surrounding air vapour barrier when it is installed. The lap should be at least 4 in. (100 mm) and occur over framing members or be sealed. Alternatively, special polyethylene box covers can be used. Ideally, it is best to avoid locating electrical outlets on exterior walls if at all possible.

It is also important to provide vapour barrier protection to insulation installed between the ends of floor joists in the header space. It is usually very difficult to achieve an effective air barrier at this location because the materials must be cut and fitted between the joists (Fig. 131). Extra care is therefore required, especially on the higher floors where air exfiltration is more likely to occur due to stack effect. When the exterior wall has sufficient insulating sheathing, it may

Installation of air vapour barrier strips in interior wall framing.

double top plate

air/vapour barrier

stud

130

be carried over the header; however, it is generally preferable to use an air barrier membrane, such as spun-bonded polyolefin or perforated poly-ethylene, at this location. (*Note: Do not use polyethylene to wrap the header on the exterior.*) If additional insulation is placed on the inside, a vapour barrier will be necessary on the inside face of the insulation to ensure that no moisture-laden air reaches the header and condenses on it.

Caulking should be used around the fitted insulation to seal the joints and prevent exfiltration. For this reason, a rigid or semi-rigid surface is preferred. Rigid board insulation is suitable for this purpose, but also some semi-rigid or soft insulation materials which come with a rein-forced aluminum backing can be used effectively. Extra care in ensuring continuity of the sheathing and sheathing membrane at this point will also help to minimize air leakage.

A potential weak point in the air/vapour barrier is the attic access hatch, which should be carefully weatherstripped.

RELATED PUBLICATIONS

The Details of Air Barrier Systems for Houses
Ontario New Home Warranty Program
CHBA Builders' Manual
Canadian Home Builders Association

Placement of vapour barrier between ends of floor joists.

corner wall joint

air barrier header wrap

wall studs

insulation along joist parallel to exterior wall

bottom wall plate (second floor)

floor joist

insulation between floor joists with vapour barrier

131

Note: Polyethylene should not be used as a header wrap

HEALTHY HOUSING INSIGHT

Airtightness and Building Envelope Integrity

There is no such thing as an airtight building; however, achieving a high degree of airtightness is important to the integrity of the building envelope. The durability of buildings is a key aspect of resource efficient and environmentally responsible healthy housing.

Research has shown that moisture can migrate into the building envelope through two mechanisms, vapour diffusion and air leakage. During the heating season, vapour diffusion is a relatively slow process which involves a high concentration of water molecules, from the air inside a building, diffusing through building materials toward a lower concentration of water molecules outdoors. A vapour barrier is required to adequately control vapour diffusion.

Air leakage from the inside of the building to the outside (exfiltration) will transport the water vapour it contains. Air leakage can transport upwards of 30 times as much moisture as vapour diffusion, depositing water within the building assembly in areas concentrated around air leakage points. This must be avoided since most building materials are highly susceptible to moisture damage. Only a continuous air barrier can prevent airborne moisture migration.

Key Points

➜ The higher the level of airtightness the better. In addition to protecting the building envelope, airtightness promotes energy efficiency, allows for better control of natural and mechanical ventilation, and reduces the transmission of outdoor noise.

➜ Properly located and sealed, polyethylene can serve as an effective air/vapour barrier — keep it on the warm side of the insulation.

➜ An exterior air barrier membrane is also recommended, particularly if the insulation being used in the walls is air permeable. Ensure that the air barrier membrane is also not a vapour barrier.

➜ Airtightness is cumulative — good workmanship in the construction of the entire building envelope is essential to its proper performance. Properly installed air barriers are not a cure-all for poor construction practices.

FIRE AND SOUND CONTROL

When a building is designed for multiple occupancy, as in the case of a duplex or semi-detached housing unit, there is a need for resistance to fire penetration and for sound transmission control between the units.

These construction methods should provide resistance to sound transmission in walls and floors to a degree that meets acceptable requirements.

Resistance to the spread of fire can be provided when the interior cladding and wall assembly meets the necessary fire resistance rating. Various claddings on the market offer ratings by recognized testing agencies.

SMOKE ALARMS

The National Building Code and most local building codes require early-warning, fire-detecting devices in dwellings, usually a self-contained combined smoke detector and an alarm that is wired into the electrical system. The two basic types of smoke alarms are: ionization (or "products-of-combustion") and photoelectric.

Location and Installation

Smoke alarms should be located in or near each bedroom and on each storey including basements. Smoke alarms should be mounted on the ceiling or on a wall between 8 and 12 in. (200 and 300 mm) from the ceiling.

Building codes usually require smoke alarms to be permanently connected (hard-wired) to an electrical circuit. There should be no disconnect switch between the smoke alarm and the electrical service panel, and the circuit should not be connected to a wall outlet.

Where electric power is not available, battery-powered smoke alarms may be used. These units are designed to operate for at least one year, followed by a seven-day trouble signal when the battery runs down.

Only install smoke alarms which are certified as meeting building code requirements. Smoke alarms labeled by a recognized testing agency, such as the Underwriters' Laboratories of Canada, conform to acceptable standards.

RELATED PUBLICATIONS

1995 National Building Code of Canada
National Research Council of Canada

VENTILATION

Ventilation of houses, and for that matter any occupied building, is needed to maintain acceptable indoor air quality (IAQ), and to control indoor moisture levels. IAQ is important for reasons of human health and well being, which may be maintained through the ventilation of contaminants and odours. Failure to control interior moisture levels within the house can also impact human health if conditions which promote the growth of molds and mildew are not prevented. Further, the control of internal moisture levels is important to the integrity of the building envelope. Moisture migrating from the interior of the house to the outdoors may accumulate within the building envelope causing severe damage to the wood-frame structure. Ventilation may also be employed to cool the interior when high humidity levels occur.

Ventilation is provided in buildings through two primary means: natural ventilation, typically through operable windows; and mechanical ventilation, through some kind of mechanical ventilation system which exhausts indoor air or supplies outdoor air to the house, or both. The sections which follow describe these two means and their key requirements under the National Building Code.

NATURAL VENTILATION

Natural ventilation through operable windows is intended for the non-heating season, when the air entering the house is at a comfortable temperature. During the heating season, the National Building Code assumes that occupants will be discouraged from opening windows which will admit cold drafts and lose heating energy, hence a controlled mechanical ventilation system is required. In some cases, windows opened during extreme cold weather lose energy and may not close properly due to ice build-up, and at such times, only a suitable mechanical ventilation system will provide the required ventilation properly.

The minimum unobstructed area of ventilation openings specified in the National Building Code applies to rooms which are not mechanically ventilated. This means that in situations where air is exhausted from, or supplied to, a room by mechanical means, no operable windows are required. In practice, however, occupants normally expect operable windows in most rooms, and in some cases, operable windows are required as a means of egress in case of fire.

By carefully planning the type, location and orientation of operable windows, it is possible to provide highly effective natural ventilation and cooling. Windows which open into prevailing summer winds can serve as scoops which capture and direct the breezes through the house. Providing both low and high openings can promote natural ventilation during calm periods.

MECHANICAL VENTILATION

The National Building Code requires the installation of a mechanical ventilation system with a prescribed capacity, which is capable of operating on a continuous basis, in all houses intended for year-round occupancy. It is not necessarily intended that house occupants operate the system at the peak capacity on a continuous basis. In households with frequent moisture-generating activities such as cooking, bathing and floor washing, continuous mechanical ventilation at a low speed may be required to control indoor humidity. There may be occasions when operating the mechanical ventilation system at its peak capacity, on a continuous basis, is needed to control contaminants arising from activities such as painting or social events. In households with sedentary occupants, or when the house is not occupied for extended periods of time, intermittent operation of the mechanical ventilation system may be all that is required to maintain acceptable indoor air quality. Within this context, mechanical ventilation systems should be viewed as appliances intended for reasons of occupant health and comfort, as well as the integrity of the building envelope. Ideally, these systems should comfortably accommodate the full range of normal household activities without over or under-ventilating the home.

Mechanical Ventilation System Options

There are essentially two mechanical ventilation system options for housing. The first option consists of a number of alternatives which are prescribed in the National Building Code. The second option involves competent mechanical design and installation in accordance with the requirements of *CAN/CSA-F326, Residential Mechanical Ventilation Systems*. The discussion which follows focuses on the prescribed alternatives noted in the National Building Code. Further information may be obtained from the reference publications listed at the end of this chapter.

Stand-alone ventilation systems, also referred to as ventilation systems not coupled to a forced-air heating system, consist of fans, ducts, grilles and controls which exhaust air from selected rooms in the house, and supply air to rooms which are not being exhausted. These systems have the advantage of being designed especially for ventilation only, independent of the need to deliver heating or cooling. Tempering incoming outdoor air is required to maintain a comfortable air supply temperature. Stand-alone ventilation systems are typically installed in houses with heating systems which do not rely on forced-air distribution of heat.

Ventilation systems coupled to a forced-air heating system are similar to stand-alone ventilation systems, but share ductwork with the heating system for the supply of fresh air to heated rooms. It is necessary to interlock ventilation system and heating system controls, so that the furnace

CHECKING BACK

Accommodating Ductwork During Framing

When planning the installation of the ventilation system, it is important to provide passageways, or chases, for ducts. Otherwise, these may have to be concealed with dropped ceilings or bulkheads in finished areas of the house. Refer to the *Planning Ahead* note in the *Floor Framing* chapter for helpful planning tips.

fan mixes and circulates the outdoor air which is delivered to the distribution ductwork. Coupled ventilation systems are generally less expensive to install since much of the ductwork is already provided by the forced-air heating system. Operating costs may be higher depending on the efficiency of the furnace circulating fan.

Heat Recovery Ventilators

Heat recovery ventilators (HRVs) are a packaged type of ventilation system which is engineered to recover heat from the air being exhausted from the house, and transfer this heat to the incoming outdoor air. Numerous studies have concluded that in the long term, HRVs are a cost-effective alternative, whose energy savings more than offset their higher initial capital costs. They also have the advantage of tempering the incoming air such that the need for auxiliary heating is avoided.

Canadian heat recovery ventilator technology is growing in affordability, effectiveness and sophistication. At present, there are two types of heat recovery ventilators manufactured in Canada: plate heat exchanger types, and heat wheel exchanger types.

Plate heat exchangers function using either a parallel flow or counter flow (Fig. 132A) of air streams through a plastic or metal core of plates. Outside air and indoor streams flow through alternate, adjacent plates. During the exchange of heat between adjacent plates, moisture from inside air condenses out and is drained to the plumbing system. As a result of this phenomenon, when plate heat exchangers are used, humidification of the house is often required to maintain suitable indoor relative humidity levels.

Heat wheel exchanger types use a heat wheel made from a desiccant material (Fig. 132B). Inside air passing through the heat wheel deposits the moisture it contains within the desiccant material, and as the wheel rotates into the outside air stream, the moisture and heat are released into the air supply. Humidification of the house air is usually not required with these HRVs, nor do they require a condensate drain.

Both types of HRV may be installed as a stand-alone ventilation system or as a ventilation system coupled to a forced-air heating system. Properly installed, HRVs deliver a balanced flow of supply and exhaust air, neither pressurizing nor depressurizing the house. This makes them ideally suited for installation in homes with spillage-susceptible combustion appliances such as fireplaces and woodstoves. As well, some types of HRVs can operate in a recirculation mode to distribute heat from

woodburning appliances throughout the house.

Mechanical Ventilation System Operation and Maintenance

Some of the most important aspects of mechanical ventilation systems are their operation and maintenance. To be effective, mechanical ventilation

Common types of heat recovery ventilators: (A) plate heat exchanger; (B) heat wheel

A

exhaust to outside

exhaust fan

plate heat exchanger

fresh air to house

stale air from house

condensate drain

supply fan

air supply from outside

B

exhaust to outside

exhaust fan

heat wheel

stale air from house

fresh air to house

supply fan

air supply from outside

132

systems must not only be properly designed and installed, but appropriately operated by the occupants.

Maintenance of the mechanical ventilation system typically includes cleaning screens and filters, as well as maintenance of the equipment according to manufacturer's instructions. Accessibility to the equipment is important.

Consult with the heating contractor prior to finalizing the house design so that the mechanical ventilation system may be properly integrated within the house, and the work coordinated accordingly.

RELATED PUBLICATIONS

Complying with Residential Ventilation Requirements in the 1995 National Building Code
Canada Mortgage and Housing Corporation

HEALTHY HOUSING INSIGHT

Ventilation, Moisture Control and Indoor Air Quality

The relationship between ventilation, moisture control and indoor air quality is important to understand when designing and building a home.

Ventilation

➤ Ventilation is needed as much in leaky houses as it is in tightly constructed houses, because the wind, the indoor-to-outdoor temperature difference, and the location and distribution of leaks cannot always be fully controlled.

➤ Ventilation may be provided naturally or mechanically, however, it should be recognized that natural ventilation cannot be controlled effectively at all times. Mechanical ventilation which exhausts air from kitchens, bathrooms and other moisture generating rooms, and supplies outside air to the other habitable rooms, is most effective in controlling indoor moisture levels.

Moisture Control

➤ Moisture control is essential in any home, but especially in those which are built in cold climates, such as in Canada. If moisture levels are too high in the home and air/vapour barriers are inadequate, it is possible for the moisture to migrate into the building assemblies. This may result

Continued on page 222

Continued from page 221

in condensation within insulated assemblies, and the accumulation of moisture which may damage the structure and components of the home. Condensation on windows may also result, leading to the deterioration of window and sill finishes.

➜ High moisture levels in the home may also promote the growth of molds and mildew. Many of these have been found harmful to human health, in addition to permanently staining finishes.

Indoor Air Quality

➜ Indoor air quality is best controlled by eliminating sources of contamination — select appropriate building materials and carefully consider products and lifestyle in the home.

➜ Operating mechanical ventilation sensibly to control moisture and odours is all that is normally required to maintain acceptable indoor air quality in a home where sources of contaminants have been eliminated or reasonably minimized.

INTERIOR WALL AND CEILING FINISHES

Interior finish describes any material used to cover the interior wall and ceiling framing. The principal type of interior finish is gypsum board, although plywood, hardboard, simulated veneer hardboard, and lumber can also be used.

GYPSUM BOARD FINISH

Gypsum board (commonly referred to as "drywall") is the most widely used interior finish because of its speed of installation, low cost and consistent result. In addition, gypsum board is manufactured in a variety of types for different uses, such as fire rated, foil backed, water resistant and prefinished. Various fasteners and glues, finishing accessories and walls systems or wall furring are also available. Thin sheet materials such as gypsum board require that studs and ceiling joists be well aligned. This is normally achieved by the use of good lumber, its proper placement (for example, crowns up for joists), and the use of additional bracing and blocking.

Gypsum board is a sheet material composed of a gypsum filler between two layers of paper. Sheets are 4 ft. (1.22 m) wide and are supplied in various lengths, 8 ft. (2.44 m) and longer. The edges along the length of the sheet are tapered on one face to receive joint compound and tape. Although gypsum board on walls may be used in 3/8 in. (9.5 mm) thickness on support spacings up to 16 in. (400 mm) on centre, a 1/2 in. (12.7 mm) board is more commonly used for its extra strength. Where supports are spaced at 24 in. (600 mm) on centre, the minimum thickness should be 1/2 in. (12.7 mm).

Gypsum wallboard is usually applied in single sheets directly on the framing members. On ceilings, the board is generally applied with the long dimension at right angles to the trusses or joists. Ceilings can also be strapped with 1 x 4 in. (19 x 89 mm) lumber, and in this case, the long dimension would run parallel to the trusses or joists. On walls, it is more common to apply the sheets horizontally rather than vertically because it reduces the amount of nailing and the length of joints. Horizontal joints at 4 ft. (1.2 m) above the floor are below eye level, making them less conspicuous. Horizontal joints are also easier to tape than vertical joints, as they are continuous and at a convenient height. Ends of sheets, which are not recessed, should terminate at a corner and always on a support. This method provides a secure attachment and reduces nail-popping.

Gypsum board panels are applied and attached with a minimum number of supplementary fasteners. Gypsum board can be attached to wood members by single nailing, double nailing, glue and nailing, or screwing. In the glue and nail-on application, a continuous bead of adhesive is applied to the face of the wood framing.

Nails used to fasten gypsum board should be ringed, with 3/32 in. (2.3 mm) shanks and 7/32 in. (5.5 mm) diameter heads. The nails should be long enough to penetrate 3/4 in. (20 mm) into the support. Where higher than normal fire-resistant ceilings are required, special gypsum board and greater penetration of fasteners may be necessary. By using special hammers, the nail heads can be set slightly below the surface without damaging the paper. A slight dimple is thus formed in the face of the board (Fig. 133A). The nails at the recessed edge of the sheet may be driven with the heads flush since they will be covered with tape and joint cement.

Gypsum board may be "double-nailed," that is, nails are driven in pairs about 2 in. (50 mm) apart at intervals of 12 in. (300 mm) along the supports (Fig. 134B) or the nails may be driven in a single pattern, spaced 4-3/4 in. to 7 in. (120 to 180 mm) along the supports on ceilings and 6 to 8 in. (150 to 200 mm) on the walls (Fig. 134A). The double-nailing method is more commonly used, because nail-popping is less likely to occur.

With special power-operated screwdrivers, screws can be used to

Finishing of gypsum board: **(A)** nail set with crowned hammer; **(B)** cementing and taping of joint; **(C)** taping at inside corners.

A

C

133

sharp fold

B

stud

gypsum board

recessed edge

joint cement

tape

joint cement

feather edge

fasten gypsum board. Screws are usually spaced 12 in. (300 mm) on centre at both the edge and intermediate supports. The distance can be increased to 16 in. (400 mm) on walls when the supports are not more than 16 in. (400 mm) on centre. The screws should be long enough to penetrate the support at least 5/8 in. (15 mm).

If two layers of gypsum board are needed, such as for sound control or additional fire rating, the boards can

Application of drywall finish: **(A)** vertical application of gypsum board showing single nailing method; **(B)** horizontal application of gypsum board showing double nailing method. Where the ceiling sheets are supported by the wall sheets around the perimeter of the ceiling, the nails along the upper edge of the gypsum board may be omitted, with the uppermost nails being not more than 8 in. (200 mm) below the ceiling. Fastening of the ceiling boards should begin approximately 8 in. (200 mm) from the wall face to allow for differential movement.

A

moderate contact

134

space 6" to 8" (150 – 200 mm) on centre

recessed edge

stud

B

Double nailing pattern nail 2" (50 mm) apart

12" (300 mm) intervals

nail or screw to stud

recessed edge

stud

be fastened in the usual manner with nails or screws, however, the penetration of fasteners for the second layer must be the same as that for the first layer.

Before the joints are taped, all loose paper must be removed and the joints cleaned. All joints wider than 1/8 in. (3 mm) are then filled with joint cement and allowed to dry. External corners are protected with corrosion-resistant corner beads or wood mouldings, and at interior corners the tape is folded as shown in Figure 133C.

Joint compound is supplied premixed or in powder form which is mixed with water to a soft putty consistency. Joint compound may be applied with hand tools, but mechanical applicators are now commonly used for both taping and filling.

The first layer of joint compound is applied in a band 5 in. (125 mm) wide along the joint. The tape is then applied and pressed into the fresh cement with trowel or wide-blade putty knife. Care should be taken to remove the excess cement, smooth the tape, and feather the compound band to zero thickness at its outer edges (Fig. 133B).

After the first layer has set, a second layer is applied in a band 8 in. (200 mm) wide on recessed joints and 10 in. (250 mm) wide where the edges of the board are not recessed. Once again, the edges are feathered.

A third layer is applied and feathered to a band 10 to 12 in. (250 to 300 mm) wide on recessed joints and 16 in. (400 mm) on joints that are not recessed. Special care should be taken with this final layer so that the joint surface is smooth, and does not form a noticeable bulge in the wall. When the third layer has set, the feathered edges should be sanded lightly with fine sand paper, care being taken to avoid damaging the paper surface of the gypsum board.

Nail heads and indentations in the centre of the board are filled with two layers of joint compound. Taping and finishing of gypsum board should be done at a temperature of 10°C or more.

OTHER FINISHES

Other products used for finishing walls and ceilings are plywood, hardboard, simulated veneer hardboard and lumber.

Plywood is usually installed vertically in panels or in strips. The minimum thickness should be 3/16 in. (4.7 mm) for supports at 16 in. (400 mm) centres and 5/16 in. (8 mm) for 24 in. (600 mm) centres. Where blocking is provided at mid-height in the walls, however, 3/16 in. (4.7 mm) thickness is used at 24 in. (600 mm) centres or less. Panels or strips are nailed on all edges with 1 1/2 in. (38 mm) finishing nails, spaced 6 in. (150 mm) along the edges and 12 in. (300 mm) at intermediate supports. Panels are available unfinished or with a factory-applied finish. For a paneled effect, plywood may be installed in strips, with a 3/4 in. (20 mm) space between strips, and supported on a backing course nailed to the framing members.

Hardboard finish is supplied in panels, and is usually installed vertically. Thin sheets 1/8 in. (3.2 mm) thick need continuous backing. Sheets may be nailed directly to the studs, provided 1/4 in. (6 mm) thick sheets are used for supports up to 16 in. (400 mm) centres and 3/8 in. (9 mm) sheets on supports up to 24 in. (600 mm) centres. Hardboard should be supported on all edges and nailed as recommended for plywood. Both finished and unfinished panels are available.

Hardboard is also supplied in tile form and used principally on ceilings. Tile size may vary from about 12 in. (300 mm) square to 16 x 32 in. (400 x 800 mm). The tile is tongue-and-grooved and is supported by concealed nails, clips or staples. It should be 1/2 in. (12.7 mm) thick when supported not more than 16 in. (400 mm) on centres.

Lumber is sometimes used as a decorative finish to walls and ceilings. Lumber is supplied in tongue-and-grooved boards about 4 to 8 in. (100 to 200 mm) wide and 5/8 to 3/4 in. (15 to 20 mm) thick. Softwood species include cedar, pine or hemlock; hardwoods include maple, birch or cherry. Some of these species are used in plywood form as well.

RELATED PUBLICATIONS

Avoiding Drywall Problems
Canada Mortgage and Housing Corporation

HEALTHY HOUSING INSIGHT

Wall and Ceiling Finish Selection

With the many choices of wall and ceiling finishes available, it is important to consider the implications for occupant health and environment of material and finish choices. As well, the long-term upkeep and adaptability of the building should also be considered. Walls and ceilings which are difficult to clean and maintain, and which do not wear well, translate into an ongoing burden for house occupants. Finishes which cannot be easily changed by painting, wallpapering or paneling may encourage replacement long before their useful service life is over. Some criteria to be considered when selecting wall and ceiling finishes are summarized below.

Appropriate Choices

➜ The use of local materials should be encouraged where possible. These stimulate the local economy and reduce the environmental impacts associated with long-distance transportation.

➜ Synthetic materials made from non-renewable materials, and materials which are not reusable or recyclable should be avoided. These materials eventually end up in landfills as waste.

Continued on page 228

Continued from page 227

➜ Select materials based on their durability and ease of maintenance. Experience has shown that finishes such as solid wood paneling and ceramic tile deliver long service. Plaster and drywall are easy to maintain, repair and refinish. Wall paper which is not recyclable should be avoided.

➜ Certain interior finishes for walls and ceilings must be attached using adhesives. Others may require special coating-type finishes. Check that these adhesives and coatings are non-toxic, and that they do not continue to off-gas for long periods of time. Fumes and vapours from such materials are known to cause discomfort, and in some cases, health problems.

There is no ideal interior finish for walls and ceilings; however, there is strong evidence of inappropriate finishes accumulating in landfill sites across the country. It should be recognized that the interior skin of the house will be exposed to wear and tear, require cleaning, and even renewal from time to time. This process should not strain the environment or the occupants, rather, it should be a natural extension of a healthy house.

FLOOR COVERINGS

Any material used as the final wearing surface on a floor is called finish flooring. There are many such materials on the market, each with specific advantages for a particular use. Two essential properties of any kind of finish flooring are durability and ease of cleaning.

Hardwoods such as birch, maple, beech and oak are used in a variety of widths and thicknesses as strip flooring. Some species are also available in parquet form. Vertical grain strips of soft woods such as fir or hemlock are sometimes used. Wood finish flooring is widely used in living and dining rooms, bedrooms, corridors and general purpose rooms such as family rooms and dens.

Other materials suitable for finish flooring include resilient flooring (in tile or sheet form) and ceramic tile. These materials are water resistant and are used in bathrooms, kitchens, public entrance halls and general storage areas. Carpets, of course, may also be used as a finish flooring except where water resistance is required.

WOOD STRIP FLOORING

Wood strip flooring is manufactured in various widths and thicknesses and is available in several grades. The strips come in random lengths in separate bundles. The thickness of wood-strip flooring required for various support conditions is shown in Table 38.

To link the wood strips together, one edge of each strip has a tongue and the other a groove. Wood flooring is generally hollow-backed, and the top face is slightly wider than the bottom so that when the strips are driven together the upper edges touch, but the lower edges are slightly apart. The tongue must fit snugly, because a loose fit may cause the floor to squeak.

The flooring should not be laid until gypsum board taping and other interior wall and ceiling finishes are completed. All windows and exterior doors should also be in place. This precaution prevents damage to the wood flooring either through wetting or other construction activities.

Strip flooring looks better when laid lengthwise in a rectangular room. When lumber subflooring is used, it is usually laid diagonally under wood strip flooring so that the strips can be laid either parallel or at right angles to the joists. Where it is necessary to place the wood strips parallel to the lumber subflooring, an underlay (described in a following section, *Underlay for Resilient Flooring*) should be used to provide a level base for the narrow strips.

Hardwood flooring should not be brought into the house until the basement floor slab has been placed and gypsum board taping is completed. Moisture given off during these operations can be absorbed by the flooring and make the wood swell; then, after being put into place, the wood strips will shrink and open the joints. The flooring should be stored in the warmest and driest place available in the house until it is installed.

Various types of nails, including annular and spiral-grooved types, are used for nailing the flooring. Minimum nail lengths and nail spacing are listed in Table 39. Various types of staples applied with manual and pneumatic tools are also available.

To nail the wood strips in place, many workers use a mallet-driven nailing tool which drives the nail in the proper location, at the correct angle, and sets the head to the proper depth. Others drive the nails using a carpenter's hammer.

Figure 135B shows the method of nailing the first strip of flooring with the nail driven down through the board at the grooved edge. The nails should be driven into the subfloor or joist and near enough to the edge so that the base or shoe moulding will cover the nail heads. The first strip of flooring should also be nailed through the tongue.

Succeeding strips of flooring can be fastened (using a carpenters' hammer) by driving nails into each strip at a 45° angle at the spot where the tongue adjoins the shoulder (Fig. 135C). Nails should not be driven home with the hammer as the wood may be struck and easily damaged (Fig. 135D). Instead, to finish the driving, nail set positioned as shown in Figure 135D is used. To avoid splitting, it is sometimes necessary to pre-drill the nail holes through the tongue. For all courses of flooring after the first, the pieces should be selected by length so that the butt joints are well separated from those in the previous course (Fig. 135A). By using a piece of scrap flooring as a driving block, each board can

be driven up tightly against the previous course with no danger of damaging the wood with the hammer.

WOOD TILE FLOORING

Flooring manufacturers have developed a wide variety of special patterns of flooring which are sometimes called floor tile and sometimes referred to as parquet flooring. One type is a block available in various thicknesses and made up of several individual strips of flooring, with two edges tongued and the opposing edges grooved. In laying, the direction of the strips is alternated to create a checkerboard effect. Manufacturers provide specific directions for laying their own type of tile. These directions should be followed carefully.

UNDERLAY FOR RESILIENT FLOORING

When the subfloor is not constructed as a combination subfloor and underlay type as described in the chapter on *Floor Framing*, an underlay should be installed under resilient flooring or carpets.

Plywood panels 1/4 in. (6 mm) thick are commonly used, although particleboard in the same thickness is also used. Ensure that the particleboard is approved for use with the finished flooring material by checking the manufacturer's installation instructions. The panels are attached to the subfloor with annular grooved nails spaced 6 in. (150 mm) apart along the edges and at 8 in. (200 mm) on centre both ways over the rest

Application of strip flooring: *(A)* general application; *(B)* laying first strip; *(C)* nailing method; *(D)* suggested method for setting nails.

A

— stagger butt joints

— subfloor

135

— joist

B

— shoe mould

— base

— wall finish

— plate

— 1/4" (6 mm) space

— when face nailed and set, shoe mould will cover nail

C

— finish floor

45°

D

— damage resulting from hammer setting

— finish floor

— nail set

of the panel. Nails should be at least 3/4 in. (19 mm long) for 1/4 in. (6 mm) panels and 7/8 in. (22 mm) long for 5/16 in. (7.9 mm) panels. Staples or screws may also be used. (See Table 38.)

Joints between panels and any defects in their surface should be filled with non-shrinking filler compound that will bond to the underlay. The filler should be sanded smooth after it has set.

Installation of Resilient Floor Covering

Resilient flooring is usually installed after other trades have finished their work. The more common types of resilient floor covering used are vinyl and rubber. Both types are available in tile and sheet form.

Resilient flooring is usually cemented to the underlay with a special adhesive. Waterproof adhesives are preferable to the non-waterproof types, especially in kitchens, bathrooms, entranceways and laundry rooms. Both tile and sheet material should be installed according to the manufacturer's recommendations. Immediately after the flooring is laid, it should be rolled in both directions, the surface cleaned and then, if necessary, sealed with the type of floor wax recommended for the material used.

Resilient flooring applied over concrete slabs must be a type recommended by the manufacturer for this use. A waterproof adhesive should be used for this application.

Seamless Resin Constituent Resilient Flooring

Resilient flooring can also be applied as a fluid, containing plastic chips or other decorative particles and fillers, that forms a resilient seamless wearing surface. Such flooring must be quality controlled as to components, application conditions and finished thickness in conformity with the manufacturer's specifications and procedures.

CARPETING

Carpeting is normally used in living rooms, bedrooms, family rooms and occasionally dining rooms. In rooms such as kitchens, laundry rooms or other areas where water damage or staining is likely to occur, carpeting should be avoided. When carpet is desired in such areas, a synthetic-fibre type should be used. For hygienic reasons, carpet is not recommended for use in rooms containing a toilet.

Carpeting should be installed over a panel-type subfloor or an underlay. Except for cushion-backed carpeting, felt or polymeric carpet underlay should be used.

CERAMIC TILE

Ceramic tile is available in different colours either with a glazed or unglazed surface. Since this tile has a hard impervious surface, it is often used as a floor covering in bathrooms and vestibules as well as for fireplace hearths.

Ceramic tile may be installed on a concrete subfloor, applied to a mortar base supported on the subfloor, or attached by a special adhesive to panel-type underlay such as plywood or hardboard.

When a mortar base is used, an asphalt-impregnated paper is placed over the subfloor to prevent moisture swelling of the subfloor. The base should be at least 1 1/4 in. (30 mm) thick and reinforced with wire mesh. The mortar may consist of 1 part Portland cement, 1/4 part lime and 3 to 5 parts coarse sand. The tiles are pressed into the fresh mortar. To ensure a good bond between the joint material and base, the joints between the tiles should be filled the same day the tile is installed. To provide sufficient depth for the mortar bed, it is often desirable to drop the wood subfloor between the joists so that the finish floor will be level with floors in adjoining rooms (Fig. 136). Where the tops of the joists have to be cut out for this purpose, the span of the joists should be calculated on the basis of the reduced depth.

When an adhesive is used to fasten the tiles to an underlay or concrete floor, the base must be smooth and free from surface irregularities. The adhesive is applied to both the tile and the base, and each tile is then pressed firmly in place.

After the adhesive is well set, the joints between the tiles are filled with the material recommended by the tile manufacturer for this purpose.

Ceramic tiles in shower bases may be laid on a plastic liner which is connected to the shower drain. This will prevent water damage to the ceiling below should the tile and its concrete base develop a crack.

Installation of ceramic tile floor.

ceramic tile
mortar setting bed
concrete
sheathing paper
ledger strips (cleats)
subfloor
floor joists

136

ceramic tile
mortar setting bed
subfloor
floor joists

HEALTHY HOUSING INSIGHT

Floor Covering Selection

The selection of finish flooring materials, adhesives and finishes has many implications for healthy housing in terms of occupant health and resource efficiency. Toxic substances should be avoided as well as materials or products which are non-renewable, non-reusable or non-recyclable. Products which are obtained from fragile ecosystems or produced using methods that are not environmentally responsible should not be selected. A large number of appropriate finish flooring options are still available after these Healthy Housing criteria are applied.

Appropriate Covering Choices

→ Stone and ceramic tile represent traditional floor coverings which are durable, easy to clean and maintain, and non-toxic provided appropriate adhesives and grouts are used.

→ Hardwood strip flooring is a product with proven performance. Hardwood trees can be found that have been sustainably harvested and processed. An appropriate finish must be selected to promote acceptable indoor air quality. Laminated (composite wood) flooring and cork tiles are suitable alternatives to hardwood strip flooring.

→ Natural or "battleship" linoleum is a highly durable floor finish made from completely renewable ingredients. Available in a wide variety of colours, it is regaining popularity over synthetic sheet and roll flooring.

→ Synthetic carpeting should be avoided since it is made from non-renewable materials and cannot be recycled. Appropriate alternatives include wool carpeting and area rugs, sisal and coir stair and hallway runners, and cotton area rugs.

Adhesives and Finishes

Many solvent-based adhesives and finishes contain toxic substances such as volatile organic compounds (VOCs). Their use may be avoided by selecting more appropriate types of products.

→ Use water-based adhesives and finishes wherever possible, since these contain fewer toxins than similar solvent-based products.

→ Look for the EcoLogo™ on products, indicating a reduced level of toxic contaminants.

INTERIOR DOORS, FRAMES AND TRIM

Interior doors, door frames and interior trim are usually installed after hardwood flooring is in place, but before it is sanded and before the resilient flooring is laid. Kitchen cabinets and other millwork are also usually installed at this stage. The decorative treatment for interior doors and trim may be paint or natural finish using stain, filler and varnish, or other selected materials. The finish selected for woodwork in various rooms may determine the type or species of wood to be used.

Wood trim should be smooth, clean, sound stock suitable for finishing. Some of the commonly used species are oak, pine, fir, basswood and poplar. The moisture content of the wood trim at the time of installation should not be more than 12 percent.

Door frames are made up of two jambs and a head, together with separate mouldings called doorstops. Stock jambs are made of 3/4 in. (19 mm) lumber and in widths to suit the thickness of the finished wall. Jambs are often dadoed at the mill, with doorstops and head cut to size (Fig. 137). Frames may also be rabbeted to form the stop, in which case the thickness of the frame is usually increased to 1 1/4 in. (32 mm). If frames are unassembled when delivered, they should be securely nailed together at each corner.

Casing is the framing or edging trim used around door openings. Many standard patterns in various widths and thicknesses are obtainable. Those with moulded forms usually require mitre joints.

There are two general types of interior doors: flush and panel. The standard thickness of interior doors is

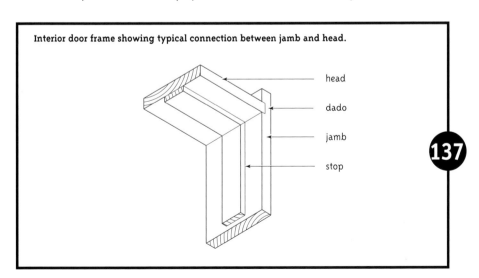

Interior door frame showing typical connection between jamb and head.

head

dado

jamb

137

stop

1 3/8 in. (35 mm). They may be obtained in various widths and heights.

The flush door is made up of facings of plywood or other sheet material glued to a light framework. For a natural or varnished finish, the face plies are selected for quality and colour. For a painted finish, the face plies may be less expensive or non-select grades.

The panel door consists of solid stiles and rails with panel fillers of various materials. These create relief panels in the door and are available in a number of styles.

Special doors are also obtainable with various kinds of closing hardware. Sliding doors and folding doors are popular for clothes closets.

Doors should be hinged so that they open in the direction of natural entry. Doors should also swing against a blank wall wherever possible and not be obstructed by other swinging doors.

Interior doors are usually 30 in. (760 mm) wide and 6 ft. 8 in. (1.98 m) high. These sizes will generally allow easy passage of furniture. The National Building Code prescribes minimum sizes for interior doors.

Setting the interior door frame is done by means of shims that are used between the jamb and rough-opening studs (Fig. 138). Wood shingles may be used for this purpose. Frames are set plumb and square, wedges are fitted snugly, and the jambs are then securely nailed to the studs through

Door frame and trim showing frame blind-nailed under doorstep.

138

framing studs

wall finish

shingle wedge

nails (under door stop)

jamb

stop

door thickness

casing

3/16" - 1/4" (5 - 6 mm)

the wedges. After nailing, the wedges are sawed flush with the face of the wall. Nails should be driven in pairs as shown in Figure 138.

Casings are nailed to both the framing studs and the jambs with finish nails. Nails should be spaced about 16 in. (400 mm) apart and the heads countersunk and filled with wood putty. The casing is placed 3/16 to 1/4 in. (5 to 6 mm) from the inner edge of the jamb.

Stops are usually 3/8 x 1 1/4 in. (10 x 32 mm) and are nailed to the jamb with finishing nails after the door is hung.

Casing joints at the head of the frame are usually mitred. Careful cutting and fitting is required to ensure a tight joint. Mitred joints are sometimes glued because a glued joint is less likely to open if slight shrinkage occurs.

Standard clearances and the location of door hardware are shown in Figure 139. The clearances may vary slightly, but those shown are most commonly used. Hinges are shown as 7 in. (175 mm) from the top and 11 in. (275 mm) from the bottom, but these distances may also vary slightly, especially in panel doors. Where three hinges are used, the centre one is spaced midway between the top and

Suggested door clearance and location of hardware.

1/16" (2 mm)

7" (175 mm)

hinge

1/16" (2 mm)

knob

1/32" (1 mm)

36" (900 mm)

hinge

11" (275 mm)

3/4" (19 mm)

139

bottom hinges. Standard knob height is 34 to 38 in. (860 to 960 mm) from the floor, and locks or latches should be installed accordingly. Lever-type handles permit easy operation by persons with limited impairments.

Clearance around the door should be 1/16 to 3/32 in. (2 to 3 mm) on the latch side, and 1/32 in. (1 mm) on the hinge side. A clearance of 1/16 in. (2 mm) at the top and 3/4 in. (19 mm) at the bottom is usual, but if the door is to open over heavy carpeting, the bottom clearance should be greater to permit air movement either into or out of the room.

Some manufacturers supply pre-fitted frames and doors, with the hinge slots already grooved for installation. Also on the market are sheet-metal door frames with formed strips and casings. Hinge slots and strike plates are integral to these units.

INSTALLATION OF DOOR HARDWARE

Hinges should be of the proper size for the door they support. For 1 3/8 in. (35 mm) thick interior doors, two 3 x 3 in. (76 x 76 mm) butt hinges are used. The door is first fitted to the jamb opening to ensure it has the proper clearances, then the door is removed, and the hinges are fitted to it. The door edge is mortised to take the two half hinges. The edge of each hinge should be at least 1/8 in. (3 mm) back from the face of the door. When the hinge halves are screwed in place, they must be flush with the surface and square.

The door is now placed in the opening and blocked up at the bottom to provide the proper clearance. The jamb is marked at the hinge locations and mortised to take the other two hinge halves which are then fastened in place. The door may now be placed in the opening, and the hinge pins inserted.

There are several types of door locks which vary both in cost and in method of installation. Lock sets are supplied with installation instructions that should be followed. Passage locks may be used where privacy is a concern, such as in bathrooms.

The location of the latch is marked on the jamb, and the strike plate located in this way. The marked outline is mortised to take the strike plate. The recess for the latch is also mortised (Fig. 140A). The strike plate is then fixed in place and should be flush with or slightly below the face of the jamb. When the door is latched, the face of the door should be flush with the edge of the jamb.

Doorstops may have been set temporarily during the installation of the hardware, but now is the time to nail them permanently in place. The stop at the jamb on the latch side is nailed first (Fig. 140B) and should be set against the door face when the door is latched. Allow space for movement and paint finishes. The stop on the hinge side is nailed next and should be given a 1/32 in. (1 mm) clearance from the door face to prevent scraping when opening the door. Finally, the head stop is nailed in place. Finishing nails should be used and heads countersunk and filled. When door and trim are painted, some of the clearances allowed will be taken up.

Installation of: (*A*) typical strike plate; (*B*) stops.

A

stop

wall finish

casing

strike plate

140

B

casing

jamb

stop

slight bevel

door

hinge

$^1/_{32}$" (1 mm)

WINDOW TRIM INSTALLATION

Casing for window trim is usually the same pattern selected for the doors. Finishing nails are applied to casing on all four sides of the window, except where a sill is used. In this instance, the casing terminates on top of the sill, and an apron is added as a finish trim below the sill.

BASE MOULDINGS

Base moulding serves as a finish between the walls and floor. They may vary in size and form, but must be sufficiently thick at the bottom to cover the flooring joint. A two-piece base moulding consists of a baseboard fitted with a shoe mould at the bottom (Fig. 141A). A one-piece base is milled with a thickened edge at the bottom to cover the flooring joint (Fig. 141B).

When a two-piece base is used, the baseboard is nailed through to the wall plate and studs, high enough so that the lower edge clears the finish floor. The shoe mould is later nailed to the subfloor using a long thin nail driven at an angle which holds the shoe mould tightly against both the baseboard and the finish floor. A one-piece base is fitted tightly to the finish floor and nailed to the wall plate or studs. The one-piece base or the shoe mould is installed after the resilient floor or carpet has been laid or after hardwood flooring has been sanded.

Joints at interior corners may either be mitred or butted and coped. Butted and coped corners are made by butting the first piece of trim against the corner. The second piece is then mitred or coped to correspond to the moulded face of the first. Exterior corners are mitred. Only use finishing nails with heads countersunk and filled.

MILLWORK

Kitchen cabinets, shelving, mantels and other items of millwork are installed at the same time as the interior trim. This work is ordinarily carried out before the hardwood floors are sanded or the resilient flooring laid.

Cabinets and similar units may be either built in place or shop-built. The cabinets, shelving and other items can be made from a variety of lumber or other wood products.

Factory-made cabinets of steel or other materials are also available and can be obtained in various sizes.

Base moulding: (A) two-piece; (B) one-piece.

A
- nail
- baseboard
- mitred or coped joint
- shoe mould
- nail
- mitre joint
- finish flooring

B
- one-piece moulding

141

KITCHEN CABINETS

The kitchen deserves special attention, since it is a focal point of household activity. An efficient arrangement of kitchen cabinets, sink, refrigerator, and appliances such as microwave ovens and range, reduces work and saves steps.

Base units of kitchen cabinets are approximately 36 in. (900 mm) high, and the counter top is 24 in. (600 mm) deep. Various combinations of drawers and doors may be included in the base. Some cabinet arrangements include a corner cabinet equipped with revolving shelves. The counter top and backsplash (added along the wall above the counter top) are faced with plastic laminate or other impervious covering. Countertops are also manufactured with a number of finishes such as laminates, and generally include the backsplash.

An arrangement of kitchen cabinets.

optional drop ceiling
wall cabinets
shelf
counter top splash back
drawer
shelf
base cabinets
toe space
space for refrigerator

142

CHECKING BACK

Advance Ordering of Cabinets

Items such as kitchen cabinets, bathroom vanities and any other custom built-in furnishings are not usually available on short notice. When planning the house, consult with suppliers to determine the lead time needed to ensure that the cabinets will be ready for delivery when the house is near completion. Allow for additional time during busy periods of construction when suppliers may be running behind schedule.

To provide work space, wall units are set about 16 in. (400 mm) above the counter. This distance should be increased to at least 24 in. (600 mm) for wall units over the range. The shelves, which can be adjustable, are usually 11 to 12 in. (275 to 300 mm) deep. The ceiling may be dropped over the cabinets as shown in Figure 142.

CLOSETS

Although many variations are possible, coat and clothes closets are commonly provided with shelves and a closet rod or metal track. A standard interior door can be installed (Fig.

143A); however, sliding doors in pairs or other multiple combinations are often used. Sliding doors are hung on a track with rollers fastened to the doors (Fig. 143C). Bifold doors, consisting of narrow wood or metal panels, or accordion-type doors consisting of a metal frame covered with a vinyl fabric, are also used.

Built-in cabinets may also be used in bedrooms. Although this type of unit costs more than a standard opening, including dressers and chests of drawers eliminate the need for much of the bedroom furniture (Fig. 143B). Many suppliers have modular arrangements of shelving and storage systems for closets.

Storage closets: **(A)** linen closet with shelves; **(B)** built-in cabinet in bedroom; **(C)** clothes closet.

143

HEALTHY HOUSING INSIGHT

Interior Trim and Cabinet Selection

When selecting interior trim and cabinets, it is important to consider the source of materials, how they are obtained and processed, their durability and reusability. Many of the hardwoods used for interior doors and trim are harvested from fragile ecosystems in a manner which is not environmentally responsible. In the case of kitchen cabinets, many products use particleboard bonded with urea-formaldehyde glues which off-gas formaldehyde — an irritant to the respiratory tract. The finishes on many cabinets employ synthetic veneers made from non-renewable and non-recyclable materials. When these become scratched or faded, the cabinets are often removed and end up in landfills. Inappropriate choices can become wasteful.

Viable Options

➡ Interior doors and trim are now available in local species, such as poplar, pine and spruce, or made using medium-density fibreboard (MDF). These products do not rely on exotic and endangered wood species, and are easy to finish and maintain.

➡ Select kitchen cabinets which are modular and made from solid wood or particleboard bonded with low toxicity glues. Standardized kitchen cabinet and drawer modules permit the easy replacing or refacing of door and drawer fronts. These cabinets may alternatively be sold for reuse to a growing number of used building supply stores, where their standard size keeps them in strong demand by homeowners with tight budgets.

➡ Select used interior doors, trims and cabinets over new products. In many cases, well-crafted products are available at a fraction of the cost for new products.

➡ Reduce the amount of built-in cabinetry and closets by opting for furniture intended to serve the same storage function. Furniture manufacturers have resumed production of more traditional items such as dry sinks, sidetables, buffets, wardrobes and buffets. Consider investing in future heirlooms that can be used by subsequent generations.

Refer to the *Painting* chapter for more insights on appropriate finishes for interior doors, trim and cabinets.

PAINTING

Painting represents the most common interior finish in wood-frame house construction. In some parts of Canada, it is widely used as an exterior finish. The finish is relatively inexpensive and may be properly applied without a great deal of skill and training. It causes minimum disruption over a short period of time, and due to the wide variety of painted finishes available, remains the most popular form of remodeling over the life of the home. This chapter presents information which is fundamental to the appropriate selection and application of painted finishes.

TYPES OF PAINTED FINISHES

Painting involves a wide range of finishes which are painted onto a surface, typically using a brush or a roller, but in some cases using sponges and rags. There are many types of paint finishes available, and the most common types are described below.

Paints Paints are opaque finishes which may either be solvent based (oil paints) or water based (latex paints). Paints come in all colours, but only in several typical surface finishes (reflectances). The most common are flat or matte finish, eggshell finish, satin finish, semi-gloss finish, and high-gloss finish. In general, the more glossy a paint, the more washable and durable it tends to be. A number of specialty paints, such as rust resistant, mildew resistant, vapour retarder, and melamine types are also available.

Stains Stains are similar to paints except that they are intended for imparting a desired colour to wood before a final finish is applied. Stains are either opaque (solid) or transparent (penetrating), and are manufactured both as solvent-based and water-based products.

Sealers and Primers Sealers and primers are specially engineered paint products intended to seal the grain in wood, or the surface of interior finishes such as drywall or plaster. Sealers and primers prepare surfaces to accept paints, stains, or varnishes.

Varnishes Varnishes represent a broad category of transparent finishes used primarily to protect wood.

Preservatives Preservative-treated wood is commonly used for exterior decks and fences. This wood is normally pressure treated with a water-borne preservative in a treating facility. The preservative can tint the wood a green colour. If pieces are cut, the ends must be treated with preservative.

Irrespective of the type of paint finish being used, it is always very important to ensure that it is suitable for its intended function, and compatible with the material it is coating. Always follow the manufacturer's application instructions when using any paint or stain product.

EXTERIOR PAINTING AND STAINING

The primary purpose of exterior painting is to protect surfaces from the weather and to enhance appearance.

A wide variety of paints, stains and other coatings are available for exterior and interior use. Good quality materials should be selected and applied according to the manufacturers' recommendations. Since the cost of the materials is nearly always a small proportion of the total cost of painting, it is false economy to use poor quality materials. Good quality house paint, properly applied, will usually last a minimum of five years between paintings.

Surfaces to be painted should be clean and free from substances that will interfere with the adhesion of the paint. After the prime coat is applied, nail holes, cracks and other defects should be filled with putty or a suitable filler. Painting should not be carried out in temperatures below 50°F (10°C). The surface to be painted should be dry.

Clear coatings that provide a protective film over the surface of wood may be adversely affected by direct sunlight, and have a short life expectancy on surfaces exposed to the sun's rays unless they contain an ultraviolet inhibitor. Direct sunlight can cause the film to disintegrate and fall off in patches, leaving parts of the wood exposed. Since the parts of the film that remain are often hard and brittle, preparing the surface for re-coating becomes difficult. Coloured stains, either transparent or semi-transparent, soak into the wood leaving no visible film on the surface and protect all sides of the house much longer than most clear finishes. Re-coating is also much easier as it can be done with a minor amount of surface preparation.

INTERIOR PAINTING

Interior surfaces are painted to provide a pleasing appearance, and to protect them from damage by moisture which is prevalent in the kitchen, bathroom and laundry room. Painted surfaces are also easier to clean.

Typically, walls and ceilings finished in drywall or plaster are painted, but doors, trim, and interior millwork may be painted, or stained and varnished. The key to success for both types of finishes involves planning, preparation and proper application.

Interior painting should not proceed until practically all of the other work in the house is complete. Unless dust can be cleaned up before, and controlled during the painting stage, it is unlikely that acceptable results will achieved.

Surfaces must be smooth, clean, dry and free of greasy or oily films. In the case of drywall, it should be dry mopped or vacuumed before applying the primer coat. Any noticeable blemishes in the taping or filling of the drywall should be corrected, then cleaned up and re-primed before proceeding with the first coat of paint. Do not apply paints in temperatures below 50°F (10°C), and always allow the required amount of time between coats. Do not excessively thin paints as this greatly decreases their wear resistance and washability — correct mixing will provide the required consistency for proper application.

When staining and varnishing wood doors, trim, interior millwork and floors, it is recommended to try the stain out on a sample of the material before proceeding with a full application. Some wood species may require a sealant prior to staining to avoid uneven penetration of the stain. Wood-strip floors are also normally sealed before applying any type of finish. When staining and sealing are completed, a light sanding is usually recommended before applying any type of varnish. Pre-finished wood flooring, which is becoming more popular, is also readily available.

Varnishes should not be applied in thick coats since they may run or sag. Two thin coats, with sufficient drying time between, are often best for most residential applications. Items such as stair treads and hand rails may warrant a third coat.

When performing any interior painting, it is important, in addition to maintaining the required indoor temperature, to provide sufficient ventilation and lighting. Store all solvent-based paints and cleaners outside of the home, if possible. Dispose of all rags, paints, stains and thinners in an appropriate manner, usually at special depots for toxic wastes.

In all cases, the manufacturer's application instructions should be followed for proper appearance and performance of finishes.

HEALTHY HOUSING INSIGHT

Paint Finishes Selection

There is a wide variety of paint products available today, and fortunately, the number of considerations involving the appropriate selection of painted finishes is far less numerous. These have been summarized below.

Environmental Concerns

➡ Indoor air quality can be jeopardized when painted finishes using toxic chemicals are used in the house. This is due to the large surface area of the finish which is exposed and may continue to off-gas contaminants for a long period of time.

➡ Local air pollution is caused where paints containing volatile organic compounds (VOCs) are manufactured.

➡ Clean-up and disposal hazards associated with painted finishes which contain VOCs, or require cleaning solvents containing VOCs, may cause local pollution problems. The cost of properly disposing of solvent-based paints, thinners and cleaners is very high.

Environmental Choices

➡ Avoid solvent-based finishes and consider water-based alternatives instead.

➡ Look for finishes which bear the EcoLogo™, and use those where the levels of toxic substances in the paint product are minimal.

➡ Choose interior finishes which do not require a painted finish, such as natural wood paneling, decorative stucco, ceramic tile, stone and masonry.

➡ Select paint products which are easy to clean and durable so that the time between painting is maximized.

➡ Store paints outside of the house and properly dispose of all paints and solvents. Never pour these down the drain or over the ground.

➡ Painted finishes for walls, ceilings, floors, and trim which have minimal health and environmental impacts are available, and should be considered as appropriate alternatives in healthy housing.

EAVESTROUGHS AND DOWNSPOUTS

The use of eavestroughs and downspouts in Canadian housing has become so common that many people regard them as mandatory. They are not required, however, by most building codes. Eavestroughs and downspouts reduce groundwater adjacent to the foundation and thus provide extra insurance against foundation leakage. They may, however, contribute to ice-damming problems. (See Figure 71 in the chapter on *Roof Sheathing and Coverings*.)

Formed metal eavestroughs are available in continuous, one-piece lengths or in several different lengths. Fittings such as inside and outside corners, downspout connectors and elbows are available in sizes and angles to suit installation requirements. Plastic materials are also used for eavestroughs and downspouts.

Eavestroughs are installed after the exterior finish is in place. They are mounted on the fascia board as close as possible to the shingle overhang, with a slight slope toward the downspouts. Eavestroughs are fastened with 6 in. (150 mm) corrosion-resistant spikes spaced about 30 in. (750 mm) apart. A sheet-metal spacer tube or ferrule is placed between the interior surfaces of the eavestrough, and the spike is driven through the eavestrough and the ferrule into the fascia board and subfascia. Another method is to mount the eavestrough on metal brackets fitted inside the trough. Joints in the eavestrough are soldered or otherwise sealed.

Downspouts may be rectangular or round. Those made from metal are usually corrugated for added strength. The corrugated patterns are also less likely to burst when plugged with ice. Goosenecks, composed of elbows and short sections of downspout piping,

CHECKING BACK

Foundation and Site Drainage

When planning and before installing eavestroughs and downspouts, check back for any impacts on the foundation and site drainage which may be caused by the shedding of rainwater and snow melt from the roof of the house. Considerations involving foundation drainage may be found under the *Foundation Drainage* section of *Footings, Foundations and Slabs.* Factors to consider regarding site drainage may be found in the *Healthy Housing Insight* titled *Siting for Sun, Wind and Water* in the *Location and Excavation* chapter.

are used to bring the downspout in line with the wall.

Downspouts are fastened to the wall by means of straps and hooks. At least two hooks or straps should be used with each 10 ft. (3 m) length of downspout.

Where the downspouts are not connected to a storm sewer, an elbow with an extension, or a splash block, is used to direct the water away from the foundation wall to avoid erosion. The final grading of the lot should be such as to ensure positive drainage away from the building and off the lot.

GARAGES AND CARPORTS

Garages can be classified as attached, detached or built-in. The type used is sometimes determined by the nature and size of the lot. Where it is feasible, the attached garage has many points in its favour. It is warmer during cold weather and, when equipped with a connecting door to the house, provides covered protection between car and house.

Built-in garages with living accommodation over the garage area are sometimes used in two-storey houses. A built-in garage may also be incorporated into the basement where reasonable access from the street can be provided. However, considering the snow and ice conditions in some regions, the slope of the driveway to the garage door should be gentle. A grated trough and drain should be installed in front of the garage door.

It is a mistake to make the garage too small for convenient use. Motor vehicles vary in size. The garage should be long and wide enough for most models and still leave space to walk around the vehicle. This requires a minimum of 20 ft. (6.1 m) between the inside face of the front and rear walls. If a work bench or storage space will be located on the rear wall, the length of the garage must be increased accordingly. A width of 10 ft. (3.05 m) clear should be a minimum, but 11 ft. 6 in. (3.5 m) or more is better so that doors on either side of the vehicle can be opened freely. A two-car garage should be at least 18 ft. 3 in. (5.55 m) wide. Since garage space is valuable for storage of garden tools and equipment, bicycles, screens and other articles, additional space should be considered for this purpose.

Footings and foundations for garages are discussed in the chapter on **Footings, Foundations and Slabs**. The framing and exterior finish of the garage's side walls and roof are similar to that of the house. Interior finish is largely a matter of choice. The wall and ceiling of attached garages should protect against fumes entering the house. These, however, need not be fire separated provided the garage serves only one single-family house, and where not required by spatial separation requirements. Common walls between the house and the garage should be insulated. If the garage is to be heated, insulation and an air barrier should be included and covered with a wall finish to protect them from damage. The door between the garage and house should be fitted with weatherstripping and a self-closing device to prevent gas and exhaust fumes from entering the house.

There are many types of doors for garages, each with different advantages. The two most commonly used are the swing-up door (Fig. 144A) and the sectional overhead door (Fig. 144B). The one-piece swing-up door operates on a pivot principle with the track mounted on the ceiling and rollers located at the centre and top of the door. Counterbalance springs are mounted on the door, one at each side to make operation easier.

The sectional overhead door has rollers at each section fitted into a track up each side of the door and along the ceiling. It also has a counterbalance spring to ease the operation of the door. These doors are also occasionally fitted with automatic openers.

Carports are generally attached to the house with all or most of the other three sides open. Carport roofs are usually supported by posts located on top of concrete piers. Piers should be at least 8 x 8 in. (190 x 190 mm). Round piers formed in paper cylinders available for this purpose are often used. The base of the pier should be sufficiently large to ensure that the safe bearing pressure for the soil is not exceeded and far enough below grade to prevent frost heaving. Where wood posts are used, piers should extend at least 6 in. (150 mm) above the ground to protect the posts from ground moisture. Posts must be securely anchored to both piers and roof framing to resist wind uplift.

Types of garage doors: (**A**) overhead swing; (**B**) overhead sectional.

A

track anchored to structural members

beam designed for span

door in one section

garage floor

sloped driveway

144

B

track anchored to structural members

each section hinged

garage floor

sloped driveway

SURFACE DRAINAGE, DRIVEWAYS AND WALKWAYS

To create a successful landscape plan, it is necessary to assess the needs for surface drainage, driveways and walkways. Driveways and walkways should be made of materials in character with the house and yard.

SURFACE DRAINAGE

A surface drainage pattern should be established which will drain the entire lot and direct water away from the house. Driveways and walkways should be set low enough to avoid interfering with the drainage pattern. If a well is used to supply water for the house, all surface drainage must be directed away from the well to avoid contaminating the water supply.

The finished grade should be sloped away from the foundation wall of the house, and provision made to carry the surface water off the property. A swale (a gently sloping ditch) is used for this purpose where the drainage slope around the house meets a reverse slope. For example, if a lot slopes up from the front to rear, the swale should be located at the rear of the house so that the surface water flows along the swale, around the house, and out toward the street or roadside ditch.

DRIVEWAYS

A safe driveway should not slope too steeply to the street and should be graded so that the water will not accumulate on the surface. The drainage slope, which may be across the driveway or along its length, should be not less than 1:60.

The commonly used materials for driveways are concrete, asphalt interlocking pavers and crushed stone. A full-width driveway is preferable, although a satisfactory driveway may be made of two ribbons at least 24 in. (600 mm) wide, spaced about 5 ft. (1.5 m) apart centre-to-centre. The ribbon type is more economical than full-width pavement. It is not, however, suitable for use where curves and turnout areas are required.

The full-width driveway is easier to drive over. In addition, by increasing its width, the full-width driveway may also serve as a walkway. A driveway should be at least 8 ft. (2.4 m) wide, and increased to 10 ft. (3 m) when it serves as a walkway.

In the construction of driveways, the area to be paved should be graded to a uniform smooth surface and be well compacted. All soft material as well as loose rocks or boulders must be removed to a depth of approximately 4 in. (100 mm) and the holes filled and well tamped with hard material. If the ground has recently been filled, it should be well compacted because any settlement in the subsoil is likely to cause cracking in the finished driveway. A well-compacted base of gravel or crushed stone, at least 4 in. (100 mm) thick, is necessary if the driveway is to be surfaced with asphalt. Asphalt is usually about 1 1/2 in. (40 mm) thick.

Concrete 5 in. (125 mm) thick may be used without a base, but this thickness can be reduced to 3 in. (75 mm) when put down over a 5 in. (125 mm) gravel base.

Concrete placing, finishing and curing should be carried out as described under Basement Floor Slabs in the chapter on **Footings, Foundations and Slabs**. Overworking the surface during bull floating operations, that is, bringing up too much paste and bleed water, will result in a less durable finish. Control joints in concrete driveways should be placed from 10 to 12 ft. (3 to 3.5 m) apart. The resulting panels should be as nearly square as possible. Isolation joints, consisting of premoulded joint filler or sheathing paper, should be used to isolate the driveway from the curb, garage slab and house foundation wall. Control joints should be made as described under **Basement Floor Slabs**. Premoulded joint filler in isolating joints should extend to the full depth of the driveway slab and be 1/4 to 1/2 in. (6 to 12 mm) thick.

WALKWAYS

Cast-in-place concrete or precast slabs are commonly used for walkways. Other types of material such as asphalt, clay or concrete brick, fine gravel or crushed stone may also be used.

Walkways should be built on a well-compacted base, with a slight slope to drain the water off the surface. A base course is not normally used under concrete walks but must be used under asphalt surfaces. Concrete walks should be at least 4 in. (100 mm) thick and asphalt about 1 1/2 in. (40 mm) thick. Control joints are included in concrete walks for the same reason as described for driveways. These joints are usually spaced apart about one-and-a-half times the walkway width. Precast slabs are generally laid in a leveling bed of sand.

HEALTHY HOUSING INSIGHT

Environmental Control of Storm Water

There are a number of cases where the placing of a house on a site may have negative impacts on the natural flow patterns of runoff. This may occur if the home is being built in a rural area with a fragile ecosystem, but is more common in areas where a large number of homes are being constructed, and the entire site is being graded into a new topography. Some important considerations have been summarized below.

➜ Site the building so that natural drainage patterns are not interrupted; when this is not possible, grade the site so that these drainage patterns are maintained.

➜ Avoid where possible the drainage of roof runoff to the municipal sewer system or the foundation drainage system. In both cases, this increases the potential for basement flooding.

➜ Connect the downspouts of eavestroughs to a storage container, such as a rain barrel or cistern, and use this water for lawn watering and car washing.

➜ Plan landscaping which will capture and retain runoff in cases where a large roof area is drained to a single point. The retention of water in areas where it will slowly percolate back into the soil is an effective alternative.

Impacts of house construction can be minimized through careful planning and design. Consult environmental authorities for further assistance in the responsible management of storm water.

PROTECTION AGAINST DECAY AND TERMITES

Wood used under conditions where it will always be dry or even where it is subject to short periods of intermittent wetting followed by rapid drying will not decay. However, all wood and wood products used in construction are subject to decay if allowed to remain wet for long periods. Most of the wood used in a house is not subject to this condition, provided suitable precautions are taken. Protection is accomplished by methods of design and construction, by use of suitable materials, and in some cases by treating the materials.

The building site should be well drained, and untreated wood should not come in contact with the soil. Foundation walls should extend at least 6 in. (150 mm) above the ground and where wood siding or wood-base sidings are used, they should be kept at least 8 in. (200 mm) from the ground. The ground level in a crawl space should be at least 12 in. (300 mm) below joists and beams, increased to 18 in. (450 mm) where termites are a problem.

Steps, porches and door and window sills should be sloped to promote water run-off. Flashing should be used over doors and windows and other projections where water is likely to seep into the structure. (See the chapter on *Flashing*.) Roofs with considerable overhang give added protection to the siding and other parts of the house. Similarly, covered entranceways protect doors.

Exterior wood steps, rails and porch floors exposed to rain and snow have a high decay potential. Unless they are pressure-treated, wood members, such applications should not be in direct contact with the ground. It is important to protect the end grain of wood at the joints since end grain absorbs water easily. If pressure-treated lumber must be cut on the job site, the cut ends should be soaked in preservative until they have absorbed as much preservative as possible. The ends and joints in siding may be treated during installation or filled later to prevent the entry of water. A good quality caulking compound should be used around the window frames, door frames, siding that comes in contact with masonry, under door sills that are not fully protected from rain, and at other similar locations to prevent the entry of water into the structure.

If a moisture barrier is not used on the ground surface, crawl spaces are apt to become very humid and expose the framing members to conditions conducive to decay. The ground cover, which prevents moisture in the ground from entering the space, should be installed as described in the *Crawl Space Ventilation and Ground Cover* section of the chapter on *Footings, Foundations and Slabs*. An unheated crawlspace should also be ventilated in the summer.

In some areas, wood is subject to attack by termites, carpenter ants and powder post beetles. In regions where these pests are known to occur, precautions should be taken to safeguard the structure against damage. The best time to provide protection is during the planning and construction of the house. Provincial or municipal building codes which outline necessary methods of protection should be followed.

MAINTENANCE

A house that is well built using suitable materials, with adequate attention to construction details as described in this publication, will require far less maintenance than a house that is not well constructed and built of poor quality materials. Yet, while sound construction methods and suitable materials in the initial construction will greatly reduce the cost of maintenance, they will not result in a "maintenance-free" house. Some maintenance can be expected even during the first year of occupancy.

In a newly built house, it is quite common, for example, for the interior wall finish to develop some minor cracks and for some of the doors to stick. These flaws usually show up during or after the first heating season when the wood-frame members may shrink slightly due to changes in moisture content or after the bearing members have settled to their final position under loading.

Quite frequently, the backfill material around the house foundation will settle which can cause the surface water to pond against the basement or foundation wall. This should be corrected by filling up any settled areas to their proper level as soon as settling has taken place.

Prudent homeowners develop a well-planned program of care and maintenance which they continue throughout the years. Just as maintenance costs are greatly reduced by adequate attention to the methods and materials used in construction, it is equally true that a continuing program of maintenance will further reduce the cost of upkeep, enhance the value of the property, and greatly increase the useful life of the wood-frame house.

RELATED PUBLICATIONS

Internal Spaces of the Dwelling
Canada Mortgage and Housing Corporation
Landscape Architectural Design and Maintenance
Canada Mortgage and Housing Corporation

Appendix — Tables

Note: The span tables included in this appendix include only the most common species, spans and grades of lumber. For other species, spans and grades of lumber, refer to the *National Building Code of Canada* (National Research Council) or *The Span Book* (Canadian Wood Council).

Table 1
Minimum Thickness of Foundation Walls

Type of Foundation Wall	Minimum Wall Thickness, in. (mm)	Maximum Height of Exterior Finish Grade Above Basement Floor or Inside Grade, ft.–in. (m)	
		Foundation Wall Laterally Unsupported at the Top[1 to 4]	Foundation Wall Laterally Supported at the Top[1 to 4]
Solid concrete, 2200 psi (15 MPa) minimum strength	6 (150) 8 (200) 10 (250) 12 (300)	2–7 (0.80) 3–11 (1.20) 4–7 (1.40) 4–11 (1.50)	4–11 (1.50) 7–0 (2.15) 7–6 (2.30) 7–6 (2.30)
Solid concrete, 2900 psi (20 MPa) minimum strength	6 (150) 8 (200) 10 (250) 12 (300)	2–7 (0.80) 3–11 (1.20) 4–7 (1.40) 4–11 (1.50)	5–10 (1.80) 7–6 (2.30) 7–6 (2.30) 7–6 (2.30)
Unit masonry	5½ (140) 9 7/16 (240) 11 7/16 (290)	1–11 (0.60) 3–11 (1.20) 4–7 (1.40)	2–7 (0.80) 5–10 (1.80) 7–2 (2.20)

Notes to Table 1

1. Foundation walls are considered laterally supported at the top if the floor joists are embedded in the top of the foundation walls, or if the floor system is anchored to the top of the foundation walls with anchor bolts, in which case the joists may run either parallel or perpendicular to the foundation wall.
2. When a foundation wall contains an opening of more than 3 ft., 11 in. (1.2 m) in length or openings in more than 25 per cent of its length, the portion of the wall beneath such openings is considered laterally unsupported unless the wall around the opening is reinforced to withstand the earth pressure.
3. When the length of solid wall between windows is less than the average length of the windows, the combined length of such windows is considered a single opening.
4. When foundation walls support solid masonry walls, the foundation wall is considered laterally supported by the first floor.

Table 2
Concrete Mixes (by Volume)

Concrete Strength	Cement (part)	Sand (parts)	Coarse Aggregate
2175 psi (15 MPa)	1	2	4 parts up to 2 in. (50 mm) in size
	1	—	6 parts pit run gravel
2900 psi (20 MPa)	1	1¾	3 parts up to 1½ in. (40 mm) in size
	1	—	4¾ parts pit run gravel

259

Table 3
Minimum Depths of Foundations

Type of Soil	Foundations Containing Heated Basement or Crawl Space		Foundations Containing No Heated Space	
	Good Soil Drainage to at Least the Depth of Frost Penetration	Poor Soil Drainage	Good Soil Drainage to at Least the Depth of Frost Penetration	Poor Soil Drainage
Clay or soils not clearly defined	4 ft. (1.2 m)	4 ft. (1.2 m)	4 ft. (1.2 m) but not less than the depth of frost penetration	4 ft. (1.2 m) but not less than the depth of frost penetration
Silt	No limit	No limit	Below the depth of frost penetration	Below the depth of frost penetration
Coarse grained soils	No limit	No limit	No limit	Below the depth of frost penetration
Rock	No limit	No limit	No limit	No limit

Table 4
Minimum Footing Sizes
(Length of Supported Joists 16 ft. [4.9 m] or less)
(Design Floor Load 50 lb./sq. ft. [2.4 kN/m²] Maximum)

No. of Floors Supported	Minimum Widths of Strip Footings, in. (mm)		Minimum Area of Column Footings[1], sq. ft. (m²)
	Supporting Exterior Walls	Supporting Interior Walls	
1	10 (250)[2]	8 (200)[3]	4.3 (0.4)
2	14 (350)[2]	14 (350)[3]	8 (0.75)
3	18 (450)[2]	20 (500)[3]	11 (1.0)

Notes to Table 4

1. Sizes are based on columns spaced 9 ft., 10 in. (3 m) (on centre). For other column spacings, footing areas must be adjusted in proportion to the distance between columns.
2. For each storey of masonry veneer over wood-frame construction, footing widths must be increased by 2 1/2 in. (65 mm). For each storey of masonry construction other than foundation walls, the footing width must be increased by 5 1/8 in. (130 mm).
3. For each storey of masonry supported by the footing, the footing width must be increased by 4 in. (100 mm).

Table 5
Mortar Mix Proportions (by Volume)

Permissible Use of Mortar	Portland Cement	Masonry Cement (Type H)	Lime	Aggregate
All locations[1]	½ to 1 1	1 —	— ¼ to ½	
All locations[1], except foundation walls and piers	— 1	1 —	— ½ to 1¼	Not less than 2¼ and not more than 3 times the sum of the
All locations, except loadbearing walls of hollow units	1	—	1¼ to 2½	volumes of the cement and lime
All non-loadbearing partitions and all loadbearing walls of solid units except foundation walls	1 —	— —	2¼ to 4 1	

Note to Table 5
1. Must not be used for sand-lime brick or concrete brick.

Table 6
Dimension Lumber — Grades and Uses

Sizes, in. (mm)	Grades	Common Grade Mix[1]	Principal Uses	Grade Category
2 to 4 in. (38 to 89 mm) thick; 2 to 4 in (38 to 89 mm) wide	Select structural No. 1 and No. 2	No. 2 and better (No. 2 & Btr.)	Most common; used in most construction. Shows high strength, stiffness and good appearance. Preferred for trusses, rafters and roof joists.	Structural light framing
	No. 3[3]	—	Used in construction where high strength and appearance are not important, such as studs in non-loadbearing walls.	
	Construction[3] Standard[3]	Standard and better (Std. & Btr.)	Most common, used in general framing work. Has less strength than No. 2 and better structural light framing, but is stronger and allows longer spans than No. 3.	Light framing
	Utility[2]	—	Used most economically where high strength is not important, such as studs and plates in partition walls, blocking,and bracing.	
	Economy[2]	—	Used in temporary or low-cost construction where strength and appearance are not important.	

Table 6 (continued)
Dimension Lumber — Grades and Uses

Sizes, in. (mm)	Grades	Common Grade Mix[1]	Principal Uses	Grade Category
2 to 4 in. (38 to 89 mm) thick; 5 in. (114 mm) and wider	Select Structural No. 1 and No. 2	No. 2 & Btr.	Most common; used in most construction where high strength and stiffness are desired, such as floor joists, roof joists and rafters.	Structural joists and planks
	No. 3[3]	—	Used in general construction where strength is not important.	
	Economy[2]	—	Used in temporary or low-cost construction where strength and appearance are not important.	
2 to 4 in. (38 to 89 mm) thick; 2 in. (38 mm) and wider	Stud[3]	—	Most common; special purpose grade intended for all stud uses, including bearing walls	Stud
	Economy stud[2]	—	Used in temporary or low-cost construction where strength and appearance are not important.	

Notes to Table 6

1. For ease in grade sorting at the mill, the higher grades are combined and sold as a grade mix. Pieces of lumber in the grade mix are still individually grade stamped.
2. Except for the utility and economy grades, all grades are stress graded, which means specified strengths have been assigned and span tables calculated.
3. Construction, Standard, Stud and No. 3 Grades are typically used in designs that are not composed of 3 or more essentially parallel members spaced on 24-in. (600 mm) centres or less, so arranged or connected to mutually support loading.

Table 7
Facsimiles of Grade Marks Used by Canadian Lumber Manufacturing
Associations and Agencies Authorized to Grade Mark Lumber in Canada[1]

Facsimile of Grade Mark	Association or organization
A.F.P.A. 00 S—P—F S-DRY STAND	Alberta Forest Products Assocation 11738 Kingsway Avenue Suite 200 Edmonton AB T5G 0X5
C L A S-P-F 100 No. 1 S-GRN.	Canadian Lumbermen's Association 27 Goulburn Avenue Ottawa ON K1N 8C7
(LMA) 1 S-GRN 1 1 D FIR-N	Cariboo Lumber Manufacturers Association 205 — 197 2nd Avenue North Williams Lake, BC V2G 1Z5
(FPA® 00 S-P-F S-DRY CONST	Central Forest Products Association P.O. Box 1169 Hudson Bay, SK S0E 0Y0
CUFA® W.CEDAR S-GRN.-(N) 100 No 3	Northern Forest Products Association 400 — 1488 Fourth Avenue Prince George, BC V2L 4Y2

Table 7 (continued)
Facsimiles of Grade Marks Used by Canadian Lumber Manufacturing Associations and Agencies Authorized to Grade Mark Lumber in Canada[1]

Facsimile of Grade Mark	Association or organization
ILMA ® S-DRY **1** **0 0** S − P − F	Interior Lumber Manufacturers' Association 360 — 1855 Kirschner Road Kelowna BC V1Y 4N7
M L B SPRUCE PINE FIR **STAND** S-GRN **MILL 11 — 466**	Maritime Lumber Bureau P.O. Box 459 Amherst NS B4H 4A1
O.L.M.A. 01-1 **CONST.** S-DRY SPRUCE - PINE - FIR	Ontario Lumber Manufacturers Association 55 University Avenue Suite 1105, Box 8 Toronto ON M5J 2H7
	Quebec Lumber Manufacturers Assocation 200 — 5055,Boulevard Hamel West Québec QC G2E 2G6
	MacDonald Inspection 211 School House Street Coquitlam BC V3K 4X9
IO CONST S·P·F S-GRN	N.W.T. Grade Stamping Agency P.O. Box 346 Sardis BC V2R 1A7

Table 7 (continued)
Facsimiles of Grade Marks Used by Canadian Lumber Manufacturing Associations and Agencies Authorized to Grade Mark Lumber in Canada[1]

Facsimile of Grade Mark	Association or organization
$\text{R} \mid \text{B}$ NLGA RULE No 1 S-GRN 00 HEM-FIR-N	Pacific Lumber Insptection Bureau P.O. Box 19118 Fourth Avenue Postal Outlet Vancouver BC V6K 4R8

Note to Table 7
1 This listing is not complete; there are other agencies authorized to grade-mark lumber. For a complete listing contact the National Lumber Grades Authority at (604) 451-7323.

Table 8
Grade Mark Facsimiles for Machine Stress-rated Lumber

Facsimile of Grade Mark	Association or organization
(Company Name) A.F.P.A.® 31 S-P-F MACHINE RATED S-DRY 2100f 1.8E	Alberta Forest Products Association 200 — 11738 Kingsway Avenue Edmonton AB T5G 0X5
ILMA® S—P—F S-DRY 15 MACHINE RATED 2400f 2.0E	Interior Lumber Manufacturers' Association 360 — 1855 Kirschner Road Kelowna BC V1Y 4N7

Table 9
Commercial Species of Lumber

Commercial Species Group Designation	Grade Stamp Identification	Species in Combination	Wood Characteristics
Spruce – Pine – Fir	S – P – F	Spruce (all species except coast sitka spruce), lodgepole pine, jack pine, alpine fir, balsam fir	Woods of similar characteristics.They work easily, take paint easily and hold nails well. Generally white to pale yellow in colour.
Douglas Fir – Larch	D. Fir – L	Douglas fir, western larch	High degree of hardness and good resistance to decay. Good nail holding, gluing and painting qualities. Colour ranges from reddish-brown to yellowish white.
Hem – Fir	Hem – Fir	Pacific coast hemlock, amabilis fir	They work easily, take paint well and hold nails well. Good gluing characteristics. Colour range pale yellow-brown to white.
Northern Species	North	Western red cedar	Wood with exceptional resistance to decay. Moderate in strength. High in appearance qualities, it works easily and takes fine finishes. Colour varies from reddish-brown heart wood to light sapwood.
	North	Red pine, ponderosa pine	Fairly strong and easy to work woods that take a good finish and hold nails and screws well. Moderately durable; they season with little checking or cupping. Sapwood is a pale yellow colour; heartwood pale brown to reddish tinge.
		Western white pine, eastern white pine	Softest of the Canadian pines, they work and finish exception ally well. Not as strong as most pines but do not tend to split or splinter. Good nail holding properties. Low shrinkage, better than all other Canadian species except the cedars. Take stains, paints and varnishes well. Colour of sapwood almost white; heartwood creamy white to light straw brown.
		Trembling aspen, largetooth aspen, balsam poplar	Light woods of moderate strength, they work easily, finish well and hold nails well. Generally light in colour, varying from almost white to greyish-white.

(Most → Less)

266

Table 10
Sizes for Dimension Lumber and Boards

	Nominal Sizes, in.	Actual Sizes, in.		Metric Equivalents, mm		Metric Nomenclature, mm
		Dry	Green	Dry	Green	
Dimension Lumber	2 x 2	1½ x 1½	1⁹⁄16 x 1⁹⁄16	38 x 38	40 x 40	38 x 38
	3	2½	2⁹⁄16	64	65	64
	4	3½	3⁹⁄16	89	90	89
	6	5½	5 ⅝	140	143	140
	8	7¼	7½	184	190	184
	10	9¼	9½	235	241	235
	12	11¼	11½	286	292	286
	3 x 3, etc.	2½ x 2½	2⁹⁄16 x 2⁹⁄16	64 x 64	65 x 65	64 x 64
	4 x 4, etc.	3½ x 3½	3⁹⁄16 x 3⁹⁄16	89 x 89	90 x 90	89 x 89
Boards	1 x 2	¾ x 1½	1³⁄16 x 1⁹⁄16	19 x 38	21 x 40	19 x 38
	3	2½	2⁹⁄16	64	65	64
	4	3½	3⁹⁄16	89	90	89
	5	4½	4⅝	114	117	114
	6	5½	5⅝	140	143	140
	8	7¼	7½	184	190	184
	10	9¼	9½	235	241	235
	12	11¼	11½	286	292	286
	1¼ x 2, etc.	1 x 1½	1¹⁄32 x 1⁹⁄16	25 x 38	26 x 40	25 x 38
	1½ x2, etc.	1¼ x 1½	1⁹⁄32 x 1⁹⁄16	32 x 38	33 x 40	32 x 38

Table 11
Maximum Spans for Built-up Floor Beams Supporting not more than One Floor[1]

			Maximum Span, ft.–in. (m)[2,3]								
			Size of Built-up Beam, in. (mm)								
		Supported Length,	2 x 8 (38 x 184)			2 x 10 (38 x 235)			2 x 12 (38 x 286)		
Commercial Designation	Grade	ft. (m)[4,5]	3-ply	4-ply	5-ply	3-ply	4-ply	5-ply	3-ply	4-ply	5-ply
Douglas fir	No. 1	8	9–9	11–3	12–7	11–11	13–9	15–4	13–10	15–11	17–10
– larch	and	(2.4)	(2.99)	(3.45)	(3.86)	(3.66)	(4.22)	(4.72)	(4.24)	(4.90)	(5.48)
(includes	No. 2	10	8–8	10–1	11–3	10–8	12–3	13–9	12–4	14–3	15–11
Douglas		(3.0)	(2.67)	(3.09)	(3.45)	(3.27)	(3.78)	(4.22)	(3.79)	(4.38)	(4.90)
fir and		12	7–11	9–2	10–3	9–9	11–3	12–7	11–3	13–0	14–7
western		(3.6)	(2.44)	(2.82)	(3.15)	(2.98)	(3.45)	(3.85)	(3.46)	(4.00)	(4.47)
larch)		14	7–4	8–6	9–6	9–0	10–5	11–7	10–5	12–1	13–6
		(4.2)	(2.26)	(2.61)	(2.92)	(2.76)	(3.19)	(3.57)	(3.21)	(3.70)	(4.14)
		16	6–11	7–11	8–11	8–5	9–9	10–10	9–9	11–3	12–7
		(4.8)	(2.11)	(2.44)	(2.73)	(2.59)	(2.98)	(3.34)	(3.00)	(3.46)	(3.87)
		18	6–6	7–6	8–5	7–11	9–2	10–3	9–2	10–8	11–11
		(5.4)	(1.99)	(2.30)	(2.57)	(2.44)	(2.81)	(3.15)	(2.83)	(3.27)	(3.65)
		20	6–2	7–1	7–11	7–6	8–8	9–9	8–9	10–1	11–3
		(6.0)	(1.89)	(2.18)	(2.44)	(2.31)	(2.67)	(2.98)	(2.68)	(3.10)	(3.46)

Table II (continued)
Maximum Spans for Built-up Floor Beams Supporting not more than One Floor[1]

			Maximum Span, ft.–in. (m)[2, 3]								
			Size of Built-up Beam, in. (mm)								
		Supported Length,	2 x 8 (38 x 184)			2 x 10 (38 x 235)			2 x 12 (38 x 286)		
Commercial Designation	Grade	ft. (m)[4, 5]	3-ply	4-ply	5-ply	3-ply	4-ply	5-ply	3-ply	4-ply	5-ply
Hem – fir	No. 1	8	10–2	11–9	13–2	12–6	14–5	16–1	14–6	16–9	18–8
(includes	and	(2.4)	(3.14)	(3.62)	(4.05)	(3.83)	(4.43)	(4.95)	(4.45)	(5.14)	(5.74)
western	No. 2	10	9–2	10–6	11–9	11–2	12–11	14–5	12–11	14–11	16–9
hemlock		(3.0)	(2.80)	(3.24)	(3.62)	(3.43)	(3.96)	(4.43)	(3.98)	(4.60)	(5.14)
and		12	8–4	9–7	10–9	10–2	11–9	13–2	11–10	13–8	15–3
amabilis fir)		(3.6)	(2.56)	(2.96)	(3.31)	(3.13)	(3.61)	(4.04)	(3.63)	(4.19)	(4.69)
		14	7–9	8–11	10–0	9–5	10–11	12–2	10–11	12–8	14–2
		(4.2)	(2.37)	(2.74)	(3.06)	(2.90)	(3.35)	(3.74)	(3.36)	(3.88)	(4.34)
		16	7–3	8–4	9–4	8–10	10–2	11–5	10–3	11–10	13–3
		(4.8)	(2.22)	(2.56)	(2.86)	(2.71)	(3.13)	(3.50)	(3.15)	(3.63)	(4.06)
		18	6–10	7–10	8–9	8–4	9–7	10–9	9–8	11–2	12–6
		(5.4)	(2.09)	(2.41)	(2.70)	(2.56)	(2.95)	(3.30)	(2.97)	(3.42)	(3.83)
		20	6–5	7–5	8–4	7–11	9–1	10–2	9–2	10–7	11–10
		(6.0)	(1.98)	(2.29)	(2.56)	(2.42)	(2.80)	(3.13)	(2.81)	(3.25)	(3.63)
Spruce –	No. 1	8	10–7	12–2	13–8	12–11	14–11	16–8	15–0	17–4	19–4
pine – fir	and	(2.4)	(3.25)	(3.75)	(4.19)	(3.97)	(4.59)	(5.13)	(4.61)	(5.32)	(5.95)
(includes	No. 2	10	9–5	10–11	12–2	11–7	13–4	14–11	13–5	15–6	17–4
spruce		(3.0)	(2.90)	(3.35)	(3.75)	(3.55)	(4.10)	(4.59)	(4.12)	(4.76)	(5.32)
[all species		12	8–8	10–0	11–2	10–7	12–2	13–7	12–3	14–2	15–10
except		(3.6)	(2.65)	(3.06)	(3.42)	(3.24)	(3.74)	(4.19)	(3.76)	(4.34)	(4.86)
coast sitka		14	8–0	9–3	10–4	9–9	11–3	12–7	11–4	13–1	14–8
spruce],		(4.2)	(2.45)	(2.83)	(3.17)	(3.00)	(3.47)	(3.88)	(3.48)	(4.02)	(4.50)
jackpine,		16	7–6	8–8	9–8	9–2	10–7	11–10	10–7	12–3	13–8
lodgepole pine,		(4.8)	(2.30)	(2.65)	(2.96)	(2.81)	(3.24)	(3.63)	(3.26)	(3.76)	(4.21)
balsam fir		18	7–1	8–2	9–1	8–7	9–11	11–1	10–0	11–7	12–11
and alpine fir)		(5.4)	(2.17)	(2.50)	(2.80)	(2.65)	(3.06)	(3.42)	(3.07)	(3.55)	(3.97)
		20	6–8	7–9	8–8	8–2	9–5	10–7	9–6	10–11	12–3
		(6.0)	(2.05)	(2.37)	(2.65)	(2.51)	(2.90)	(3.24)	(2.91)	(3.37)	(3.76)
Northern	No. 1	8	8–6	9–10	10–11	10–4	12–0	13–5	12–0	13–11	15–6
species	and	(2.4)	(2.61)	(3.01)	(3.36)	(3.19)	(3.68)	(4.11)	(3.70)	(4.27)	(4.77)
(includes	No. 2	10	7–7	8–9	9–10	9–3	10–9	12–0	10–9	12–5	13–11
any		(3.0)	(2.33)	(2.69)	(3.01)	(2.85)	(3.29)	(3.68)	(3.31)	(3.82)	(4.27)
Canadian		12	6–11	8–0	8–11	8–6	9–9	10–11	9–10	11–4	12–8
species		(3.6)	(2.13)	(2.46)	(2.75)	(2.60)	(3.00)	(3.36)	(3.02)	(3.49)	(3.90)
covered by		14	6–5	7–5	8–3	7–10	9–1	10–1	9–1	10–6	11–9
the NLGA		(4.2)	(1.97)	(2.27)	(2.54)	(2.41)	(2.78)	(3.11)	(2.80)	(3.23)	(3.61)
Standard		16	6–0	6–11	7–9	7–4	8–6	9–6	8–6	9–10	11–0
Grading		(4.8)	(1.84)	(2.13)	(2.38)	(2.25)	(2.60)	(2.91)	(2.61)	(3.02)	(3.38)
Rules)		18	5–8	6–6	7–4	6–11	8–0	8–11	8–0	9–3	10–4
		(5.4)	(1.74)	(2.01)	(2.24)	(2.12)	(2.45)	(2.74)	(2.47)	(2.85)	(3.18)
		20	5–4	6–2	6–11	6–7	7–7	8–6	7–7	8–9	9–10
		(6.0)	(1.65)	(1.90)	(2.13)	(2.02)	(2.33)	(2.60)	(2.34)	(2.70)	(3.02)

Notes to Table 11

1. Spans apply only where the floors serve residential areas.
2. Spans are clear spans between supports. For total span, add two bearing lengths.
3. Provide minimum 3½ in. (89 mm) of bearing.
4. Supported length means half the sum of the joist spans on both sides of the beam.
5. Straight interpolation may be used for other supported lengths.

Table 12
Maximum Spans for Built-up Floor Beams Supporting not more than Two Floors[1]

			Maximum Span, ft.–in. (m)[2,3]								
			Size of Built-up Beam, in. (mm)								
		Supported Length,	2 x 8 (38 x 184)			2 x 10 (38 x 235)			2 x 12 (38 x 286)		
Commercial Designation	Grade	ft. (m)[4,5]	3-ply	4-ply	5-ply	3-ply	4-ply	5-ply	3-ply	4-ply	5-ply
Douglas fir – larch (includes Douglas fir and western larch)	No. 1 and No. 2	8 (2.4)	7–5 (2.27)	8–6 (2.62)	9–6 (2.93)	9–0 (2.77)	10–5 (3.20)	11–8 (3.58)	10–6 (3.22)	12–1 (3.72)	13–6 (4.16)
		10 (3.0)	6–7 (2.03)	7–8 (2.34)	8–6 (2.62)	8–1 (2.48)	9–4 (2.86)	10–5 (3.20)	9–4 (2.88)	10–10 (3.32)	12–1 (3.72)
		12 (3.6)	6–0 (1.85)	7–0 (2.14)	7–9 (2.39)	7–4 (2.26)	8–6 (2.62)	9–6 (2.92)	8–7 (2.63)	9–11 (3.03)	11–1 (3.39)
		14 (4.2)	5–7 (1.71)	6–5 (1.98)	7–2 (2.21)	6–10 (2.10)	7–11 (2.42)	8–10 (2.71)	7–11 (2.43)	9–2 (2.81)	10–3 (3.14)
		16 (4.8)	5–3 (1.60)	6–0 (1.85)	6–9 (2.07)	6–5 (1.96)	7–4 (2.26)	8–3 (2.53)	7–5 (2.28)	8–7 (2.63)	9–7 (2.94)
		18 (5.4)	4–11 (1.51)	5–8 (1.75)	6–4 (1.95)	6–0 (1.85)	6–11 (2.14)	7–9 (2.39)	7–0 (2.15)	8–1 (2.48)	9–0 (2.77)
		20 (6.0)	4–8 (1.43)	5–5 (1.66)	6–0 (1.85)	5–9 (1.75)	6–7 (2.03)	7–4 (2.26)	6–8 (2.04)	7–8 (2.35)	8–7 (2.63)
Hem – fir (includes western hemlock and amabilis fir)	No. 1 and No. 2	8 (2.4)	7–9 (2.38)	8–11 (2.75)	10–0 (3.07)	9–6 (2.91)	10–11 (3.36)	12–3 (3.76)	11–0 (3.38)	12–8 (3.90)	14–2 (4.36)
		10 (3.0)	6–11 (2.13)	8–0 (2.46)	8–11 (2.75)	8–6 (2.60)	9–9 (3.00)	10–11 (3.36)	9–10 (3.02)	11–4 (3.49)	12–8 (3.90)
		12 (3.6)	6–4 (1.94)	7–4 (2.24)	8–2 (2.51)	7–9 (2.38)	8–11 (2.74)	10–0 (3.07)	8–11 (2.75)	10–4 (3.18)	11–7 (3.56)
		14 (4.2)	5–10 (1.80)	6–9 (2.08)	7–7 (2.32)	7–0 (2.15)	8–3 (2.54)	9–3 (2.84)	7–11 (2.44)	9–7 (2.95)	10–9 (3.29)
		16 (4.8)	5–3 (1.63)	6–4 (1.94)	7–1 (2.17)	6–4 (1.94)	7–9 (2.38)	8–8 (2.66)	7–2 (2.20)	8–11 (2.75)	10–0 (3.08)
		18 (5.4)	4–10 (1.49)	6–0 (1.83)	6–8 (2.05)	5–9 (1.78)	7–2 (2.22)	8–2 (2.50)	6–7 (2.02)	8–1 (2.50)	9–5 (2.91)
		20 (6.0)	4–6 (1.37)	5–7 (1.71)	6–4 (1.94)	5–4 (1.65)	6–7 (2.04)	7–9 (2.38)	6–1 (1.88)	7–6 (2.31)	8–11 (2.75)
Spruce – pine – fir (includes spruce [all species except coast sitka spruce], jack pine, lodgepole pine, balsam fir and alpine fir)	No. 1 and No. 2	8 (2.4)	8–0 (2.46)	9–3 (2.85)	10–4 (3.18)	9–10 (3.01)	11–4 (3.48)	12–8 (3.89)	11–5 (3.50)	13–2 (4.04)	14–8 (4.51)
		10 (3.0)	7–2 (2.20)	8–3 (2.55)	9–3 (2.85)	8–9 (2.70)	10–2 (3.11)	11–4 (3.48)	10–2 (3.13)	11–9 (3.61)	13–2 (4.04)
		12 (3.6)	6–7 (2.01)	7–7 (2.32)	8–5 (2.60)	8–0 (2.46)	9–3 (2.84)	10–4 (3.18)	9–4 (2.85)	10–9 (3.30)	12–0 (3.69)
		14 (4.2)	6–1 (1.86)	7–0 (2.15)	7–10 (2.40)	7–5 (2.28)	8–7 (2.63)	9–7 (2.94)	8–7 (2.64)	9–11 (3.05)	11–1 (3.41)
		16 (4.8)	5–8 (1.74)	6–7 (2.01)	7–4 (2.25)	6–10 (2.11)	8–0 (2.46)	8–11 (2.75)	7–9 (2.38)	9–4 (2.85)	10–5 (3.19)
		18 (5.4)	5–3 (1.61)	6–2 (1.90)	6–11 (2.12)	6–3 (1.93)	7–7 (2.32)	8–5 (2.59)	7–1 (2.18)	8–9 (2.69)	9–10 (3.01)
		20 (6.0)	4–10 (1.49)	5–10 (1.80)	6–7 (2.01)	5–9 (1.78)	7–2 (2.20)	8–0 (2.46)	6–7 (2.02)	8–1 (2.50)	9–4 (2.85)

Table 12 (continued)
Maximum Spans for Built-up Floor Beams Supporting not more than Two Floors[1]

			Maximum Span, ft.–in. (m)[2, 3]								
			Size of Built-up Beam, in. (mm)								
		Supported Length,	2 x 8 (38 x 184)			2 x 10 (38 x 235)			2 x 12 (38 x 286)		
Commercial Designation	Grade	ft. (m)[4, 5]	3-ply	4-ply	5-ply	3-ply	4-ply	5-ply	3-ply	4-ply	5-ply
Northern	No. 1	8	6–5	7–5	8–4	7–10	9–1	10–2	9–2	10–7	11–9
species	and	(2.4)	(1.98)	(2.28)	(2.55)	(2.42)	(2.79)	(3.12)	(2.81)	(3.24)	(3.62)
(includes	No. 2	10	5–9	6–8	7–5	7–0	8–2	9–1	8–2	9–5	10–7
any		(3.0)	(1.77)	(2.04)	(2.28)	(2.16)	(2.50)	(2.79)	(2.51)	(2.90)	(3.24)
Canadian		12	5–3	6–1	6–9	6–5	7–5	8–4	7–5	8–7	9–8
species		(3.6)	(1.61)	(1.86)	(2.08)	(1.97)	(2.28)	(2.55)	(2.29)	(2.65)	(2.96)
covered by		14	4–10	5–7	6–3	5–11	6–10	7–8	6–11	8–0	8–11
the NLGA		(4.2)	(1.49)	(1.73)	(1.93)	(1.83)	(2.11)	(2.36)	(2.12)	(2.45)	(2.74)
Standard		16	4–7	5–3	5–11	5–7	6–5	7–2	6–6	7–5	8–4
Grading Rules)		(4.8)	(1.40)	(1.61)	(1.81)	(1.71)	(1.97)	(2.21)	(1.98)	(2.29)	(2.56)
		18	4–3	4–11	5–6	5–3	6–1	6–9	6–1	7–0	7–10
		(5.4)	(1.32)	(1.52)	(1.70)	(1.61)	(1.86)	(2.08)	(1.87)	(2.16)	(2.42)
		20	4–1	4–8	5–3	5–0	5–9	6–5	5–9	6–8	7–5
		(6.0)	(1.25)	(1.44)	(1.61)	(1.53)	(1.77)	(1.97)	(1.77)	(2.05)	(2.29)

Notes to Table 12

1. Spans apply only where the floors serve residential areas.
2. Spans are clear spans between supports. For total span, add two bearing lengths.
3. Provide minimum 3½ in. (89 mm) of bearing.
4. Supported length means half the sum of the joist spans on both sides of the beam.
5. Straight interpolation may be used for other supported lengths.

Table 13
Maximum Spans for Built-up Floor Beams Supporting not more than Three Floors[1]

			Maximum Span, ft.-in. (m)[2, 3]								
			Size of Built-up Beam, in. (mm)								
		Supported Length,	2 x 8 (38 x 184)			2 x 10 (38 x 235)			2 x 12 (38 x 286)		
Commercial Designation	Grade	ft. (m)[4, 5]	3-ply	4-ply	5-ply	3-ply	4-ply	5-ply	3-ply	4-ply	5-ply
Douglas fir	No. 1	8	6–2	7–2	8–0	7–7	8–9	9–9	8–9	10–2	11–4
– larch	and	(2.4)	(1.90)	(2.19)	(2.45)	(2.32)	(2.68)	(3.00)	(2.70)	(3.11)	(3.48)
(includes	No. 2	10	5–6	6–5	7–2	6–9	7–10	8–9	7–10	9–1	10–2
Douglas fir		(3.0)	(1.70)	(1.96)	(2.19)	(2.08)	(2.40)	(2.68)	(2.41)	(2.79)	(3.11)
and western		12	5–1	5–10	6–6	6–2	7–2	8–0	7–2	8–3	9–3
larch)		(3.6)	(1.55)	(1.79)	(2.00)	(1.90)	(2.19)	(2.45)	(2.20)	(2.54)	(2.84)
		14	4–8	5–5	6–0	5–9	6–7	7–5	6–8	7–8	8–7
		(4.2)	(1.44)	(1.66)	(1.86)	(1.76)	(2.03)	(2.27)	(2.04)	(2.35)	(2.63)
		16	4–4	5–1	5–8	5–4	6–2	6–11	6–2	7–2	8–0
		(4.8)	(1.34)	(1.55)	(1.74)	(1.64)	(1.90)	(2.12)	(1.91)	(2.20)	(2.46)
		18	4–1	4–9	5–4	5–1	5–10	6–6	5–10	6–9	7–7
		(5.4)	(1.27)	(1.46)	(1.64)	(1.55)	(1.79)	(2.00)	(1.80)	(2.08)	(2.32)
		20	3–11	4–6	5–1	4–9	5–6	6–2	5–6	6–5	7–2
		(6.0)	(1.20)	(1.39)	(1.55)	(1.47)	(1.70)	(1.90)	(1.69)	(1.97)	(2.20)
Hem – fir	No. 1	8	6–6	7–6	8–5	7–11	9–2	10–3	9–2	10–8	11–11
(includes	and	(2.4)	(1.99)	(2.30)	(2.57)	(2.44)	(2.81)	(3.15)	(2.83)	(3.27)	(3.65)
western	No. 2	10	5–9	6–8	7–6	6–11	8–2	9–2	7–9	9–6	10–8
hemlock		(3.0)	(1.78)	(2.06)	(2.30)	(2.13)	(2.52)	(2.81)	(2.40)	(2.92)	(3.27)
and		12	5–0	6–1	6–10	6–0	7–6	8–4	6–10	8–5	9–8
amabilis fir)		(3.6)	(1.55)	(1.88)	(2.10)	(1.85)	(2.30)	(2.57)	(2.10)	(2.61)	(2.98)
		14	4–6	5–7	6–4	5–4	6–8	7–9	6–1	7–6	8–11
		(4.2)	(1.38)	(1.71)	(1.95)	(1.65)	(2.05)	(2.38)	(1.88)	(2.32)	(2.75)
		16	4–1	5–0	5–11	4–11	6–0	7–1	5–7	6–10	8–0
		(4.8)	(1.25)	(1.55)	(1.82)	(1.50)	(1.85)	(2.19)	(1.72)	(2.10)	(2.48)
		18	3–9	4–7	5–5	4–6	5–6	6–6	5–2	6–3	7–4
		(5.4)	(1.15)	(1.42)	(1.68)	(1.39)	(1.70)	(2.00)	(1.59)	(1.93)	(2.27)
		20	3–6	4–3	5–0	4–3	5–1	6–0	4–10	5–10	6–10
		(6.0)	(1.07)	(1.31)	(1.55)	(1.30)	(1.57)	(1.85)	(1.49)	(1.79)	(2.10)
Spruce –	No. 1	8	6–9	7–9	8–8	8–3	9–6	10–7	9–6	11–0	12–4
pine – fir	and	(2.4)	(2.06)	(2.38)	(2.67)	(2.52)	(2.92)	(3.26)	(2.93)	(3.38)	(3.78)
(includes	No. 2	10	6–0	6–11	7–9	7–4	8–6	9–6	8–5	9–10	11–0
spruce [all		(3.0)	(1.85)	(2.13)	(2.38)	(2.26)	(2.61)	(2.92)	(2.61)	(3.03)	(3.38)
species		12	5–5	6–4	7–1	6–6	7–9	8–8	7–4	9–0	10–1
except		(3.6)	(1.68)	(1.95)	(2.18)	(2.00)	(2.38)	(2.66)	(2.27)	(2.76)	(3.09)
coast sitka		14	4–10	5–10	6–7	5–9	7–2	8–0	6–7	8–2	9–4
spruce],		(4.2)	(1.49)	(1.80)	(2.02)	(1.78)	(2.20)	(2.46)	(2.03)	(2.51)	(2.86)
jack pine,		16	4–5	5–5	6–2	5–3	6–6	7–6	6–0	7–4	8–8
lodgepole pine,		(4.8)	(1.35)	(1.68)	(1.88)	(1.62)	(2.00)	(2.30)	(1.84)	(2.27)	(2.67)
balsam fir and		18	4–0	5–0	5–9	4–10	5–11	7–0	5–6	6–9	8–0
alpine fir)		(5.4)	(1.24)	(1.53)	(1.78)	(1.49)	(1.83)	(2.17)	(1.70)	(2.08)	(2.46)
		20	3–9	4–7	5–5	4–6	5–6	6–6	5–2	6–3	7–4
		(6.0)	(1.15)	(1.42)	(1.68)	(1.39)	(1.70)	(2.00)	(1.59)	(1.93)	(2.27)

Table 13 (continued)
Maximum Spans for Built-up Floor Beams Supporting not more than Three Floors[1]

			Maximum Span, ft.-in. (m)[2, 3]								
			Size of Built-up Beam, in. (mm)								
		Supported	2 x 8			2 x 10			2 x 12		
		Length,	(38 x 184)			(38 x 235)			(38 x 286)		
Commercial		ft.									
Designation	Grade	(m)[4, 5]	3-ply	4-ply	5-ply	3-ply	4-ply	5-ply	3-ply	4-ply	5-ply
Northern	No.	8	5–5	6–3	7–0	6–7	7–7	8–6	7–8	8–10	9–11
species	and	(2.4)	(1.66)	(1.91)	(2.14)	(2.03)	(2.34)	(2.62)	(2.35)	(2.72)	(3.04)
(includes	No. 2	10	4–10	5–7	6–3	5–11	6–10	7–7	6–10	7–11	8–10
any		(3.0)	(1.48)	(1.71)	(1.91)	(1.81)	(2.09)	(2.34)	(2.10)	(2.43)	(2.72)
Canadian		12	4–5	5–1	5–8	5–5	6–3	6–11	6–3	7–3	8–1
species		(3.6)	(1.35)	(1.56)	(1.75)	(1.65)	(1.91)	(2.14)	(1.92)	(2.22)	(2.48)
covered by		14	4–1	4–8	5–3	5–0	5–9	6–5	5–9	6–8	7–6
the NLGA		(4.2)	(1.25)	(1.45)	(1.62)	(1.53)	(1.77)	(1.98)	(1.78)	(2.05)	(2.29)
Standard		16	3–10	4–5	4–11	4–8	5–5	6–0	5–5	6–3	7–0
Grading Rules)		(4.8)	(1.17)	(1.35)	(1.51)	(1.43)	(1.65)	(1.85)	(1.66)	(1.92)	(2.15)
		18	3–7	4–2	4–8	4–5	5–1	5–8	5–1	5–11	6–7
		(5.4)	(1.10)	(1.28)	(1.43)	(1.35)	(1.56)	(1.74)	(1.57)	(1.81)	(2.02)
		20	3–5	3–11	4–5	4–2	4–10	5–5	4–10	5–7	6–3
		(6.0)	(1.05)	(1.21)	(1.35)	(1.28)	(1.48)	(1.65)	(1.49)	(1.72)	(1.92)

Notes to Table 13

1. Spans apply only where the floors serve residential areas.

2. Spans are clear spans between supports. For total span, add two bearing lengths.

3. Provide minimum $3\frac{1}{2}$ in. (89 mm) of bearing.

4. Supported length means half the sum of the joist spans on both sides of the beam.

5. Straight interpolation may be used for other supported lengths.

272

Table 14
Maximum Spans for Glue-laminated Floor Beams — 2of-E Grade[1]

			Maximum Span, ft.-in. (m)[2 to 5]						
		Supported				Beam Depth, in. (mm)			
Number of Floors Supported	Beam Width, in. (mm)	Length, ft. (m)[6,7]	9 (228)	10½ (266)	12 (304)	13½ (342)	15 (380)	16½ (418)	18 (456)
1	3 (80)	8 (2.4)	14–1 (4.32)	16–5 (5.04)	18–9 (5.76)	21–1 (6.48)	23–5 (7.20)	25–9 (7.92)	28–2 (8.64)
		10 (3.0)	12–7 (3.87)	14–8 (4.51)	16–9 (5.15)	18–10 (5.80)	21–0 (6.44)	23–1 (7.09)	25–2 (7.73)
		12 (3.6)	11–6 (3.53)	13–5 (4.12)	15–4 (4.70)	17–3 (5.29)	19–2 (5.88)	21–1 (6.47)	23–0 (7.06)
		14 (4.2)	10–8 (3.27)	12–5 (3.81)	14–2 (4.36)	15–11 (4.90)	17–9 (5.44)	19–6 (5.99)	21–3 (6.53)
		16 (4.8)	9–11 (3.06)	11–7 (3.57)	13–3 (4.07)	14–11 (4.58)	16–7 (5.09)	18–3 (5.60)	19–11 (6.11)
		18 (5.4)	9–5 (2.88)	10–11 (3.36)	12–6 (3.84)	14–1 (4.32)	15–8 (4.80)	17–2 (5.28)	18–9 (5.76)
		20 (6.0)	8–11 (2.73)	10–5 (3.19)	11–10 (3.64)	13–4 (4.10)	14–10 (4.56)	16–4 (5.01)	17–10 (5.47)
1	5 (130)	8 (2.4)	17–11 (5.51)	20–11 (6.43)	23–11 (7.35)	26–11 (8.26)	29–11 (9.18)	32–11 (10.10)	35–10 (11.02)
		10 (3.0)	16–0 (4.93)	18–9 (5.75)	21–5 (6.57)	24–1 (7.39)	26–9 (8.21)	29–5 (9.03)	32–1 (9.86)
		12 (3.6)	14–8 (4.50)	17–1 (5.25)	19–6 (6.00)	22–0 (6.75)	24–5 (7.50)	26–10 (8.25)	29–3 (9.00)
		14 (4.2)	13–7 (4.16)	15–10 (4.86)	18–1 (5.55)	20–4 (6.25)	22–7 (6.94)	24–10 (7.64)	27–1 (8.33)
		16 (4.8)	12–8 (3.90)	14–10 (4.54)	16–11 (5.19)	19–0 (5.84)	21–2 (6.49)	23–3 (7.14)	25–4 (7.79)
		18 (5.4)	11–11 (3.67)	13–11 (4.28)	15–11 (4.90)	17–11 (5.51)	19–11 (6.12)	21–11 (6.73)	23–11 (7.35)
		20 (6.0)	11–4 (3.48)	13–3 (4.07)	15–1 (4.65)	17–0 (5.23)	18–11 (5.81)	20–10 (6.39)	22–8 (6.97)
2	3 (80)	8 (2.4)	10–8 (3.28)	12–5 (3.83)	14–3 (4.37)	16–0 (4.92)	17–9 (5.47)	19–7 (6.01)	21–4 (6.56)
		10 (3.0)	9–7 (2.93)	11–2 (3.42)	12–9 (3.91)	14–4 (4.40)	15–11 (4.89)	17–6 (5.38)	19–1 (5.87)
		12 (3.6)	8–9 (2.68)	10–2 (3.12)	11–7 (3.57)	13–1 (4.02)	14–6 (4.46)	16–0 (4.91)	17–5 (5.36)
		14 (4.2)	8–1 (2.48)	9–5 (2.89)	10–9 (3.31)	12–1 (3.72)	13–5 (4.13)	14–10 (4.54)	16–2 (4.96)
		16 (4.8)	7–7 (2.32)	8–10 (2.71)	10–1 (3.09)	11–4 (3.48)	12–7 (3.86)	13–10 (4.25)	15–1 (4.64)
		18 (5.4)	7–1 (2.19)	8–4 (2.55)	9–6 (2.91)	10–8 (3.28)	11–10 (3.64)	13–1 (4.01)	14–3 (4.37)
		20 (6.0)	6–9 (2.07)	7–11 (2.42)	9–0 (2.77)	10–2 (3.11)	11–3 (3.46)	12–5 (3.80)	13–6 (4.15)

Table 14 (continued)
Maximum Spans for Glue-laminated Floor Beams — 20f-E Grade[1]

			Maximum Span, ft.-in. (m)[2 to 5]						
Number of Floors Supported	Beam Width, in. (mm)	Supported Length, ft. (m)[6,7]	Beam Depth, in. (mm)						
			9 (228)	10½ (266)	12 (304)	13½ (342)	15 (380)	16½ (418)	18 (456)
2	5 (130)	8 (2.4)	13–7 (4.18)	15–10 (4.88)	18–2 (5.57)	20–5 (6.27)	22–8 (6.97)	24–11 (7.66)	27–3 (8.36)
		10 (3.0)	12–2 (3.74)	14–2 (4.36)	16–3 (4.99)	18–3 (5.61)	20–3 (6.23)	22–4 (6.85)	24–4 (7.48)
		12 (3.6)	11–1 (3.41)	13–0 (3.98)	14–10 (4.55)	16–8 (5.12)	18–6 (5.69)	20–4 (6.26)	22–3 (6.83)
		14 (4.2)	10–3 (3.16)	12–0 (3.69)	13–9 (4.21)	15–5 (4.74)	17–2 (5.27)	18–10 (5.79)	20–7 (6.32)
		16 (4.8)	9–7 (2.96)	11–3 (3.45)	12–10 (3.94)	14–5 (4.43)	16–0 (4.93)	17–8 (5.42)	19–3 (5.91)
		18 (5.4)	9–1 (2.79)	10–7 (3.25)	12–1 (3.72)	13–7 (4.18)	15–1 (4.64)	16–8 (5.11)	18–2 (5.57)
		20 (6.0)	8–7 (2.64)	10–0 (3.08)	11–6 (3.53)	12–11 (3.97)	14–4 (4.41)	15–9 (4.85)	17–3 (5.29)
3	3 (80)	8 (2.4)	8–11 (2.75)	10–5 (3.21)	11–11 (3.66)	13–5 (4.12)	14–11 (4.58)	16–5 (5.04)	17–11 (5.50)
		10 (3.0)	8–0 (2.46)	9–4 (2.87)	10–8 (3.28)	12–0 (3.69)	13–4 (4.10)	14–8 (4.51)	16–0 (4.92)
		12 (3.6)	7–4 (2.24)	8–6 (2.62)	9–9 (2.99)	10–11 (3.37)	12–2 (3.74)	13–5 (4.11)	14–7 (4.49)
		14 (4.2)	6–9 (2.08)	7–11 (2.42)	9–0 (2.77)	10–2 (3.12)	11–3 (3.46)	12–5 (3.81)	13–6 (4.15)
		16 (4.8)	6–4 (1.94)	7–5 (2.27)	8–5 (2.59)	9–6 (2.91)	10–6 (3.24)	11–7 (3.56)	12–8 (3.89)
		18 (5.4)	6–0 (1.83)	6–11 (2.14)	7–11 (2.44)	8–11 (2.75)	9–11 (3.05)	10–11 (3.36)	11–11 (3.66)
		20 (6.0)	5–8 (1.74)	6–7 (2.03)	7–7 (2.32)	8–6 (2.61)	9–5 (2.90)	10–4 (3.19)	11–4 (3.48)
3	5 (130)	8 (2.4)	11–5 (3.50)	13–4 (4.09)	15–2 (4.67)	17–1 (5.25)	19–0 (5.84)	20–11 (6.42)	22–10 (7.01)
		10 (3.0)	10–2 (3.13)	11–11 (3.66)	13–7 (4.18)	15–4 (4.70)	17–0 (5.22)	18–8 (5.74)	20–5 (6.27)
		12 (3.6)	9–4 (2.86)	10–10 (3.34)	12–5 (3.81)	14–0 (4.29)	15–6 (4.77)	17–1 (5.24)	18–7 (5.72)
		14 (4.2)	8–7 (2.65)	10–1 (3.09)	11–6 (3.53)	12–11 (3.97)	14–4 (4.41)	15–10 (4.85)	17–3 (5.30)
		16 (4.8)	8–1 (2.48)	9–5 (2.89)	10–9 (3.30)	12–1 (3.72)	13–5 (4.13)	14–9 (4.54)	16–1 (4.95)
		18 (5.4)	7–7 (2.34)	8–10 (2.72)	10–2 (3.11)	11–5 (3.50)	12–8 (3.89)	13–11 (4.28)	15–2 (4.67)
		20 (6.0)	7–3 (2.22)	8–5 (2.58)	9–7 (2.95)	10–10 (3.32)	12–0 (3.69)	13–3 (4.06)	14–5 (4.43)

Notes to Table 14

1. Spans apply only where the floors serve residential areas.
2. Spans are valid for glue-laminated timber conforming to CAN/CSA-O122-M and CAN/CSA-O177-M.
3. Spans are clear spans between supports. For total span, add two bearing lengths.
4. Provide a minimum bearing length of 3½ in. (89 mm).
5. Top edge of beam assumed to be fully laterally supported by joists.
6. Supported length means half the sum of the joist spans on both sides of the beam.
7. Straight interpolation may be used for other supported lengths.

Table 15
Maximum Spans for Floor Joists — General Cases[1, 2]

			Maximum Span, ft.-in. (m)								
			Joist Spacing, in. (mm)								
		Joist	With Strapping			With Bridging			With Strapping and Bridging		
Commercial Designation	Grade	Size, ft. (m)	12 (300)	16 (400)	24 (600)	12 (300)	16 (400)	24 (600)	12 (300)	16 (400)	24 (600)
Douglas fir – larch (includes Douglas fir and western larch)	No. 1 and No. 2	2x6 (38x140)	10–2 (3.09)	9–7 (2.91)	8–7 (2.62)	10–10 (3.29)	9–10 (2.99)	8–7 (2.62)	10–10 (3.29)	9–10 (2.99)	8–7 (2.62)
		2x8 (38x184)	12–2 (3.71)	11–7 (3.53)	11–0 (3.36)	13–1 (4.00)	12–4 (3.76)	11–3 (3.44)	13–9 (4.19)	12–10 (3.90)	11–3 (3.44)
		2x10 (38x235)	14–4 (4.38)	13–8 (4.16)	13–0 (3.96)	15–3 (4.66)	14–4 (4.38)	13–6 (4.11)	15–10 (4.84)	14–10 (4.51)	13–10 (4.20)
		2x12 (38x286)	16–5 (4.99)	15–7 (4.75)	14–10 (4.52)	17–2 (5.26)	16–2 (4.94)	15–3 (4.65)	17–10 (5.43)	16–7 (5.06)	15–6 (4.72)
Hem – fir (includes western hemlock and amabilis fir)	No. 1 and No. 2	2x6 (38x140)	10-2 (3.09)	9–7 (2.91)	8–7 (2.62)	10–10 (3.29)	9–10 (2.99)	8–7 (2.62)	10–10 (3.29)	9–10 (2.99)	8–7 (2.62)
		2x8 (38x184)	12–2 (3.71)	11–7 (3.53)	11–0 (3.36)	13–1 (4.00)	12–4 (3.76)	11–3 (3.44)	13–9 (4.19)	12–10 (3.90)	11–3 (3.44)
		2x10 (38x235)	14–4 (4.38)	13–8 (4.16)	13–0 (3.96)	15–3 (4.66)	14–4 (4.38)	13–6 (4.11)	15–10 (4.84)	14–10 (4.51)	13–10 (4.20)
		2x12 (38x286)	16–5 (4.99)	15–7 (4.75)	14–10 (4.52)	17–2 (5.26)	16–2 (4.94)	15–3 (4.65)	17–10 (5.43)	16–7 (5.06)	15–6 (4.72)
Spruce – pine – fir (includes spruce [all species except coast sitka spruce], jack pine, lodgepole pine, balsam fir and alpine fir)	No. 1 and No. 2	2x6 (38x140)	9–7 (2.92)	8–11 (2.71)	8–2 (2.49)	10–4 (3.14)	9–4 (2.85)	8–2 (2.49)	10–4 (3.14)	9–4 (2.85)	8–2 (2.49)
		2x8 (38x184)	11–7 (3.54)	11–0 (3.36)	10–6 (3.20)	12–5 (3.81)	11–9 (3.58)	10–9 (3.27)	13–1 (3.99)	12–2 (3.72)	10–9 (3.27)
		2x10 (38x235)	13–8 (4.17)	13–0 (3.96)	12–4 (3.77)	14–6 (4.44)	14–1 (4.17)	12–10 (3.92)	15–1 (4.60)	14–1 (4.29)	13–2 (4.00)
		2x12 (38x286)	15–7 (4.75)	14–10 (4.52)	14–1 (4.30)	16–4 (5.01)	15–5 (4.71)	14–6 (4.42)	17–0 (5.17)	15–10 (4.82)	14–9 (4.49)
Northern species (includes any Canadian species covered by the NLGA Standard Grading Rules)	No. 1 and No. 2	2x6 (38x140)	8–3 (2.51)	7–8 (2.33)	7–1 (2.16)	9–3 (2.83)	8–5 (2.57)	7–5 (2.25)	9–4 (2.83)	8–5 (2.57)	7–5 (2.25)
		2x8 (38x184)	10–6 (3.19)	10–0 (3.04)	9–4 (2.84)	11–3 (3.44)	10–7 (3.23)	9–8 (2.96)	11–10 (3.60)	11–0 (3.36)	9–8 (2.96)
		2x10 (38x235)	12–4 (3.76)	11–9 (3.58)	11–2 (3.41)	13–1 (4.01)	12–4 (3.77)	11–7 (3.54)	13–8 (4.16)	12–9 (3.88)	11–10 (3.62)
		2x12 (38x286)	14–1 (4.29)	13–5 (4.08)	12–9 (3.88)	14–9 (4.53)	13–11 (4.25)	13–1 (4.00)	15–4 (4.67)	14–4 (4.35)	13–4 (4.06)

Note to Table 15
1. Spans apply only where the floors serve residential areas.
2. Subfloor must comply with minimum requirements from tables 17 and 18.

Table 16
Maximum Spans for Floor Joists — Special Cases[1, 2]

			Maximum Span, ft.–in. (m)								
			Joists with Ceilings Attached to Wood Furring						Joists with Concrete Topping		
			Joist Spacing, in. (mm)						Joist Spacing, in (mm)		
			Without Bridging			With Bridging			With or Without Bridging[3]		
Commercial Designation	Grade	Joist Size, ft. (m)	12 (300)	16 (400)	24 (600)	12 (300)	16 (400)	24 (600)	12 (300)	16 (400)	24 (600)
Douglas fir – larch (includes Douglas fir and western larch)	No. 1 and No. 2	2x6 (38x140)	10-10 (3.29)	9-10 (2.99)	8-7 (2.62)	10-10 (3.29)	9-10 (2.99)	8-7 (2.62)	10-10 (3.29)	9-10 (2.99)	8-5 (2.55)
		2x8 (38x184)	13-4 (4.06)	12-7 (3.83)	11-3 (3.44)	14-2 (4.33)	12-11 (3.93)	11-3 (3.44)	14-2 (4.33)	12-6 (3.81)	10-2 (3.11)
		2x10 (38x235)	15-8 (4.78)	14-9 (4.50)	13-6 (4.11)	17-2 (5.24)	16-4 (4.98)	14-2 (4.31)	17-8 (5.37)	15-3 (4.65)	12-6 (3.80)
		2x12 (38x286)	17-10 (5.44)	16-10 (5.12)	15-4 (4.68)	19-5 (5.93)	18-6 (5.64)	16-5 (5.00)	20-6 (6.24)	17-9 (5.40)	14-6 (4.41)
Hem – fir (includes western hemlock and amabilis fir)	No. 1 and No. 2	2x6 (38x140)	10-10 (3.29)	9-10 (2.99)	8-7 (2.62)	10-10 (3.29)	9-10 (2.99)	8-7 (2.62)	10-10 (3.29)	9-10 (2.99)	8-7 (2.62)
		2x8 (38x184)	13-4 (4.06)	12-7 (3.83)	11-3 (3.44)	14-2 (4.33)	12-11 (3.93)	11-3 (3.44)	14-2 (4.33)	12-11 (3.93)	10-8 (3.26)
		2x10 (38x235)	15-8 (4.78)	14-9 (4.50)	13-6 (4.11)	17-2 (5.24)	16-4 (4.98)	14-5 (4.39)	18-2 (5.53)	16-0 (4.88)	13-1 (3.99)
		2x12 (38x286)	17-10 (5.44)	16-10 (5.12)	15-4 (4.68)	19-5 (5.93)	18-6 (5.64)	17-3 (5.25)	21-6 (6.54)	18-7 (5.66)	15-2 (4.63)
Spruce – pine – fir (includes spruce [all species except coast sitka spruce], jack pine, lodgepole pine, balsam fir and alpine fir)	No. 1 and No. 2	2x6 (38x140)	10-4 (3.14)	9-4 (2.85)	8-2 (2.49)	10-4 (3.14)	9-4 (2.85)	8-2 (2.49)	10-4 (3.14)	9-4 (2.85)	8-2 (2.49)
		2x8 (38x184)	12-8 (3.87)	11-11 (3.64)	10-9 (3.27)	13-6 (4.12)	12-4 (3.75)	10-9 (3.27)	13-6 (4.12)	12-4 (3.75)	10-9 (3.27)
		2x10 (38x235)	14-11 (4.55)	14-1 (4.28)	12-10 (3.91)	16-4 (4.99)	15-7 (4.75)	13-9 (4.18)	17-3 (5.27)	15-8 (4.79)	13-7 (4.13)
		2x12 (38x286)	17-0 (5.18)	16-0 (4.88)	14-7 (4.46)	18-6 (5.65)	17-7 (5.37)	16-7 (5.06)	20-5 (6.23)	19-1 (5.81)	15-9 (4.79)
Northern species (includes any Canadian species covered by the NLGA Standard Grading Rules)	No. 1 and No. 2	2x6 (38x140)	9-4 (2.83)	8-5 (2.57)	7-5 (2.25)	9-4 (2.83)	8-5 (2.57)	7-5 (2.25)	9-4 (2.83)	8-5 (2.57)	7-4 (2.23)
		2x8 (38x184)	11-6 (3.50)	10-10 (3.29)	9-8 (2.96)	12-3 (3.72)	11-1 (3.38)	9-8 (2.96)	12-3 (3.72)	10-11 (3.32)	8-11 (2.71)
		2x10 (38x235)	13-6 (4.11)	12-8 (3.87)	11-7 (3.54)	14-9 (4.51)	14-1 (4.29)	12-4 (3.76)	15-4 (4.69)	13-4 (4.06)	10-10 (3.31)
		2x12 (38x286)	15-4 (4.68)	14-5 (4.40)	13-2 (4.03)	16-9 (5.10)	15-11 (4.85)	14-4 (4.36)	17-10 (5.44)	15-5 (4.71)	12-7 (3.84)

Notes to Table 16

1. Spans apply only where the floors serve residential areas.
2. Subfloor must comply with minimum requirements from tables 17 and 18.
3. No bridging is assumed for spans for floor joists with concrete topping.

Table 17
Minimum Thickness of Subflooring

	Minimum Subflooring Thickness, in. (mm), for Maximum Joist Spacing at		
	16 (400)	20 (500)	24 (600)
Plywood and OSB, 0-2 grade	5⁄8 (15.5)	5⁄8 (15.5)	23⁄32 (18.5)
OSB, 0-1 grade, and waferboard, R-1 Grade	5⁄8 (15.9)	5⁄8 (15.9)	3⁄4 (19.0)
Particleboard	5⁄8 (15.9)	3⁄4 (19.0)	1 (25.4)
Lumber	11⁄16 (17.0)	3⁄4 (19.0)	3⁄4 (19.0)

Table 18
Sheathing and Subfloor Attachment

	Minimum Length of Fasteners for Sheathing and Subfloor Attachment, in. (mm)				
Element	Common or Spiral Nails	Ring Thread Nails or Screws	Roofing Nails	Staples	Minimum No. or Maximum Spacing of Fasteners
Plywood, OSB or waferboard up to 3⁄8 in. (10 mm) thick	2 (51)	1¾ (45)	N/A	1½ (38)	
Plywood, OSB or waferboard 3⁄8 in. (10 mm) to 13⁄16 in. (20 mm) thick	2 (51)	1¾ (45)	N/A	2 (51)	
Plywood, OSB or waferboard over 13⁄16 in. (20 mm) thick	2¼ (57)	2 (51)	N/A	N/A	6 in. (150 mm) o.c. along edges and 12 in. (300 mm) o.c. along intermediate supports
Fibreboard sheathing up to ½ in. (13 mm) thick	N/A	N/A	1¾ (44)	1⅛ (28)	
Gypsum sheathing up to ½ in. (13mm) thick	N/A	N/A	1¾ (44)	N/A	
Board lumber 8 in. (184 mm) or less wide	2 (51)	1¾ (45)	N/A	2 (51)	2 per support
Board lumber more than 8 in. (184 mm) wide	2 (51)	1¾ (45)	N/A	2 (51)	3 per support

Table 19
Nailing for Framing[1]

Construction Detail	Minimum Length of Nails, in. (mm)		Minimum Number or Maximum Spacing of Nails
Floor joist to plate – toe nail	3¼	(82)	2
Wood or metal strapping to underside of floor joists	2¼	(57)	2
Cross bridging to joists	2¼	(57)	2 at each end
Double header or trimmer joists	3	(76)	12 in. (300 mm) (o.c.)
Floor joist to stud (balloon construction)	3	(76)	2
Ledger strip to wood beam	3¼	(82)	2 per joist
Joist to joist splice (See Table 29)	3	(76)	2 at each end
Tail joist to adjacent header joist (end nailed) around openings	3¼ 4	(82) (101)	5 3
Each header joist to adjacent trimmer joist (end nailed) around openings	3¼ 4	(82) (101)	5 3
Stud to wall plate (each end) toe nail or end nail	2½ 3¼	(63) (82)	4 2
Doubled studs at openings, or studs at walls or wall intersections and corners	3	(76)	30 in. (750 mm) (o.c.)
Doubled top wall plates	3	(76)	24 in. (600 mm) (o.c.)
Bottom wall plate or sole plate to joists or blocking (exterior walls)[1]	3¼	(82)	16 in. (400 mm) (o.c)
Interior walls to framing or subflooring	3¼	(82)	24 in. (600 mm) (o.c.)
Horizontal members over openings in non-loadbearing walls – each end	3¼	(82)	2
Lintels to studs	3¼	(82)	2 at each end
Ceiling joist to plate – toe nail each end	3¼	(82)	2
Roof rafter, roof truss or roof joist to plate – toe nail	3¼	(82)	3
Rafter plate to each ceiling joist	4	(101)	2
Rafter to joist (with ridge supported)	3	(76)	3
Rafter to joist (with ridge unsupported)	3	(76)	See Table 29
Gusset plate to each rafter at peak	2¼	(57)	4

Table 19 (continued)
Nailing for Framing[1]

Construction Detail	Minimum Length of Nails, in. (mm)		Minimum Number or Maximum Spacing of Nails
Rafter to ridge board – toe nail – end nail	3¼	(82)	3
Collar tie to rafter – each end	3	(76)	3
Collar tie lateral support to each collar tie	2¼	(57)	2
Jack rafter to hip or valley rafter	3¼	(82)	2
Roof strut to rafter	3	(76)	3
Roof strut to loadbearing wall – toe nail	3¼	(82)	2
2 in.x6 in. (38 mmx140 mm) or less plank decking to support	3¼	(82)	2
Plank decking wider than 2 in.x6 in. (38 mmx140 mm) to support	3¼	(82)	3
2 in. (38 mm) edge laid plank decking to support (toe nail)	3	(76)	1
2 in. (38 mm) edge laid plank to each other	3	(76)	18 in. (450 mm) (o.c.)

Note to Table 19

1. Where the bottom wall plate or sole plate of an exterior wall is not nailed to joists or blocking, the exterior wall is permitted to be fastened to the floor framing by plywood, OSB, or waferboard sheathing that extends down over the floor framing and is fastened to that framing by nails or staples. The wall can also be fastened by tying the wall framing to the floor framing with galvanized strips that are 2 in. (50 mm) wide, 0.016 in. (0.41 mm) in thickness or more, spaced not more than 48 in. (1.2 m) apart and fastened at each end with at least two 2 ½-in. (63 mm) nails.

279

Table 20
Size and Spacing of Studs

Type of Wall	Supported Loads (including dead loads)	Minimum Stud Size in. (mm)	Maximum Stud Spacing, in. (mm)	Maximum Unsupported Height ft.–in. (m),
	No load	2 x 2 (38 x 38) 2 x 4 (38 x 89) flat[1]	16 (400) 16 (400)	8–0 (2.4) 11–10 (3.6)
	Attic not accessible by a stairway	2 x 3 (38 x 64) 2 x 3 (38 x 64) flat[1] 2 x 4 (38 x 89) 2 x 4 (38 x 89) flat[1]	24 (600) 16 (400) 24 (600) 16 (400)	9–10 (3.0) 8–0 (2.4) 11–10 (3.6) 8–0 (2.4)
Interior	Attic accessible by a stairway plus one floor Roof load plus one floor Attic not accessible by a stairway plus two floors	2 x 4 (38 x 89	16 (400)	11–10 (3.6)
	Roof load Attic accessible by a stairway Attic not accessible by a stairway plus one floor	2 x 3 (38 x 64) 2 x 4 (38 x 89)	16 (400) 24 (600)	8–0 (2.4) 11–10 (3.6)
	Attic accessible by a stairway plus two floors Roof load plus two floors	2 x 4 (38 x 89) 2 x 6 (38 x 140)	12 (300) 16 (400)	11–10 (3.6) 13–9 (4.2)
	Attic accessible by a stairway plus three floors	2 x 6 (38 x 140)	12 (300)	13–9 (4.2)
Exterior	Roof with or without attic storage	2 x 3 (38 x 64) 2 x 4 (38 x 89)	16 (400) 24 (600)	8–0 (2.4) 9–10 (3.0)
	Roof with or without attic storage plus one floor	2 x 4 (38 x 89) 2 x 6 (38 x 140)	16 (400) 24 (600)	9–10 (3.0) 9–10 (3.0)
	Roof with or without attic storage plus two floors	2 x 4 (38 x 89) 2 x 6 (38 x 140)	12 (300) 16 (400)	9–10 (3.0) 11–10 (3.6)
	Roof with or without attic storage plus three floors	2 x 6 (38 x 140)	12 (300)	6–0 (1.8)

Note to Table 20

1. Studs on the flat are permitted to be used in gable ends of roofs that contain only unfinished space or in non-loadbearing interior walls within the limits described in the National Building Code of Canada. Studs supporting only a load from an attic not accessible from a stairway are permitted to be placed on the flat, in accordance with this table, if they are clad on not less than one side with plywood, OSB, or waferboard sheathing fastened to the face of the studs with a structural adhesive, and if the portion of the roof supported by the studs does not exceed 6 ft., 10 in. (2.1 m) in width.

Table 21
Maximum Spans for Spruce — Pine — Fir Lintels — No. 1 or No. 2 Grade — Non-Structural Sheathing

		Maximum Span, ft.–in. (m)[1 to 3]					
		Exterior Walls					
	Lintel Size,	Specified Snow Load, psf (kPa)[6]					
Lintel Supporting	in. (mm)[4], 2-ply	20.9 (1.0)	31.3 (1.5)	41.8 (2.0)	52.2 (2.5)	62.7 (3.0)	Interior Walls
Limited attic storage and ceiling	2 x 4 (38 x 89)						4–2 (1.27)
	2 x 6 (38 x 140)						6–6 (1.99)
	2 x 8 (38 x 184)		This area intentionally left blank				8–3 (2.51)
	2 x 10 (38 x 235)						10–1 (3.07)
	2 x 12 (38 x 286)						11–9 (3.57)
Roof and ceiling only	2 x 4 (38 x 89)	4–2 (1.27)	3–8 (1.11)	3–4 (1.01)	3–1 (0.93)	2–10 (0.87)	3–1 (0.93)
	2 x 6 (38 x 140)	6–4 (1.93)	5–5 (1.66)	4–10 (1.48)	4–5 (1.35)	4–1 (1.25)	4–5 (1.35)
	2 x 8 (38 x 184)	7–9 (2.35)	6–8 (2.02)	5–11 (1.80)	5–5 (1.64)	5–0 (1.52)	5–5 (1.64)
	2 x 10 (38 x 235)	9–5 (2.88)	8–1 (2.47)	7–3 (2.20)	6–7 (2.01)	6–0 (1.84)	6–7 (2.01)
	2 x 12 (38x286)	10–11 (3.34)	9–5 (2.87)	8–5 (2.56)	7–8 (2.33)	6–10 (2.09)	7–8 (2.33)
Roof, ceiling and 1 storey[5]	2 x 4 (38 x 89)	3–5 (1.05)	3–2 (0.96)	2–11 (0.89)	2–9 (0.84)	2–7 (0.79)	2–5 (0.74)
	2 x 6 (38 x 140)	4–11 (1.49)	4–6 (1.37)	4–2 (1.27)	3–11 (1.19)	3–8 (1.13)	3–4 (1.02)
	2 x 8 (38 x 184)	6–0 (1.82)	5–6 (1.67)	5–1 (1.55)	4–9 (1.44)	4–4 (1.33)	3–11 (1.20)
	2 x 10 (38 x 235)	7–3 (2.22)	6–8 (2.04)	6–2 (1.89)	5–8 (1.73)	5–3 (1.59)	4–9 (1.45)
	2 x 12 (38 x 286)	8–5 (2.58)	7–9 (2.36)	7–1 (2.15)	6–5 (1.96)	5–11 (1.81)	5–5 (1.66)
Roof, ceiling and 2 storeys[5]	2 x 4 (38 x 89)	3–1 (0.94)	2–11 (0.88)	2–9 (0.83)	2–7 (0.79)	2–6 (0.76)	2–1 (0.64)
	2 x 6 (38 x 140)	4–5 (1.34)	4–2 (1.26)	3–11 (1.19)	3–8 (1.13)	3–6 (1.06)	2–11 (0.88)
	2 x 8 (38 x 184)	5–4 (1.63)	5–0 (1.53)	4–9 (1.44)	4–4 (1.33)	4–1 (1.25)	3–5 (1.05)
	2 x 10 (38 x 235)	6–6 (1.99)	6–2 (1.87)	5–8 (1.72)	5–3 (1.60)	4–11 (1.50)	4–2 (1.27)
	2 x 12 (38 x 286)	7–7 (2.31)	6–11 (2.12)	6–5 (1.96)	6–0 (1.82)	5–7 (1.71)	4–9 (1.45)

Table 21 (continued)
Maximum Spans for Spruce — Pine — Fir Lintels — No. 1 or No. 2 Grade — Non-Structural Sheathing

Lintel Supporting	Lintel Size, in. (mm)[4], 2-ply	Specified Snow Load, psf (kPa)[6]					Interior Walls
		20.9 (1.0)	31.3 (1.5)	41.8 (2.0)	52.2 (2.5)	62.7 (3.0)	
Roof, ceiling and 3 storeys[5]	2 x 4 (3 x 89)	2–11 (0.88)	2–9 (0.83)	2–8 (0.80)	2–6 (0.77)	2–5 (0.74)	1–11 (0.59)
	2 x 6 (38 x 140)	4–1 (1.25)	3–11 (1.19)	3–9 (1.14)	3–6 (1.08)	3–4 (1.02)	2–8 (0.81)
	2 x 8 (38 x 184)	5–0 (1.52)	4–9 (1.44)	4–5 (1.35)	4–2 (1.27)	4–0 (1.21)	3–2 (0.97)
	2 x 10 (38 x 235)	6–1 (1.86)	5–8 (1.73)	5–4 (1.62)	5–0 (1.53)	4–9 (1.45)	3–10 (1.17)
	2 x 12 (38 x 286)	6–11 (2.11)	6–5 (1.96)	6–0 (1.84)	5–9 (1.74)	5–5 (1.66)	4–5 (1.35)

Maximum Span, ft.–in. (m)[1 to 3], Exterior Walls

Notes to Table 21

1. Spans are calculated based on a maximum supported joist or rafter length of 16 ft., 0 in. (4.9 m) and a maximum supported truss length of 32 ft., 0 in. (9.8 m). Spans may be increased by 5% for supported lengths not more than 14 ft., 1 in. (4.3 m) or by 10% for supported lengths not more than 12 ft., 1 in. (3.7 m). Supported length means half the span of the longest supported members.
2. If floor joists span the full width of the building without support, lintel spans shall be reduced by 15% for "Roof, ceiling and 1 storey," by 20% for "Roof, ceiling and 2 storeys," and by 25% for "Roof, ceiling and 3 storeys."
3. For ends of lintels fully supported by walls, provide minimum 1½ in. (38 mm) of bearing for lintel spans up to 9 ft., 10 in. (3 m) or minimum 3 in. (76 mm) of bearing for lintel spans greater than 9 ft., 10 in. (3 m).
4. A single piece of 3½ in. (89 mm)-thick lumber may be used in lieu of 2 pieces of 1½ in. (38 mm)-thick lumber on edge.
5. Spans apply only where the floors serve residential areas.
6. To determine the specified snow load in your location, contact your municipal building department.

Table 22
Maximum Spans for Spruce — Pine — Fir Lintels — No. 1 or No. 2 Grade — Structural Sheathing[1]

Lintel Supporting	Lintel Size, in. (mm)[5], 2-ply	Specified Snow Load, psf (kPa)[7]				
		20.9 (1.0)	31.3 (1.5)	41.8 (2.0)	52.2 (2.5)	62.7 (3.0)
Roof and ceiling only	2 x 4 (38 x 89)	4–7 (1.40)	4–0 (1.23)	3–8 (1.11)	3–5 (1.03)	3–2 (0.97)
	2 x 6 (38 x 140)	7–3 (2.21)	6–4 (1.93)	5–8 (1.73)	5–2 (1.57)	4–9 (1.45)
	2 x 8 (38 x 184)	9–0 (2.75)	7–9 (2.36)	6–11 (2.10)	6–4 (1.92)	5–10 (1.77)
	2 x 10 (38 x 235)	11–0 (3.36)	9–6 (2.89)	8–5 (2.57)	7–8 (2.34)	7–1 (2.16)
	2 x 12 (38 x 286)	12–10 (3.90)	11–0 (3.35)	9–10 (2.99)	8–11 (2.72)	8–3 (2.51)

Maximum Span, ft.–in. (m)[2 to 4], Exterior Walls

Table 22 (continued)
Maximum Spans for Spruce — Pine — Fir Lintels — No. 1 or No. 2 Grade — Structural Sheathing[1]

		Maximum Span, ft.–in. (m)[2 to 4]				
		Exterior Walls				
	Lintel Size,	Specified Snow Load, psf (kPa)[7]				
Lintel Supporting	in. (mm)[5], 2-ply	20.9 (1.0)	31.3 (1.5)	41.8 (2.0)	52.2 (2.5)	62.7 (3.0)
Roof, ceiling and 1 storey[6]	2 x 4 (38 x 89)	3–10 (1.16)	3–6 (1.08)	3–4 (1.01)	3–2 (0.96)	3–0 (0.92)
	2 x 6 (38 x 140)	5–9 (1.74)	5–3 (1.60)	4–10 (1.48)	4–7 (1.39)	4–4 (1.32)
	2 x 8 (38 x 184)	6–11 (2.12)	6–5 (1.95)	5–11 (1.81)	5–6 (1.69)	5–3 (1.60)
	2 x 10 (38 x 235)	8–6 (2.59)	7–10 (2.38)	7–3 (2.21)	6–9 (2.07)	6–4 (1.93)
	2 x 12 (38 x 286)	9–10 (3.01)	9–1 (2.76)	8–5 (2.56)	7–10 (2.38)	7–2 (2.19)
Roof, ceiling and 2 storeys[6]	2 x 4 (38 x 89)	3–7 (1.09)	3–5 (1.03)	3–2 (0.97)	3–0 (0.92)	2–11 (0.88)
	2 x 6 (38 x 140)	5–1 (1.56)	4–10 (1.47)	4–7 (1.39)	4–4 (1.32)	4–2 (1.26)
	2 x 8 (38 x 184)	6–3 (1.90)	5–10 (1.79)	5–6 (1.69)	5–3 (1.61)	4–11 (1.51)
	2 x 10 (38 x 235)	7–8 (2.33)	7–2 (2.19)	6–9 (2.07)	6–4 (1.94)	5–11 (1.81)
	2 x 12 (38 x 286)	8–10 (2.70)	8–4 (2.54)	2–9 (2.37)	7–3 (2.20)	6–9 (2.05)
Roof, ceiling and 3 storeys[6]	2 x 4 (38 x 89)	3–4 (1.02)	3–2 (0.97)	3–1 (0.93)	2–11 (0.89)	2–10 (0.86)
	2 x 6 (38 x 140)	4–9 (1.46)	4–7 (1.39)	4–4 (1.33)	4–2 (1.28)	4–0 (1.23)
	2 x 8 (38 x 184)	5–10 (1.78)	5–6 (1.69)	5–4 (1.62)	5–1 (1.54)	4–9 (1.46)
	2 x 10 (38 x 235)	7–1 (2.17)	6–9 (2.07)	6–5 (1.96)	6–0 (1.84)	5–9 (1.74)
	2 x 12 (38 x 286)	8–3 (2.52)	7–10 (2.38)	7–3 (2.22)	6–10 (2.09)	6–6 (1.98)

Notes to Table 22

1. A minimum 3/8 in. (9.5 mm)-thick structural panel conforming to CSA O121-M, CSA O151-M, CAN/CSA-O325.0 or CAN/CSA-O437.0 shall be fastened with at least 2 rows of fasteners conforming to Table 19 to the exterior face of the lintel, and a single row to the top plates and studs.
2. Spans are calculated based on a maximum supported joist or rafter length of 16 ft. (4.9 m) and a maximum supported truss length of 32 ft. (9.8 m). Spans may be increased by 5% for supported lengths not more than 14 ft., 1 in. (4.3 m) or by 10% for supported lengths not more than 12 ft., 1 in. (3.7 m). Supported length means half the span of the longest supported members.
3. If floor joists span the full width of the building without support, lintel spans shall be reduced by 15% for "Roof, ceiling and 1 storey," by 20% for "Roof, ceiling and 2 storeys," and by 25% for "Roof, ceiling and 3 storeys."
4. For ends of lintels fully supported by walls, provide minimum 1½ in. (38 mm) of bearing for lintel spans up to 9 ft., 10 in. (3 m) or minimum 3 in. (76 mm) of bearing for lintel spans greater than 9 ft., 10 in. (3 m).
5. A single piece of 3½ in. (89 mm)-thick lumber may be used in lieu of 2 pieces of 1½ in (38 mm)-thick lumber on edge.
6. Spans apply only where the floors serve residential areas.
7. To determine the specified snow load in your location, contact your municipal building department.

Table 23
Maximum Spans for Built-up Lintels — Roof and Ceiling Load Only — No. 1 or No. 2 Grade

Commercial Designation	Lintel Size, in. (mm)		Maximum Span, ft.–n. (m)[1, 2]				
			Specified Snow Load, psf (kPa)[3]				
			20.9 (1.0)	31.3 (1.5)	41.8 (2.0)	52.2 (2.5)	62.7 (3.0)
Spruce – pine – fir (includes spruce [all species except coast sitka spruce], jack pine, lodgepole pine, balsam fir and alpine fir)	2 x 8 (38 x 184)	3-ply	9–10 (3.00)	8–5 (2.58)	7–7 (2.30)	6–10 (2.09)	6–4 (1.93)
		4-ply	10–10 (3.30)	9–5 (2.88)	8–7 (2.62)	7–11 (2.42)	7–4 (2.23)
		5-ply	11–8 (3.55)	10–2 (3.10)	9–3 (2.82)	8–7 (2.62)	8–1 (2.46)
	2 x 10 (38 x 235)	3-ply	12–0 (3.67)	10–4 (3.15)	9–3 (2.81)	8–5 (2.56)	7–9 (2.36)
		4-ply	13–10 (4.21)	11–11 (3.64)	10–8 (3.24)	9–8 (2.95)	8–11 (2.73)
		5-ply	14–11 (4.54)	13–0 (3.96)	11–10 (3.60)	10–10 (3.30)	10–0 (3.05)
	2 x 12 (38 x 286)	3-ply	14–0 (4.26)	12–0 (3.66)	10–8 (3.26)	9–9 (2.97)	9–0 (2.74)
		4-ply	16–2 (4.92)	13–11 (4.23)	12–4 (3.76)	11–3 (3.43)	10–5 (3.17)
		5-ply	18–0 (5.49)	15–6 (4.73)	13–10 (4.21)	12–7 (3.83)	11–7 (3.54)

Notes to Table 23

1. Spans are calculated based on a maximum supported joist or rafter length of 16 ft. (4.9 m) and a maximum supported truss length of 32 ft. (9.8 m). Spans may be increased by 15% for supported lengths not more than 12 ft., 1 in. (3.7 m) or by 35% for supported lengths not more than 8 ft. (2.4 m). Supported length means half the span of the trusses, roof joists or rafters supported by the lintel plus the length of the overhanging beyond the lintel.
2. For ends of lintels fully supported by walls, provide minimum 1½ in. (38 mm) of bearing for lintel spans up to 9 ft., 10 in. (3 m) or minimum 3 in. (76 mm) of bearing for lintel spans greater than 9 ft., 10 in. (3 m).
3. To determine the specified snow load in your location, contact your municipal building department.

Table 24
Maximum Spans for Roof Joists — Specified Roof Snow Loads 20.9 to 41.8 psf (1.0 to 2.0 kPa)

			Maximum Span, ft.–in. (m)								
			Specified Snow Load, psf (kPa)[1]								
			20.9 (1.0)			31.3 (1.5)			41.8 (2.0)		
		Joist Size,	12 (300)	16 (400)	24 (600)	12 (300)	16 (400)	24 (600)	12 (300)	16 (400)	24 (600)
Commercial Designation	Grade	ft. (m)	Joist Spacing, in. (mm)			Joist Spacing, in. (mm)			Joist Spacing, in. (mm)		
Douglas fir – larch (includes Douglas fir and western larch)	No. 1 and No. 2	2x4 (38x89)	8–6 (2.59)	7–9 (2.36)	6–9 (2.06)	7–5 (2.27)	6–9 (2.06)	5–11 (1.80)	6–9 (2.06)	6–2 (1.87)	5–4 (1.63)
		2x6 (38x140)	13–5 (4.08)	12–2 (3.71)	10–8 (3.24)	11–8 (3.57)	10–8 (3.24)	9–3 (2.83)	10–8 (3.24)	9–8 (2.94)	8–5 (2.57)
		2x8 (38x184)	17–7 (5.36)	16–0 (4.87)	14–0 (4.26)	15–4 (4.69)	14–0 (4.26)	12–2 (3.72)	14–0 (4.26)	12–8 (3.87)	11–1 (3.38)
		2x10 (38x235)	22–6 (6.85)	20–5 (6.22)	17–10 (5.44)	19–8 (5.98)	17–10 (5.44)	15–7 (4.74)	17–10 (5.44)	16–2 (4.94)	13–10 (4.22)
		2x12 (38x286)	27–4 (8.34)	24–10 (7.57)	21–0 (6.40)	23–11 (7.28)	21–9 (6.62)	18–1 (5.50)	21–9 (6.62)	19–8 (6.00)	16–1 (4.90)
Hem – fir (includes western hemlock and amabilis fir)	No. 1 and No. 2	2x4 (38x89)	8–6 (2.59)	7–9 (2.36)	6–9 (2.06)	7–5 (2.27)	6–9 (2.06)	5–11 (1.80)	6–9 (2.06)	6–2 (1.87)	5–4 (1.63)
		2x6 (38x140)	13–5 (4.08)	12–2 (3.71)	10–8 (3.24)	11–8 (3.57)	10–8 (3.24)	9–3 (2.83)	10–8 (3.24)	9–8 (2.94)	8–5 (2.57)
		2x8 (38x184)	17–7 (5.36)	16–0 (4.87)	14–0 (4.26)	15–4 (4.69)	14–0 (4.26)	12–2 (3.72)	14–0 (4.26)	12–8 (3.87)	11–1 (3.38)
		2x10 (38x235)	22–6 (6.85)	20–5 (6.22)	17–10 (5.44)	19–8 (5.98)	17–10 (5.44)	15–7 (4.75)	17–10 (5.44)	16–2 (4.94)	14–2 (4.32)
		2x12 (38x286)	27–4 (8.34)	24–10 (7.57)	21–9 (6.62)	23–11 (7.28)	21–9 (6.62)	18–11 (5.77)	21–9 (6.62)	19–9 (6.01)	16–10 (5.25)
Spruce – pine – fir (includes spruce [all species except coast sitka spruce], jack pine, lodgepole pine, balsam fir and alpine fir)	No. 1 and No. 2	2x4 (38x89)	8–1 (2.47)	7–4 (2.24)	6–5 (1.96)	7–1 (2.16)	6–5 (1.96)	5–7 (1.71)	6–5 (1.96)	5–10 (1.78)	5–1 (1.56)
		2x6 (38x140)	12–9 (3.89)	11–7 (3.53)	10–1 (3.08)	11–2 (3.40)	10–1 (3.08)	8–10 (2.69)	10–1 (3.08)	9–2 (2.80)	8–0 (2.45)
		2x8 (38x184)	16–9 (5.11)	15–3 (4.64)	13–4 (4.05)	14–8 (4.46)	13–4 (4.05)	11–7 (3.54)	13–4 (4.05)	12–1 (3.68)	10–7 (3.22)
		2x10 (38x35)	21–5 (6.52)	19–5 (5.93)	17–0 (5.18)	18–8 (5.70)	17–0 (5.18)	14–10 (4.52)	17–0 (5.18)	15–5 (4.70)	13–6 (4.11)
		2x12 (38x286)	26–1 (7.94)	23–8 (7.21)	20–8 (6.30)	22–9 (6.94)	20–8 (6.30)	18–1 (5.50)	20–8 (6.30)	18–9 (5.73)	16–5 (5.00)
Northern species (includes any Canadian species covered by the NLGA Standard Grading Rules)	No. 1 and No. 2	2x4 (38x89)	7–4 (2.23)	6–8 (2.03)	5–10 (1.77)	6–5 (1.95)	5–10 (1.77)	5–1 (1.55)	5–10 (1.77)	5–3 (1.61)	4–7 (1.41)
		2x6 (38x140)	11–6 (3.51)	10–6 (3.19)	9–2 (2.79)	10–1 (3.07)	9–2 (2.79)	8–0 (2.43)	9–2 (2.79)	8–4 (2.53)	7–3 (2.21)
		2x8 (38x184)	15–2 (4.61)	13–9 (4.19)	12–0 (3.66)	13–3 (4.03)	12–0 (3.66)	10–6 (3.20)	12–0 (3.66)	10–11 (3.33)	9–6 (2.91)
		2x10 (38x235)	19–4 (5.89)	17–7 (5.35)	15–4 (4.68)	16–11 (5.15)	15–4 (4.68)	13–5 (4.09)	15–4 (4.68)	13–11 (4.25)	12–1 (3.68)
		2x12 (38x286)	23–6 (7.17)	21–5 (6.52)	18–4 (5.58)	20–7 (6.26)	18–8 (5.69)	15–9 (4.80)	18–8 (5.69)	17–0 (5.17)	14–0 (4.27)

Note to Table 24
1. To determine the specified snow load in your location, contact your municipal building department.

Table 25
Maximum Spans for Roof Joists — Specified Roof Snow Loads 52.2 and 62.7 psf (2.5 and 3.0 kPa)

			Maximum Span, ft.–in. (m)					
			Specified Snow Load, psf (kPa)[1]					
			52.2 (2.5)			62.7 (3.0)		
		Joist Size,	Joist Spacing, in. (mm)			Joist Spacing, in. (mm)		
Commercial		ft.	12	16	24	12	16	24
Designation	Grade	(m)	(300)	(400)	(600)	(300)	(400)	(600)
Douglas fir	No. 1	2x4	6–3	5–8	5–0	5–11	5–4	4–8
– larch	and	(38x89)	(1.91)	(1.74)	(1.52)	(1.80)	(1.63)	(1.43)
(includes	No. 2	2x6	9–10	9–0	7–10	9–3	8–5	7–4
Douglas fir		(38x140)	(3.01)	(2.73)	(2.39)	(2.83)	(2.57)	(2.25)
and		2x8	13–0	11–9	10–3	12–2	11–1	9–6
western		(38x184)	(3.95)	(3.59)	(3.14)	(3.72)	(3.38)	(2.90)
larch)		2x10	16–7	15–1	12–7	15–7	14–2	11–8
		(38x235)	(5.05)	(4.59)	(3.84)	(4.75)	(4.32)	(3.55)
		2x12	20–2	17–11	14–8	19–0	16–7	13–6
		(38x286)	(6.14)	(5.46)	(4.46)	(5.78)	(5.05)	(4.12)
Hem – fir	No. 1	2x4	6–3	5–8	5–0	5–11	5–4	4–8
(includes	and	(38x89)	(1.91)	(1.74)	(1.52)	(1.80)	(1.63)	(1.43)
western	No. 2	2x6	9–10	9–0	7–10	9–3	8–5	7–4
hemlock		(38x140)	(3.01)	(2.73)	(2.39)	(2.83)	(2.57)	(2.25)
and		2x8	13–0	11–9	10–3	12–2	11–1	9–8
amabilis fir)		(38x184)	(3.95)	(3.59)	(3.14)	(3.72)	(3.38)	(2.95)
		2x10	16–7	15–1	13–2	15–7	14–2	12–3
		(38x235)	(5.05)	(4.59)	(4.01)	(4.75)	(4.32)	(3.72)
		2x12	20–2	18–4	15–4	19–0	17–3	14–2
		(38x286)	(6.14)	(5.58)	(4.68)	(5.78)	(5.25)	(4.32)
Spruce –	No. 1	2x4	6–0	5–5	4–9	5–7	5–1	4–6
pine – fir	and	(38x89)	(1.82)	(1.65)	(1.44)	(1.71)	(1.56)	(1.36)
(includes	No. 2	2x6	9–5	8–6	7–5	8–10	8–0	7–0
spruce [all		(38x140)	(2.86)	(2.60)	(2.27)	(2.69)	(2.45)	(2.14)
species		2x8	12–4	11–3	9–10	11–7	10–7	9–3
except		(38x184)	(3.76)	(3.42)	(2.99)	(3.54)	(3.22)	(2.81)
coast sitka		2x10	15–9	14–4	12–6	14–10	13–6	11–9
spruce],		(38x235)	(4.81)	(4.37)	(3.82)	(4.52)	(4.11)	(3.59)
jack pine,		2x12	19–2	17–5	15–3	18–1	16–5	14–4
lodgepole pine,		(38x286)	(5.85)	(5.31)	(4.64)	(5.50)	(5.00)	(4.37)
balsam fir and								
alpine fir)								
Northern	No. 1	2x4	5–5	4–11	4–3	5–1	4–7	4–0
species	and	(38x89)	(1.64)	(1.49)	(1.31)	(1.55)	(1.41)	(1.23)
(includes	No. 2	2x6	8–6	7–9	6–9	8–0	7–3	6–4
any		(38x140)	(2.59)	(2.35)	(2.05)	(2.43)	(2.21)	(1.93)
Canadian		2x8	11–2	10–2	8–10	10–6	9–6	8–4
species		(38x184)	(3.40)	(3.09)	(2.70)	(3.20)	(2.91)	(2.53)
covered by		2x10	14–3	12–11	11–0	13–5	12–2	10–2
the NLGA		(38x235)	(4.34)	(3.94)	(3.35)	(4.09)	(3.71)	(3.10)
Standard		2x12	17–4	15–7	12–9	16–4	14–5	11–9
Grading Rules)		(38x286)	(5.28)	(4.76)	(3.89)	(4.97)	(4.40)	(3.59)

Note to Table 25
1. To determine the specified snow load in your location, contact your municipal building department.

Table 26 Maximum Spans for Roof Rafters — Specified Roof Snow Loads 20.9 to 41.8 psf (1.0 to 2.0 kPa)

			Maximum Span, ft.–in. (m)								
			Specified Snow Load, psf (kPa)[1]								
			20.9 (1.0)			31.3 (1.5)			41.8 (2.0)		
Commercial Designation	Grade	Rafter Size, in. (mm)	12 (300)	16 (400)	24 (600)	12 (300)	16 (400)	24 (600)	12 (300)	16 (400)	24 (600)
			Rafter Spacing, in. (mm)			Rafter Spacing, in. (mm)			Rafter Spacing, in. (mm)		
Douglas fir – larch (includes Douglas fir and western larch)	No. 1 and No. 2	2x4 (38x89)	10–9 (3.27)	9–9 (2.97)	8–6 (2.59)	9–4 (2.86)	8–6 (2.59)	7–5 (2.27)	8–6 (2.59)	7–9 (2.36)	6–9 (2.06)
		2x6 (38x140)	16–10 (5.14)	15–4 (4.67)	12–11 (3.95)	14–9 (4.49)	13–5 (4.08)	10–11 (3.34)	13–5 (4.08)	11–10 (3.60)	9–8 (2.94)
		2x8 (38x184)	22–2 (6.76)	19–4 (5.88)	15–9 (4.80)	18–10 (5.74)	16–4 (4.97)	13–4 (4.06)	16–7 (5.06)	14–5 (4.38)	11–9 (3.58)
		2x10 (38x235)	27–3 (8.30)	23–7 (7.19)	19–3 (5.87)	23–0 (7.02)	19–11 (6.08)	16–3 (4.96)	20–4 (6.19)	17–7 (5.36)	14–4 (4.38)
		2x12 (38x286)	31–7 (9.63)	27–5 (8.34)	22–4 (6.81)	26–9 (8.14)	23–2 (7.05)	18–11 (5.76)	23–7 (7.18)	20–5 (6.22)	16–8 (5.08)
Hem – fir (includes western hemlock and amabilis fir)	No. 1 and No. 2	2x4 (38x89)	10–9 (3.27)	9–9 (2.97)	8–6 (2.59)	9–4 (2.86)	8–6 (2.59)	7–5 (2.27)	8–6 (2.59)	7–9 (2.36)	6–9 (2.06)
		2x6 (38x140)	16–10 (5.14)	15–4 (4.67)	13–5 (4.08)	14–9 (4.49)	13–5 (4.08)	11–6 (3.50)	13–5 (4.08)	12–2 (3.71)	10–1 (3.08)
		2x8 (38x184)	22–2 (6.76)	20–2 (6.14)	16–6 (5.04)	19–4 (5.90)	17–1 (5.21)	14–0 (4.26)	17–5 (5.31)	15–1 (4.60)	12–4 (3.75)
		2x10 (38x235)	28–4 (8.63)	24–9 (7.54)	20–2 (6.16)	24–2 (7.36)	20–11 (6.37)	17–1 (5.20)	21–4 (6.49)	18–5 (5.62)	15–1 (4.59)
		2x12 (38x286)	33–2 (10.11)	28–9 (8.75)	23–5 (7.15)	28–0 (8.54)	24–3 (7.40)	19–10 (6.04)	24–9 (7.53)	21–5 (6.52)	17–6 (5.33)
Spruce – pine – fir (includes spruce [all species except coast sitka spruce], jack pine, lodgepole pine, balsam fir and alpine fir)	No. 1 and No. 2	2x4 (38x89)	10–3 (3.11)	9–3 (2.83)	8–1 (2.47)	8–11 (2.72)	8–1 (2.47)	7–1 (2.16)	8–1 (2.47)	7–4 (2.24)	6–5 (1.96)
		2x6 (38x140)	16–1 (4.90)	14–7 (4.45)	12–9 (3.89)	14–0 (4.28)	12–9 (3.89)	11–2 (3.40)	12–9 (3.89)	11–7 (3.53)	10–1 (3.08)
		2x8 (38x184)	21–1 (6.44)	19–2 (5.85)	16–9 (5.11)	18–5 (5.62)	16–9 (5.11)	14–6 (4.41)	16–9 (5.11)	15–3 (4.64)	12–9 (3.89)
		2x10 (38x235)	27–0 (8.22)	24–6 (7.47)	20–11 (6.38)	23–7 (7.18)	21–5 (6.52)	17–8 (5.39)	21–5 (6.52)	19–1 (5.82)	15–7 (4.75)
		2x12 (38x286)	32–10 (10.00)	29–9 (9.06)	24–3 (7.40)	28–8 (8.74)	25–2 (7.66)	20–6 (6.25)	25–7 (7.80)	22–2 (6.76)	18–1 (5.52)
Northern species (includes any Canadian species covered by the NLGA Standard Grading Rules)	No. 1 and No. 2	2x4 (38x89)	9–3 (2.81)	8–5 (2.55)	7–4 (2.23)	8–1 (2.46)	7–4 (2.23)	6–5 (1.95)	7–4 (2.23)	6–8 (2.03)	5–10 (1.77)
		2x6 (38x140)	14–6 (4.42)	13–2 (4.02)	11–3 (3.44)	12–8 (3.86)	11–6 (3.51)	9–6 (2.91)	11–6 (3.51)	10–4 (3.14)	8–5 (2.56)
		2x8 (38x184)	19–1 (5.81)	16–10 (5.13)	13–9 (4.19)	16–5 (5.00)	14–3 (4.33)	11–7 (3.54)	14–6 (4.41)	12–6 (3.82)	10–3 (3.12)
		2x10 (38x235)	23–9 (7.24)	20–7 (6.27)	16–10 (5.12)	20–1 (6.12)	17–5 (5.30)	14–2 (4.33)	17–8 (5.40)	15–4 (4.67)	12–6 (3.82)
		2x12 (38x286)	27–7 (8.40)	23–10 (7.27)	19–6 (5.94)	23–3 (7.10)	20–2 (6.15)	16–6 (5.02)	20–6 (6.26)	17–9 (5.42)	14–6 (4.43)

Note to Table 26
1. To determine the specified snow load in your location, contact your municipal building department.

Table 27 Maximum Spans for Roof Rafters — Specified Roof Snow Loads 52.2 and 62.7 psf (2.5 and 3.0 kPa)

			Maximum Span, ft.–in. (m)					
			Specified Snow Load, psf (kPa)[1]					
			52.2 (2.5)			62.7 (3.0)		
		Rafter Size,	Raft Spacing, in. (mm)			Raft Spacing, in. (mm)		
Commercial Designation	Grade	in. (mm)	12 (300)	16 (400)	24 (600)	12 (300)	16 (400)	24 (600)
Douglas fir	No. 1	2x4	7–11	7–2	6–1	7–5	6–9	5–7
– larch	and	(38x89)	(2.41)	(2.19)	(1.86)	(2.27)	(2.06)	(1.71)
(includes	No. 2	2x6	12–4	10–8	8–9	11–4	9–10	8–0
Douglas fir		(38x140)	(3.76)	(3.26)	(2.66)	(3.46)	(3.00)	(2.45)
and		2x8	15–0	13–0	10–7	13–10	12–0	9–9
western		(38x184)	(4.58)	(3.96)	(3.24)	(4.21)	(3.65)	(2.98)
larch)		2x10	18–4	15–11	13–0	16–11	14–8	11–11
		(38x235)	(5.60)	(4.85)	(3.96)	(5.15)	(4.46)	(3.64)
		2x12	21–4	18–5	15–1	19–7	17–0	13–10
		(38x 286)	(6.50)	(5.63)	(4.59)	(5.98)	(5.17)	(4.23)
Hem – fir	No. 1	2x4	7–11	7–2	6–3	7–5	6–9	5–11
(includes	and	(38x89)	(2.41)	(2.19)	(1.91)	(2.27)	(2.06)	(1.80)
western	No. 2	2x6	12–5	11–3	9–2	11–8	10–4	8–5
hemlock		(38x140)	(3.79)	(3.42)	(2.79)	(3.57)	(3.14)	(2.57)
and		2x8	15–9	13–8	11–2	14–6	12–7	10–3
amabilis fir)		(38x184)	(4.80)	(4.16)	(3.40)	(4.42)	(3.83)	(3.12)
		2x10	19–3	16–8	13–7	17–9	15–4	12–6
		(38x235)	(5.87)	(5.08)	(4.15)	(5.40)	(4.68)	(3.82)
		2x12	22–4	19–4	15–10	20–7	17–10	14–6
		(38x286)	(6.81)	(5.90)	(4.82)	(6.27)	(5.43)	(4.43)
Spruce –	No. 1	2x4	7–6	6–10	6–0	7–1	6–5	5–7
pine – fir	and	(38x89)	(2.29)	(2.08)	(1.82)	(2.16)	(1.96)	(1.71)
(includes	No. 2	2x6	11–10	10–9	9–5	11–2	10–1	8–9
spruce [all		(38x140)	(3.61)	(3.28)	(2.86)	(3.40)	(3.08)	(2.66)
species		2x8	15–7	14–2	11–6	14–8	13–0	10–7
except		(38x184)	(4.74)	(4.31)	(3.52)	(4.46)	(3.96)	(3.23)
coast sitka		2x10	19–10	17–3	14–1	18–4	15–11	13–0
spruce],		(38x235)	(6.06)	(5.27)	(4.30)	(5.59)	(4.84)	(3.96)
jack pine,		2x12	23–2	20–1	16–4	21–4	18–5	15–1
lodgepole pine,		(38x286)	(7.06)	(6.11)	(4.99)	(6.49)	(5.62)	(4.59)
balsam fir and								
alpine fir)								
Northern	No. 1	2x4	6–10	6–2	5–4	6–5	5–10	4–11
species	and	(38x89)	(2.07)	(1.88)	(1.62)	(1.95)	(1.77)	(1.49)
(includes	No. 2	2x6	10–8	9–4	7–7	9–11	8–7	7–0
any		(38x140)	(3.26)	(2.84)	(2.32)	(3.02)	(2.61)	(2.13)
Canadian		2x8	13–1	11–4	9–3	12–1	10–5	8–6
species		(38x184)	(3.99)	(3.46)	(2.82)	(3.67)	(3.18)	(2.60)
covered by		2x10	16–0	13–10	11–4	14–9	12–9	10–5
the NLGA		(38x235)	(4.88)	(4.23)	(3.45)	(4.49)	(3.89)	(3.17)
Standard		2x12	18–7	16–1	13–2	17–1	14–10	12–1
Grading Rules)		(38x286)	(5.66)	(4.90)	(4.00)	(5.21)	(4.51)	(3.68)

Note to Table 27
1. To determine the specified snow load in your location, contact your municipal building department.

Table 28 Maximum Spans for Ceiling Joists — Attic not Accessible by a Stairway

Commercial Designation	Grade	Joist Size, in. (mm)	Maximum Span, ft.–in. (m)		
			Joist Spacing, in. (mm)		
			12 (300)	16 (400)	24 (600)
Douglas fir	No. 1	2x4 (38x89)	10–9 (3.27)	9–9 (2.97)	8–6 (2.59)
– larch	and	2x6 (38x140)	16–10 (5.14)	15–4 (4.67)	13–5 (4.08)
(includes	No. 2	2x8 (38x184)	22–2 (6.76)	20–2 (6.14)	17–7 (5.36)
Douglas fir and		2x10 (38x235)	28–4 (8.63)	25–9 (7.84)	22–6 (6.85)
western larch)		2x12 (38x286)	34–5 (10.50)	31–3 (9.54)	27–4 (8.34)
Hem – fir	No. 1	2x4 (38x89)	10–9 (3.27)	9–9 (2.97)	8–6 (2.59)
(includes	and	2x6 (38x140)	16–10 (5.14)	15–4 (4.67)	13–5 (4.08)
western	No. 2	2x8 (38x184)	22–2 (6.76)	20–2 (6.14)	17–7 (5.36)
hemlock		2x10 (38x235)	28–4 (8.63)	25–9 (7.84)	22–6 (6.85)
and amabilis fir)		2x12 (38x286)	34–5 (10.50)	31–3 (9.54)	27–4 (8.34)
Spruce – pine – fir	No. 1	2x4 (38x89)	10–3 (3.11)	9–3 (2.83)	8–1 (2.47)
(includes spruce	and	2x6 (38x140)	16–1 (4.90)	14–7 (4.45)	12–9 (3.89)
[all species	No. 2	2x8 (38x184)	21–1 (6.44)	19–2 (5.85)	16–9 (5.11)
except coast sitka		2x10 (38x235)	27–0 (8.22)	24–6 (7.47)	21–5 (6.52)
spruce], jack pine,		2x12 (38x286)	32–10 (10.00)	29–10 (9.09)	26–1 (7.94)
lodgepole pine,					
balsam fir and					
alpine fir)					
Northern species	No. 1	2x4 (38x89)	9–3 (2.81)	8–5 (2.55)	7–4 (2.23)
(includes any	and	2x6 (38–140)	14–6 (4.42)	13–2 (4.02)	11–6 (3.51)
Canadian species	No. 2	2x8 (38x184)	19–1 (5.81)	17–4 (5.28)	15–2 (4.61)
covered by the		2x10 (38x235)	24–4 (7.42)	22–2 (6.74)	19–4 (5.89)
NLGA Standard		2x12 (38x286)	29–8 (9.03)	26–11 (8.21)	23–6 (7.17)
Grading Rules)					

289

Table 29
Minimum Rafter-to-Joist Nailing

		Rafter Tied to Every Joist						Rafter Tied to Joist Every 3 ft., 11 in. (1.2 m)					
		Building Width up to						Building Width up to					
		26 ft., 3 in. (8 m)			32 ft., 2 in. (9.8 m)			26 ft., 3 in. (8 m)			32 ft., 2 in. (9.8 m)		
		Roof Snow Load, psf (kPa)[3]						Roof Snow Load, psf (kPa)[3]					
Roof Slope	Rafter Spacing, in. (mm)	20 (1) or less	30 (1.5)	40 (2.0) or more	20 (1) or less	30 (1.5)	40 (2.0) or more	20 (1) or less	30 (1.5)	40 (2.0) or more	20 (1) or less	30 (1.5)	40 (2.0) or more
1:3	16 (400)	4	5	6	5	7	8	11	–	–	–	–	–
	24 (600)	6	8	9	8	–	–	11	–	–	–	–	–
1:2.4	16 (400)	4	4	5	5	6	7	7	10	–	9	–	–
	24 (600)	5	7	8	7	9	11	7	10	–	–	–	–
1:2	16 (400)	4	4	4	4	4	5	6	8	9	8	–	–
	24 (600)	4	5	6	5	7	8	6	8	9	8	–	–
1:1.71	16 (400)	4	4	4	4	4	4	5	7	8	7	9	11
	24 (600)	4	4	5	5	6	7	5	7	8	7	9	11
1:1.33	16 (400)	4	4	4	4	4	4	4	5	6	5	6	7
	24 (600)	4	4	4	4	4	5	4	5	6	5	6	7
1:1	16 (400)	4	4	4	4	4	4	4	4	4	4	4	5
	24 (600)	4	4	4	4	4	4	4	4	4	4	4	5

Notes to Table 29
1. Nails not less than $3^{1}/8$ in. (79 mm).
2. Ceiling joists must be fastened together with at least one more nail per joist splice than required for the rafter-to-joist connection.
3. To determine the specified snow load in your location, contact your municipal building department.

Table 30
Maximum Spans for Built-up Roof Ridge Beams — No. 1 or No. 2 Grade

			Maximum Span, ft.-in. (m)[1, 2]				
			Specified Snow Load, psf (kPa)[3]				
Commercial Designation	Beam Size, in. (mm)		20.9 (1.0)	31.3 (1.5)	41.8 (2.0)	52.2 (2.5)	62.7 (3.0)
Spruce – pine – fir (includes spruce [all species except coast sitka spruce], jack pine, lodgepole pine, balsam fir and alpine fir)	2x8 (38x184)	3-ply	8–7 (2.63)	7–5 (2.26)	6–7 (2.02)	6–0 (1.83)	5–6 (1.69)
		4-ply	10–0 (3.04)	8–7 (2.61)	7–8 (2.33)	6–11 (2.12)	6–5 (1.96)
		5-ply	11–0 (3.40)	9–6 (2.92)	8–6 (2.60)	7–9 (2.37)	7–2 (2.19)
	2x10 (38x235)	3-ply	10–7 (3.22)	9–1 (2.77)	8–1 (2.46)	7–4 (2.24)	6–9 (2.07)
		4-ply	12–2 (3.72)	10–6 (3.20)	9–4 (2.85)	8–6 (2.59)	7–10 (2.39)
		5-ply	13–8 (4.16)	11–8 (3.57)	10–5 (3.18)	9–6 (2.90)	8–9 (2.68)
	2x12 (38x286)	3-ply	12–3 (3.73)	10–6 (3.21)	9–4 (2.86)	8–6 (2.60)	7–10 (2.40)
		4-ply	14–2 (4.31)	12–2 (3.71)	10–10 (3.30)	9–10 (3.01)	9–1 (2.78)
		5-ply	15–10 (4.82)	13–7 (4.15)	12–1 (3.69)	11–0 (3.36)	10–2 (3.10)

Notes to Table 30

1. The spans are calculated based on a maximum supported length of 16 ft. (4.9 m), where supported length means half the sum of the rafter, joist or truss spans on both sides of the beam. Spans may be increased by 5% for supported lengths not more than 14 ft., 1 in. (4.3 m) or by 10% for supported lengths not more than 12 ft., 1 in. (3.7 m).
2. Provide minimum 31/2 in. (89 mm) bearing.
3. To determine the specified snow load in your location, contact your municipal building department.

Table 31
Minimum Thickness of Flashing Materials

Material	Minimum Thickness, in. (mm)			
	Roof Flashing	Wall flashing		
		Cladding	Above Grade Masonry	
			Exposed	Concealed
Aluminum	0.019 (0.48)	0.019 (0.48)	0.019 (0.48)	–
Copper	0.018 (0.46)	0.018 (0.46)	0.014 (0.36)	0.014 (0.36)
Copper or aluminum laminated to felt or kraft paper	–	–	–	0.002 (0.05)
Galvanized steel	0.013 (0.33)	0.013 (0.33)	0.013 (0.33)	0.013 (0.33)
Lead sheet	0.068 (1.73)	0.068 (1.73)	0.068 (1.73)	0.068 (1.73)
Polyethylene	–	–	–	0.02 (0.50)
Roll roofing, types	–	–	–	Standard
Zinc	0.018 (0.46)	0.018 (0.46)	0.018 (0.46)	0.018 (0.46)
Vinyl	–	0.04 (1.02)	–	–

Table 32
Minimum Thickness of Roof Sheathing for Sloping Roofs[1]

		Sheathing Thickness, in. (mm), for Truss or Rafter Spacing at		
		12 (300)	16 (400)	24 (600)
Plywood and OSB, 0-2 grade	Supported[2] edges	5/16 (7.5)	5/16 (7.5)	3/8 (9.5)
	Unsupported edges	5/16 (7.5)	3/8 (9.5)	1/2 (12.7)
OSB, 0-1 grade and waferboard R-1 grade	Supported edges	3/8 (9.5)	3/8 (9.5)	7/16 (11.1)
	Unsupported edges	3/8 (9.5)	7/16 (11.1)	1/2 (12.7)
Lumber[3]		11/16 (17)	11/16 (17)	3/4 (19)

Notes for Table 32

1. The thickness of sheathing for flat roofs used as walking decks is the same as for subfloors (see Table 17).
2. Supported edges between panels by means of H clips or minimum 2 in.x2 in. (38mmx38 mm) blocking between trusses or rafters.
3. For eastern white pine and red pine, minimum lumber grade is No. 4 common. For all other species, the minimum grades shall be standard or No. 3 common.

Table 33
Stapling Table, in. (mm)

A) Asphalt shingles to wood decks
   (1) 16 gauge (1.6 mm) thick, $7/8$ (22.2) long, $7/16$ (11.1) crown
   Corrosion resistant
   $1/3$ more staples than the number of nails required
   (2) 16 gauge (1.6 mm) thick, $3/4$ (19) long, 1 (25.4) crown
   Corrosion resistant
   Equivalent to number of nails required

B) Cedar shingles to wood decks
   16 gauge (1.6 mm) thick, $11/8$ (28.6) long, $3/8$ (9.5) crown
   Corrosion resistant

C) Gypsum plaster lath, $3/8$ (9.5) thick
   16 gauge (1.6 mm) thick, 1 (25.4) long, $3/4$ (19) crown
   Gypsum plaster lath, $3/8$ (9.5) thick
   16 gauge (1.6 mm) thick, $11/8$ (28.6) long, $3/4$ (19) crown

D) $5/16$ and $3/8$ (7.5 and 9.5) plywood wall sheathing
   16 gauge (1.6 mm) thick, $11/2$ (38.1) long, $3/8$ (9.5) crown

E) $3/8$ (9.5) plywood roof sheathing
   16 gauge (1.6 mm) thick, $11/2$ (38.1) long, $3/8$ (9.5) crown

F) $7/16$ and $1/2$ (11.1 and 12.7) fibreboard wall sheathing
   16 gauge (1.6 mm) thick, $11/2$ (38.1) long, $3/8$ (9.5) crown

G) $1/4$ (6.4) underlayment
   18 gauge (1.2 mm) thick, $11/8$ (28.6) long, $3/8$ (9.5) crown

H) $5/16$ and $3/8$ (7.9 and 9.5) hardboard underlayment
   18 gauge (1.2 mm) thick, $11/8$ (28.6) long, $5/16$ (7.9) crown

I) Metal plaster lath
   14 gauge (2mm) thick, $11/2$ (38.1) long, $3/4$ (19) crown

Table 34
Roofing Types and Slope Limits for Roofs

Type of Roofing	Slope	
	Minimum	Maximum
Built-up roofing		
Asphalt base (graveled)	1 in 50	1 in 4
Asphalt base (without gravel)	1 in 25	1 in 2
Coal-tar base (graveled)	1 in 50	1 in 25
Cold process	1 in 25	1 in 1.33
Asphalt shingles		
Normal Application	1 in 3	No limit
Low slope application	1 in 6	No limit
Roll roofing		
Smooth and mineral surfaced	1 in 4	No limit
19 in. (480 mm) wide selvage asphalt roofing	1 in 6	No limit
Cold application felt	1 in 50	1 in 1.33
Wood shingles	1 in 4	No limit
Handsplit shakes	1 in 3	No limit
Asbestos-cement corrugated sheets	1 in 4	No limit
Corrugated metal roofing	1 in 4	No limit
Sheet metal shingles	1 in 4	No limit
Slate shingles	1 in 2	No limit
Clay tile	1 in 2	No limit
Glass fibre reinforced polyester roofing panels	1 in 4	No limit

Table 35
Minimum Thickness of Wall Sheathing

Type of Sheathing	Minimum Thickness, in. (mm)		Material Standards
	With Supports 16 (400) o.c.	With Supports 24 (600) o.c.	
Structural			
Fibreboard (insulating)	3/8 (9.5)	7/16 (11.1)	CAN/CSA-A247
Gypsum sheathing	3/8 (9.5)	1/2 (12.7)	CAN/CSA-A82.27-M
Plywood (exterior type)	1/4 (6.0)	5/16 (7.5)	CSA 0121-M
			CSA 0151-M
			CSA 0153-M
OSB, 0-1 grade, and waferboard, R-1 grade	1/4 (6.35)	5/16 (7.9)	CSA 0437.0
Lumber	11/16 (17.0)	11/16 (17.0)	See Table 6
Mineral fibre, rigid board, type 2	1 (25)	1 (25)	CSA A101-M
OSB, 0-2 grade	1/4 (6.0)	5/16 (7.5)	CSA 0437.0
Phenolic, faced	1 (25)	1 (25)	CAN/CGSB-51.25-M
Non-Structural			
Expanded Polystyrene (Types 1 and 2)	11/2 (38)	11/2 (38)	CAN/CGSB-51.20-M
Expanded Polystyrene (Types 3 and 4)	1 (25)	1 (25)	CAN/CGSB-51.20-M
Urethane and isocyanurate (Types 1, 2 and 4)	11/2 (38)	11/2 (38)	CGSB 51-GP-21M
Urethane and isocyanurate (Type 3)	1 (25)	1 (25)	CGSB 51-GP-21M
Urethane and isocyanurate (Types 1 and 2), faced	1 (25)	1 (25)	CAN/CGSB-51.26-M

Table 36
Exposure and Thickness of Wood Shingles and Machine-grooved Shakes — Walls

Shake or Shingle Length, in. (mm)	Maximum Exposure, in. (mm)		Minimum Butt Thickness, in. (mm)
	Single Coursing	Double Coursing	
16 (400)	71/2 (190)	12 (305)	3/8 (10)
18 (450)	81/2 (216)	14 (356)	7/16 (11)
24 (600)	111/2 (292)	16 (406)	1/2 (13)

Table 37
Stucco Mixes (by Volume)

Portland Cement	Masonry Cement, Type H	Lime	Aggregate
1	—	1/4 to 1	31/4 to 4 parts per
1	1	1	part of cementitious material

Table 38
Dimensions for Wood-strip Flooring

Type of Flooring	Maximum Joist Spacing, in, (mm)	Minimum Thickness of	
		Flooring, in, (mm)	
		With Subfloor	No Subfloor
Matched hardwood	16 (400)	5/16 (7.9)	3/4 (19.0)
(interior use only)	24 (600)	5/16 (7.9)	15/16 (33.3)
Matched softwood	16 (400)	3/4 (19.0)	3/4 (19.0)
(interior or exterior use)	24 (600)	3/4 (19.0)	11/4 (31.7)
Square edge softwood	16 (400)	–	1 (25.4)
(exterior use only)	24 (600)	–	11/2 (38.1)

Table 39
Nailing of Wood-strip Flooring

Finish Floor Thickness, in. (mm)	Minimum Length of Flooring Nails, in. (mm)	Maximum Spacing of Flooring Nails, in. (mm)
5/16 (7.9)	11/2 (38)	8 (200)
7/16 (11.1)	2 (51)	12 (300)
3/4 (19.0)	21/4 (57)	16 (400)
1 (25.4)	21/2 (63)	16 (400)
1 1/4 (31.7)	23/4 (70)	24 (600)
1 1/2 (38.1)	31/4 (83)	24 (600)

Note to Table 39

1. Staples are permitted to be used to fasten wood strip flooring not more than 5/16 in. (7.9 mm) in thickness provided the staples are not less than 13/16 in. (29 mm) long with a shank diameter of 0.047 in. (1.19 mm) and a width of 3/16 in. (4.7 mm) crowns.

INDEX